E. Kyriakopoulos

Interior Solutions to the Solutions of Schwarzschild and Kerr

E. Kyriakopoulos

Interior Solutions to the Solutions of Schwarzschild and Kerr

Second Edition

LAP LAMBERT Academic Publishing

Imprint
Any brand names and product names mentioned in this book are subject to trademark, brand or patent protection and are trademarks or registered trademarks of their respective holders. The use of brand names, product names, common names, trade names, product descriptions etc. even without a particular marking in this work is in no way to be construed to mean that such names may be regarded as unrestricted in respect of trademark and brand protection legislation and could thus be used by anyone.

Cover image: www.ingimage.com

Publisher:
LAP LAMBERT Academic Publishing
is a trademark of
Dodo Books Indian Ocean Ltd., member of the OmniScriptum S.R.L Publishing group
str. A.Russo 15, of. 61, Chisinau-2068, Republic of Moldova Europe
Printed at: see last page
ISBN: 978-620-4-98207-6

Preface of the First Edition

In this book we present a method of finding interior solutions to the solution of Schwarzschild or to the solution of Kerr. We do not present solutions of this kind which have been found before. The work is the result of an original research on this field.

January 2021

Preface of the Second Edition

Since after the publication of my book entitled "Interior Solutions to the Solution of Schwarzschild and to the solution of Kerr" I made significant progress in the problem of finding regular interior solutions to the solution of Kerr which satisfy the Weak and the Strong Energy Conditions a Second Edition of the book should be published in order to include the recent results. The Second Edition of the book contains two papers one entitled "Interior Solutions to the Solution of Schwarzschild and to the solution of Kerr" which is in fact the whole book of the First Edition and a second paper which was published after the publication of this book: E Kyriakopoulos, Regular Interior Solutions to the Solution of Kerr which satisfy the Weak and the Strong Energy Conditions, J. Math. Phys. 63, 012501 (2022). In the second paper interior solutions to the solution of Kerr are found which are physical in all respects since they are regular and satisfy the Weak and the Strong Energy Conditions. It should be stressed that in both papers we have matching not only according to the Darmois boundary conditions but also according to the boundary conditions of Lichnerowicz.

August 2022

Interior Solutions to the Solution of Schwarzschild and to the Solution of Kerr

E. Kyriakopoulos
Department of Physics
National Technical University15780 Zografou, Athens, GREECE
E-mail: kyriakop@central.ntua.gr

Abstract

We present a big number of solutions and a big number of families of solution which are interior solutions to the solution of Schwarzschild or to the solution of Kerr. These interior solutions match to the corresponding exterior solution on a surface $r = k =$ constant, which in Kerr' s case is an oblate spheroid. All interior solutions to the solution of Schwarzschild are in the interior region $0 \leq r \leq k$ regular in the sense that their Ricci scalar R and their second order curvature invariant R^2 are regular in this region. The interior metric in Schwarzschild' s case is expressed in term of two functions $f(r)$ and $h(r)$. The solution for arbitrary $f(r)$ and $h(r)$ is an anisotropic fluid solution. The differential equation, which the functions $f(r)$ and $h(r)$ should satisfy in order to have a perfect fluid solution is given. It is shown that in our model perfect fluid solutions with $f(r) = r^2$ interior to the solution of Schwarzchild do not exist. Also it is shown that solutions whose $f(r)$ and $h(r)$ satisfy the matching conditions and have an equation of state of the forn $\mu + P_r = 0$, where μ is the energy density and P_r the radial pressure are obtained only if $f(r) = r^2$ and all solutions with $f(r) = r^2$ have an equation of state of this form. In addition it is shown that the radial pressure of all solutions without rotation of the model vanishes at the matching surface and the positions of the horizons of the solutions after matching are presented.

A function $h(r)$ is presented, which together with the function $f(r) = r^2$ gives an interior solution to the solution of Schwarzschild, which for some values of its parameters is regular, for some values of its paramerers its line element has the form of De Sitter' s line element and for some values of its parameter does not have a horizon.

To find other interior solutions to the solution of Schwarzschild we take $f(r)$ and $h(r)$ from a list of functions we give. We get the simplest solutions if we take $h(r)$ from this list of functions and also take $f(r) = (h(r))^2$. Seven families of such solutions are presented.

We give explicitly for the solutions of all families and also for the solutions which are obtained for certain values of their parameters the
non zero components of the Ricci tensor $R_{\mu\nu}$, the Ricci scalar R, the
second order curvature invariant R^2 (exept of Example 2.3.1.4), the
eigenvalues $B_i, i = t, r, \theta, \phi$ of the Ricci tensor R_μ^ν, the energy density
μ, the radial pressure P_r, the tangential pressure $P_\perp$, the quantities
$\mu + P_r$ and $\mu + P_\perp$, the equations of state, the values of their parameters for which the solutions are regular and satisfy the Weak Energy
Conditions (WEC), the graphs of $k^2\mu$, k^2P_r, $k^2P_\perp$, $k^2(\mu + P_r)$ and
$k^2(\mu + P_\perp)$ for certain values of their parameters and of $n = \frac{2M}{k}$, their
line element and the positions of their horizons.

Subsequently six families of solutions are given the functions $f(r)$
and $h(r)$ of which are taken from the list of functions $f(r)$ and $h(r)$ we
have found, which however are not connected by some relation. For
these solutions and also for the solutions which are obtained for certain
values of their parameters we present explicitly the same quantities as
for the previous seven families, with same exeptions. A special feature
of four of these families is that for certain values of their parameters
P_r is non positive and monotonically increasing in the interior region
and for some other values non negative and monotonically decreasing.

Also several perfect fluid solutions are presented, which match to
the solution of Schwarzschild. For all of them we give explicitly the
non zero components of the Ricci tensor $R_{\mu\nu}$, the Ricci scalar R, the
second order curvature invariant R^2 (exept of Example 2.3.3.2), the
eigenvalues $B_i, i = t, r, \theta, \phi$ of the Ricci tensor R_μ^ν, the energy density
μ, the pressure $P = P_r = P_\theta = P_\phi$, the quantity $\mu + P$, the values
of the parameters for which the solutions are regular and satisfy the
WEC, the graphs of $k^2\mu$, k^2P and $k^2(\mu + P)$ for certain values of their
parameters and of $n = \frac{2M}{k}$, the line element and for some of them the
equation of state.

To find interior solutions to the solution of Kerr we start from
a metric which depends on two functions $F(r)$ and $H(r)$, which for
$F(r) = r^2$ and $H(r) = -2Mr$ becomes Kerr' s metric. The Dur-
mois and the Lichnerowicz matching conditions, which are briefly dis-
cussed, give the relations $F(r)$ and $H(r)$ should satisfy in order to have
matching of the above metric to Kerr' s metric on a surface $r = k$.
We shall consider two cases of solutions, the solutions of Case A with
$F(r) = r^2$ and the solutions Case B with $F(r) \neq r^2$. In Case A writing
$H(r) = -2Mh(r)$ we compute the non vanishing components of the
Ricci tensor $R_{\mu\nu}$ the quantities R, R^2, B_i $i = t, r, \theta, \phi$ and the quanti-

2

ties $V_i(r,x)$ $i = t, \phi$, which are obtained for B_i $i = t, \phi$ and which tell if B_i is the eigenvalue of a timelike or a spacelike eigenvector. Also we calculate $\mu, P_r, P_\perp, \mu + P_r$ and $\mu + P_\perp$. We show that all solutions of the model with $F(r) = r^2$ satisfy the relation $\mu + P_r = 0$, are anisotropic fluid solutions and that there is no perfect fluid solution of this type. Also we show that in the framework of the model with $F(r) = r^2$ there is no regular solution which satisfy the WEC. We can however find solutions with Kerr' s ring singularity only, which satisfy the WEC (Case A1) and also regular solutions which have μ but not $\mu + P_\perp$ non negative in the whole interior region (Case A2).

In Case A1 we find general expressions of $h(r)$ which contain powers of $1 - \frac{r}{k}$, $Sinh(1 - \frac{r}{k})$ and $Cosh(1 - \frac{r}{k})$ and give solutions which satisfy the WEC. The solutions with these $h(r)$ satisfy also the strong energy conditions but not the dominant energy conditions. We give three examples with $h(r)$ of the above form for which we find explicitly the non vanishing components of the Ricci tensor $R_{\mu\nu}$ and the quantities R, R^2, B_i, μ, $P_\perp$ and $\mu + P_\perp$. Also the graphs of $k^2\mu$, $k^2 P_\perp$ and $k^2(\mu + P_\perp)$ for certain values of their parameters are given.

In Case A2 we start from an $h(r)$ which depends besides k on two constants b and p and calculate the same quantities as in Case A1. We show that for certain values of b and p the solution is regular and has non negative in the whole interior region only the energy density μ not the quantity $\mu + P_\perp$. The graphs of $k^2\mu$, $k^2 P_\perp$ and $k^2(\mu + P_\perp)$ for certain values of their parameters are given.

In Case B we calculate the non vanishing components of the Ricci tensor $R_{\mu\nu}$ and the quantities R, R^2, B_i and $V_i(r,x)$. Also we calculate the quantities μ, P_r, P_θ, P_ϕ, $\mu + P_r$, $\mu + P_\theta$ and $\mu + P_\phi$ where P_r, P_θ and P_ϕ are the three pressures. Assuming a scaling behavior of F (r) and H (r) we find that the functions V_i, $k^2\mu$, $k^2 P_r$, $k^2 P_\theta$ and $k^2 P_\phi$ are independent of k. In addition we find that in our model with $F(r) \neq r^2$ there is no perfect fluid solution interior to the solution of Kerr. Also we find that for $F(r) \neq r^2$ the matching occurs outside or on the outer horizon of the exterior solution of Kerr or inside or on the inner horizon of Kerr. Finally we present three examples of solutions of Case B which are regular their $F(r)$ and $H(r)$ satisfy the matching conditions, satisfy the relations $V_1(r,x) \leq 0$, $V_2(r,x) \geq 0$, $\mu \geq 0$, $\mu + P_\theta \geq 0$, $\mu + P_\phi \geq 0$ and only the expression $\mu + P_r$ has a small negative value in a small part of the interior region. Graphs of $k^2\mu$, $k^2(\mu + P_r)$, $k^2(k + P_\theta)$, $k^2(\mu + P_\phi)$, $k^2 P_r$, $k^2 P_\theta$ and $k^2 P_\phi$ of these solutions are given.

Contents

1 **Introduction**   **7**

2 **Interior Solutions to Schwarzschild's Solution**   **15**

  2.1   The General Case   15

  2.2   Regular Solutions with $f(r) = r^2$ and Regular $\frac{h(r)}{r^2}$ in the Interior Region   22

      2.2.1   Example 2.2.1 : Solution with $f(r)$ and $h(r)$ of Eq (38)   22

               Example 2.2.1.1 : Solution with $f(r)$ and $h(r)$ of Eq (58)   26

                      Example 2.2.1.1.1 : Solution with $f(r)$ and $h(r)$ of Eq (76)   28

  2.3   Solutions with non vanishing $f(r)$ in the Interior Region . . .   31

      2.3.1   Solutions with $f(r) = (h(r))^2$ 33

               Example 2.3.1.1 : Solution with $f(r) = (h(r))^2$ and $h(r)$ of Eq (135)   35

                      Example 2.3.1.1.1 : Solution with $f(r) = (h(r))^2$ and $h(r)$ of Eq (162)   39

                      Example 2.3.1.1.2 : Solution with $f(r) = (h(r))^2$ and $h(r)$ of Eq (179)   44

                      Example 2.3.1.1.3 : Solution with $f(r) = (h(r))^2$ and $h(r)$ of Eq (195)   50

               Example 2.3.1.2 : Solution with $f(r) = (h(r))^2$ and $h(r)$ of Eq (211)   56

                      Example 2.3.1.2.1 : Solution with $f(r) = (h(r))^2$ and $h(r)$ of Eq (238)   60

               Example 2.3.1.3: Solution with $f(r) = (h(r))^2$ and $h(r)$ of Eq (253)   65

                      Example 2.3.1.3.1: Solution with $f(r) = (h(r))^2$ and $h(r)$ of Eq (279)   68

                      Example 2.3.1.3.2: Solution with $f(r) = (h(r))^2$ and $h(r)$ of Eq (295)   74

               Example 2.3.1.4: Solution with $f(r) = (h(r))^2$ and $h(r)$ of Eq (311)   80

                      Example 2.3.1.4.1: Solution with $f(r) = (h(r))^2$ and $h(r)$ of Eq (339)   84

Example 2.3.1.4.2: Solution with $f(r) = (h(r))^2$
and $h(r)$ of Eq (355) 90
Example 2.3.1.5: Solution with $f(r) = (h(r))^2$ and
$h(r)$ of Eq (371) 96
Example 2.3.1.5.1 : Solution with $f(r) = (h(r))^2$
and $h(r)$ of Eq (408) 103
Example 2.3.1.5.2 : Solution with $f(r) = (h(r))^2$
and $h(r)$ of Eq (424) 109
Example 2.3.1.6: Solution with $f(r) = (h(r))^2$ and
$h(r)$ of Eq (440) 115
Example 2.3.1.6.1 : Solution with $f(r) = (h(r))^2$
and $h(r)$ of Eq (464) 118
Example 2.3.1.6.2 : Solution with $f(r) = (h(r))^2$
and $h(r)$ of Eq (480) 124
Example 2.3.1.7: Solution with $f(r) = (h(r))^2$ and
$h(r)$ of Eq (496) 130
Example 2.3.1.7.1 : Solution with $f(r) = (h(r))^2$
and $h(r)$ of Eq (523) 134
Example 2.3.1.7.2 : Solution with $f(r) = (h(r))^2$
and $h(r)$ of Eq (540) 140
2.3.2   Solutions with $f(r)$ and $h(r)$ of General Form 146
Example 2.3.2.1 : Solution with the $f(r)$ and the $h(r)$
of Eq (555) 146
Example 2.3.2.1.1 : Solution with the $f(r)$ and
the $h(r)$ of Eq (582) 151
Example 2.3.2.1.2 : Solution with the $f(r)$ and
the $h(r)$ of Eq (598) 157
Example 2.3.2.2 : Solution with the $f(r)$ and the $h(r)$
of Eq (614) 163
Example 2.3.2.2.1 : Solution with the $f(r)$ and
the $h(r)$ of Eq (635) 168
Example 2.3.2.2.2 : Solution with the $f(r)$ and
the $h(r)$ of Eq (650) 174
Example 2.3.2.3 : Solution with the $f(r)$ and the $h(r)$
of Eq (665) 181
Example 2.3.2.3.1 : Solution with the $f(r)$ and
the $h(r)$ of Eq (684) 185

Example 2.3.2.3.2 : Solution with the $f(r)$ and
the $h(r)$ of Eq (700) 191
Example 2.3.2.4 : Solution with the $f(r)$ and the $h(r)$
of Eq (716) 197
Example 2.3.2.4.1 : Solution with the $f(r)$ and
the $h(r)$ of Eq (732) 201
Example 2.3.2.4.2 : Solution with the $f(r)$ and
the $h(r)$ of Eq (747) 207
Example 2.3.2.5 : Solution with the $f(r)$ and the $h(r)$
of Eq (762) 213
Example 2.3.2.5.1 : Solution with the $f(r)$ and
the $h(r)$ of Eq (778) 216
Example 2.3.2.5.2 : Solution with the $f(r)$ and
the $h(r)$ of Eq (793) 223
Example 2.3.2.6 : Solution with the $f(r)$ and the $h(r)$
of Eq (808) 229
Example 2.3.2.6.1 : Solution with the $f(r)$ and
the $h(r)$ of Eq (823) 233
Example 2.3.2.6.2 : Solution with the $f(r)$ and
the $h(r)$ of Eq (838) 239
2.3.3   Perfect Fluid Solutions 246
Example 2.3.3.1 : Perfect Fluid Solution with the $f(r)$
of Eq (853) 246
Example 2.3.3.2 : Perfect Fluid Solution with the $f(r)$
of Eq (872) 251
Example 2.3.3.2.1 : Perfect Fluid Solution with
the $f(r)$ of Eq (888) 255
Example 2.3.3.2.2 : Perfect Fluid Solution with
the $f(r)$ of Eq (904) 261
Example 2.3.3.2.3 : Perfect Fluid Solution with
the $f(r)$ of Eq (919) 267
Example 2.3.3.2.4 : Perfect Fluid Solution with
the $f(r)$ of Eq (932) 272
Example 2.3.3.2.5 : Perfect Fluid Solution with
the $f(r)$ of Eq (944) 278
Example 2.3.3.2.6 : Perfect Fluid Solution with
the $f(r)$ of Eq (961) 283

6

Example 2.3.3.3: Perfect Fluid Solution with the $f(r)$
of Eq (977) 290

3 Interior Solutions to the Solution of Kerr   **296**
3.1   Case A : Interior Solutions to the Solution of Kerr with $F(r) =$
r^2 298
3.1.1   Case A1 : Interior Solutions with $F(r) = r^2$ and Kerr's
Ring Singularity which satisfy the WEC 304
Example 3.1.1.1: Solution with $F(r) = r^2$ and the $h(r)$
of Eq (1053) 306
Example 3.1.1.2: Solution with $F(r) = r^2$ and the $h(r)$
of Eq (1069) 311
Example 3.1.1.3: Solution with $F(r) = r^2$ and the $h(r)$
of Eq (1084) 317
3.1.2   Case A2: Regular Interior Solutions with $F(r) = r^2$
which have in the whole interior region the energy density μ non-negative but not the quantity $\mu + P_\perp$ . . . 323
Example 3.1.2.1 : Solution with $F(r) = r^2$ and the
$h(r)$ of Eq (1099) 323
3.2   Case B : Interior Solutions to the Solution of Kerr with $F(r) \neq$
r^2. 328
3.2.1   Example 3.2.1 337
3.2.2   Example 3.2.2 344
3.2.3   Example 3.2.3 351

1   Introduction

In recent years several people tried to find regular black hole models without
rotation [1], [2] as possible end products of gravitational collapse. The models
can be divided into three classes.

First class: It contains models with no junction. The solution is continuous throughout the space-time. A general characteristic of these models is
that the solution behaves for big r like Schwarzschild's solution and for small
r like de Sitter's solution. Several models of this class have been found [3]-[6].

Second Class: The solutions of this class have two regions and a surface
layer, i.e. thin shell, joining these regions. Usually a de Sitter core is joined
with a Schwarzschild or Reissner-Nordstrom space. Regular black holes with

7

thin shells of spacelike and timelike character have been found. Several papers of this class have been published [7]-[12].

Third Class: In this case we have two regions and a boundary surface joining them. Thin shell is not needed. Relatively little work has been done to find solutions of this class [13]-[15].

In the first part of this work, which refers to interior solutions to the solution of Schwarzschild, we present models of the third class. We start from a metric which depends on two functions $f(r)$ and $h(r)$, and which satisfies some conditions so that the interior solution is regular and matches to the solution of Schwarzschild. The calculations of this work were done with the help of Bonanos's computer program [16]. Using this program we calculated for the above metric the non zero components of the Ricci tensor $R_{\mu\nu}$, the Ricci scalar R, the second order curvature invariant R^2, the eigenvalues B_i, $i = t, r, \theta, \phi$ of the Ricci tensor R_μ^ν, the energy density μ, the radial pressure R_r, the tangential pressure $P_\perp$ and the quantities $\mu + P_r$ and $\mu + P_\perp$. From the expressions for μ, $P_\perp$ and $\mu + P_r$ we can calculate $h(r)$, $h'(r)$ and $h''(r)$, which can be used to find equations of state. The differential equation the functions $f(r)$, $h(r)$ and their first and second order derivatives with respect to r should satisfy in order to get a perfect fluid solution is given. Also we show that solutions with arbitrary $h(r)$ and the equation of state $\mu + P_r = 0$, which satisfy the matching conditions are obtained only if $f(r) = r^2$ [17]-[21]. In addition we show that all solutions with metric of the form of Eq (1) have energy-momentum tensor $T_{\mu\nu}$ of the form of the energy-momentum tensor of an anisotropic fluid or perfect fluid solution [22], which means that all solutions with this metric are anisotropic fluid or perfect fluid solutions.

An interesting feature of all solutions of the model without rotation is that their radial pressure P_r vanishes at the matching surface and that their energy density also vanishes at the matching surface if at least one of the relations $\frac{2M}{k} = n = 1$ and $f''(k) - 2 = 0$ hold.

The exterior Schwarzschild's solution gives to the solution we get after matching a horizon at $r = 2M$ if this is in the exterior region that is if $k \leq 2M$. We determine also the positions r_{int} of the horizons which the interior solution gives to the solution we get after matching, which satisfy the relation $0 < r_{int} \leq k$.

In Section 2.2 we consider solutions with $f(r) = r^2$ and regular $\frac{h(r)}{f(r)}$, which are regular. This is done in Example 2.2.1, where we give a function h(r) which depends besides k on three parameters $b \neq 0$, p and q. The solution we get for this $h(r)$ is regular if $p-4 \geq 0$ and $p+b-4 \geq 0$. Since we want to get a solution which satisfies the WEC we must have $b > 0$ and $p+b+q-1 \neq 0$. The line element we get for this $h(r)$ with $p = 4$ takes for $r \to 0$ the form of the line element of the de Sitter solution.

The $h(r)$ of Example 2.2.1.1 is obtained from the $h(r)$ of Example 2.2.1 for $p = 4$. For the solution of this example we calculate the non vanishing components of the Ricci tensor $R_{\mu\nu}$ and also R, R^2, $B_t = B_r$, $B_\theta = B_\phi$, $\mu = -P_r$, $P_\perp$ and $\mu+P_\perp$. With numerical computer calculations we find the values or the range of values of the constants b and q for which μ and $\mu + P_\perp$ are non negative. Also for $p = 4$ and $b = 1$ we find the values of q for which the solution satisfy the WEC.

The $h(r)$ of Example 2.2.1.1.1 is obtained from the $h(r)$ of Example 2.2.1 for $p = 4$, $b = 1$ and $q = 0$. For this solution we give the non vanishing components of $R_{\mu\nu}$ and also R, R^2, $B_t = B_r$, $B_\theta = B_\phi$, $\mu = -P_r$, $P_\perp$ and $\mu + P_\perp$. This solution which is regular and satisfies the WEC is the only solution of the paper which is examined in details from the physical point of view. For some values of $\frac{k}{M}$ the interior solution does not have a horizon and the event horizon of the exterior Schwarzschild's solution is inside the matching surface. Therefore it describes a gravitational soliton since after matching the solution does not have a horizon.

In Section 2.3 we describe solutions with non vanishing $f(r)$ in the interior region. We give a list of such $f(r)$ which satisfy the matching conditions and a list of $h(r)$ which also satisfy the matching conditions. We get the simplest solutions of this kind if we take $f(r) = (h(r))^2$. In Subsection 2.3.1 for this choice of $f(r)$ we give the non vanishing components of $R_{\mu\nu}$ and also R, R^2, B_t, B_r, $B_\theta = B_\phi$, μ, P_r, $P_\perp$, $\mu + P_r$, and $\mu + P_\perp$. From the expressions for P_r, $P_\perp$ and $\mu + P_r$ we calculate $h(r)$, $h'(r)$ and $h''(r)$, which we shall use to find the equation of state of the corresponding solution. We show also that for this choice of $f(r)$ we cannot get an interior perfect fluid solution, which satisfies the WEC.

We shall consider seven families of solutions with $f(r) = (h(r))^2$, which are described in Example 2.3.1.1 - Example 2.3.1.7. For the solutions of these Examples as well as for all solutions we shall get if we give some values to their parameters we shall give explicitly the non vanishing components of $R_{\mu\nu}$ and also R, R^2, B_i, $i = t, r, \theta, \phi$, μ, P_r, $P_\perp$, $\mu + P_r$ and $\mu + P_\perp$, except the second order curvature invariant R^2 of Example 2.3.1.4. The solutions of all Examples except the solution of Example 2.3.1.5 and the solution of Example 2.3.1.7 depend beside M and k on one more constant b, while the solution of Example 2.3.1.5 depends on two more constants p and q and the solution of Example 2.3.1.7 depends on two more constants b and $C(b)$. For all solutions the value of the constant or the values of the constants for which the solutions are regular and satisfy the WEC are given. Also with the help of the expressions for $h(r)$, $h'(r)$ and $h''(r)$ we find the equation of state of the solutions of Example 2.3.1.1 - Example 2.3.1.7. In all Examples the positions of the horizons are given. From Example 2.3.1.1 we get for $b = 1$, 2 and -2 Example 2.3.1.1.1, Example 2.3.1.1.2,and Example 2.3.1.1.3 respectively, from Example 2.3.1.2 for $b = 2$ Example 2.3.1.2.1, from Example 2.3.1.3.for $b = 1$ and 2 Example 2.3.1.3.1, and Example 2.3,1,3.2, from Example 2.3.1.4 for $b = -1$ and -2 Example 2.3.1.4.1 and Example 2.3.1.4.2, from Example 2.3.1.5 for $q = 2$ and $p = 3$ and for $q = 2$ and $p = -1$ Example 2.3.1.5.1 and Example 2.3.1.5.2, from Example 2.3.1.6 for $b = \frac{1}{2}$ and $\frac{3}{2}$ Example 2.3.1.6.1 and Example 2.3.1.6.2 and finally from Example 2.3.1.7 for $b = 2$ and $C(b) = 0.1$ and also for $b = 4$ and $C(b) = 0.1$ Example 2.3.1.7.1 and Example 2.3.1.7.2. Also for the above Examples with numerical values of b, p, q and $C(b)$ we give the graphs of $k^2\mu$, $k^2(\mu + P_r)$, $k^2(\mu + P_\perp)$ and $k^2 P_\perp$ for $n = 1$ and 2 and the graph of $k^2 P_r$ which is independent of n. From the above graphs we conclude immediately that the solutions we consider satisfy the WEC. We get the simplest solutions of the parer for $f(r) = (h(r))^2$. For example the g_{tt} of Example 2.3.1.1.1 is linear in r.

In Subsection 2.3.2 the functions $f(r)$ and $h(r)$ are not connected by some relation. They are taken from the list of functions we have found. We give in Example 2.3.2.1 - Example 2.3.2.6 six families of such solutions.The solutions of Example 2.3.2.1 and Example 2.3.2.3 - Example 2.3.2.6 have besides M and k one more parameter b while the solution of Example 2.3.2.2 two more parameters b and p. For these families of solutions and also for the solutions which are obtained from them for some values of b and p we give explicitly the non vanishing components of $R_{\mu\nu}$ and also R, R^2, B_i $i = t, r, \theta, \phi$, μ, P_r, $P_\perp$, $\mu + P_r$ and $\mu + P_\perp$ except the second order curvature invariant R^2 of Example 2.3.2.2. For all solutions we give the values of their constants for which they are regular. In Example 2.3.2.1 the values of b for which the solution satisfies the WEC are given and its equation of state is found. For the solution of Example 2.3.2.1.1 and for the solution of Example 2.3.2.1.2 which are obtained from the solution of Example 2.3.2.1 for $b = 2$ and $b = 3$ respectively the graphs of $k^2\mu$, $k^2(\mu + P_r)$, $k^2(\mu + P_\perp)$, $k^2 P_r$ and $k^2 P_\perp$ for $n = 1$ and $n = 2$ are given.

We find the values of b and n for which the solution of Example 2.3.2.2 with $p = 4$ satisfies the WEC. The solutions of Example 2.3.2.2.1 and of Example 2.3.2.2.2 which are obtained from the solution of Example 2.3.2.2 for $(p, b) = (4, 3)$ and $(p, b) = (4, 4)$ respectively have P_r non positive and monotonically increasing for some values of n for example for $n = 1$ and non negative and monotonically decreasing for some other values of n for example the solution of Example 2.3.2.2.1 for $n = 6$ and the solution of Example 2.3.2.2.2 for $n = 4$. We give the graphs of $k^2\mu$, $k^2(\mu + P_r)$, $k^2(\mu + P_\perp)$, $k^2 P_r$ and $k^2 P_\perp$ of the solution of Example 2.3.2.2.1 for $n = 1$ and 6 and of the solution of Example 2.3.2.2.2 for $n = 1$ and 4.

For the solution of Example 2.3.2.3 we estimate with numerical computer calculations the values of $k^2\mu$, $k^2 P_r$, $k^2 P_\perp$, $k^2(\mu + P_r)$ and $k^2(\mu + P_\perp)$ for $n = 1$, 2, 10 and 13 and various values of b. From these calculations we conclude that there are solutions with non negative P_r in the whole interior region which satisfy the WEC, for example the solution of Example 2.3.2.3.1 and solutions with non positive P_r in the whole interior region, which again satisfy the WEC, for example the solution of Example 2.3.2.3.2. From the expressions for $h(r)$, $h'(r)$ and $h''(r)$ we calculate the equation of state of the solution. Also the graphs of $k^2\mu$, $k^2(\mu + P_r)$, $k^2(\mu + P_\perp)$, $k^2 P_r$ and $k^2 P_\perp$ of the solution of Example 2.3.2.3.1 for $n = 10$ and 13 and of the solution of Example 2.3.2.3.2 for 1 and 2 are given.

For the solution of Example 2.3.2.4 we estimate with numerical computer calculations the values of $k^2\mu$, $k^2 P_r$, $k^2 P_\perp$, $k^2(\mu + P_r)$ and $k^2(\mu + P_\perp)$ for $n = 1$, 2 and 3 and various values of b. From these calculations we conclude that there are solutions with non negative P_r in the whole interior region which satisfy the WEC, for example the solution of Example 2.3.2.4.1 which is obtained from the solution of Example 2.3.2.4. for $b = 4$ and solutions with non positive P_r in the whole interior region, which again satisfy the WEC, for example the solution of Example 2.3.2.3.2 which is obtained from the solution of Example 2.3.2.4. for $b = 6$. Also we give the graphs of $k^2\mu$, $k^2(\mu + P_r)$, $k^2(\mu + P_\perp)$, $k^2 P_r$ and $k^2 P_\perp$ of the solution of Example 2.3.2.4.1 for $n = 2$ and 3 and of the solution of Example 2.3.2.4.2 for 1 and 2.

For the solution of Example 2.3.2.5 we estimate with numerical computer calculations the values of $k^2\mu$, $k^2 P_r$, $k^2 P_\perp$, $k^2(\mu + P_r)$ and $k^2(\mu + P_\perp)$ for $n = 1$, 2 and 3 and various values of b. Also we give the graphs of $k^2\mu$, $k^2(\mu + P_r)$, $k^2(\mu + P_\perp)$, $k^2 P_r$ and $k^2 P_\perp$ of the solution of Example 2.3.2.5.1, which is obtained from the solution of Example 2.3.2.5 for $b = 3$, for $n = 1$ and 2 and of the solution of Example 2.3.2.5.2, which is obtained from the solution of Example 2.3.2.5 for $b = 4$, for $n = 2$ and 3.

In Example 2.3.2.6 we estimate with numerical computer calculations the values of $k^2\mu$, k^2P_r, $k^2P_\perp$, $k^2(\mu + P_r)$ and $k^2(\mu + P_\perp)$ for $n = 1$, 2, 10 and 20 and various values of b. For the solution of Example 2.3.2.6.1, which is obtained from the solution of Example 2.3.2.6 for $b = 0.5$, which satisfies the WEC and which has P_r non positive and monotonically increasing in the whole interior region we give the graphs of $k^2\mu$, $k^2(\mu + P_r)$, $k^2(\mu + P_\perp)$, k^2P_r and $k^2P_\perp$ for $n = 1$ and 2. Also for the solution of Example 2.3.2.6.2, which is obtained from the solution of Example 2.3.2.6 for $b = 0.9$, which satisfies the WEC and which has P_r non negative and monotonically decreasing in the whole interior region we give the same graphs for $n = 10$ and 20.

In Subsection 2.3.3 we presents two perfect fluid solutions and a family of such solutions, which are interior solutions to the solution of Schwarzschild. The functions $f(r)$ and $h(r)$ of a perfect fluid solution satisfy a differential equation. Inserting in this equation a function $f(r)$ which satisfies the matching conditions, solving for $h(r)$ the resulting equation and choosing the constants of integration such that $h(r)$ satisfies the matching conditions we get the functions $f(r)$ and $h(r)$ of a perfect fluid solution interior to the solution of Schwarzschild. For the perfect fluid solutions we present we give explicitly the non vanishing components of the Ricci tensor $R_{\mu\nu}$, the Ricci scalar R, the eigenvalues B_t and $B_r = B_\theta = B_\phi$ of the Ricci tensor R^ν_μ, the energy density μ, the pressure $P = P_r = P_\theta = P_\phi$ and the quantity $\mu + P$. Also for all perfect fluid solutions except the solution of Example 2.3.3.2 we give explicitly the second order curvature invariant R^2. The solution of Example 2.3.3.1 is regular and satisfies the WEC if $\frac{2M}{k} \geq 1$. Also the solution of Example 2.3.3.3 is regular if its constants satisfy some relations. We give the equations of state of the solutions of Example 2.3.3.1 and of Example 2.3.3.3, which are very simple. Also we give the graphs of $k^2\mu$, k^2P and $k^2(\mu + P)$ of the solution of Example 2.3.3.1 for $n = 1$ and 2 and of the solution of Example 2.3.3.3 for $n = 1$, 2 and some values of its constants. From these graphs we find that the solutions for these values of their constants satisfy the WEC.

For the family of perfect fluid solutions of Example 2.3.3.2, which besides M and k depend on a parameter b, we find the values of b for which the solutions are regular. With numerical computer calculations we find that for $b > 2$ and $n = 1$ and 2 the energy density μ and the quantity $\mu + p$ are non negative and monotonically decreasing and the pressure P is non positive and monotonically increasing in the whole interior region. Therefore for $n = 1$ and 2 the solution satisfies the WEC. The solutions we get for $b = 3$, 4, 6, $\frac{15}{4}$, -2 and -3 are the solutions of Example 2.3.3.2.1 - Example 2.3.3.2.6. We present the graphs of $k^2\mu$, k^2P and $k^2(\mu + P)$ of the solutions of these Examples for $n = 1$ and 2.

Soon after the discovery of the solution of Kerr the problem of finding interior solutions to this solution became a major problem of the general theory of relativity. The efforts before 1978 are described in Ref [23]. According to this reference since all efforts were unsuccessful there appear an opinion, without however some proof, that the metric of Kerr may have no other source than a black hole. In recent years many people tried to find solutions to this problem and to related problems [24] - [34].

In this work we find interior solutions to the solution of Kerr. We start from a metric which contains two functions $F(r)$ and $H(r)$ and a constant a and which becomes Kerr's metric in Boyer- Lindquist coordinates [35] if $F(r) = r^2$ and $H(r) = -2Mr$. We discuss briefly the Darmois and the Lichnerowicz matching conditions for the matching of an interior to an exterior region [36], [37] and we give the conditions $F(r)$ and $H(r)$ should satisfy in order to have matching of the above metric to the metric of Kerr on a surface $r = k = $ constant, which in Boyer- Lindquist coordinates is an oblate spheroid [38]. The matching conditions of $F(r)$ and $H(r)$ are the same with the matching conditions of $f(r)$ and $-2Mh(r)$ of the Schwarzschild's case and therefore can be used to find interior solutions to the solution of Schwarzschild for proper values of their parameters.

In Section 3.1 we find interior solutions with $F(r) = r^2$ (Case A). Writing $H(r) = -2Mh(r)$ we compute the non vanishing components of the Ricci tensor $R_{\mu\nu}$ the Ricci scalar R, the second order curvature invariant R^2 the eigenvalues B_1, B_2, B_r and B_θ of the Ricci tensor R_μ^ν and the quantities $V_1(r,x)$ which is obtained from B_1 and $V_2(r,x)$ which is obtained from B_2 and which tell that $B_i = B_t$ if $V_i(r,x) < 0$ and $B_i = B_\phi$ if $V_i(r,x) > 0$. Also we compute the energy density μ, the radial pressure P_r, the tangential pressure $P_\perp$ and the quantity $\mu + P_\perp$. For all solutions with $F(r) = r^2$ we have the equation of stare $\mu = -P_r$, as in the previous case of Schwarzschild.

Calculating the energy - momentum tensor $T_{\mu\nu}$ we find that all solutions with $F(r) = r^2$ are anisotropic fluid solutions, as in the case of Schwarzschild. Also we find that in our model there is no perfect fluid solution with $F(r) = r^2$ interior to the solution of Kerr. In addition in our model with $F(r) = r^2$ we show that solutions which are regular and satisfy the WEC do not exist, in agreement with reference [39]. We can however find solutions which satisfy the WEC but which have Kerr's ring singularity (Case A1) and also regular solutions with non negative only the energy density μ not both μ and $\mu + P_\perp$ (Case A2)

In Case A1 we write $H(r) = r + L(r)$ in which case $H(r)$ satisfies the matching conditions if $L(k) = L'(k) = 0$ and we can prove that the solution satisfies the WEC if $L(r) \leq 0$, $L'(r) \geq 0$ and $L''(r) \leq 0$ in the whole interior region. These conditions are satisfied if $L(r)$ is a linear combination of expressions of the form $(1 - \frac{r}{k})^p$, $Sinh^q(1 - \frac{r}{k})$ and $Cosh^w(1 - \frac{r}{k})$ or products of expressions of this form multiplied by some coefficients for proper values of p, q, w and also for proper values of the coefficients. As we see from the explicit expressions of R and R^2 the only singularity these solutions have is Kerr's ring singularity. Also we can easily prove that these solutions satisfy the strong energy conditions but not the dominant energy conditions. In Example 3.1.1.1, Example 3.1.1.2 and Example 3.1.1.3 we present three solutions of this type and give their line elements. Also we present the graphs of $k^2\mu$, $k^2P_\perp$ and $k^2(\mu + P_\perp)$ of these solutions with certain values of their parameters for $0 \leq \frac{r}{k} \leq 1$ and $0 \leq x \leq 1$. From these graphs we find that the solutions satisfy the WEC.

In Case A2 we consider a solution whose $h(r)$ depends on k and two more parameters p and b. From the explicit expressions of R and R^2 we find that for certain values of p and b the solution is regular.We calculate $k^2\mu$, $k^2P_\perp$ and $k^2(\mu + P_\perp)$ and present their graphs for certain values of their constants. From the graph of $k^2\mu$ we conclude that it is everywhere non negative, while from the graph of $k^2(\mu + P_\perp)$ we find that this quantity is negative in a small part of the interior region. We have chosen the constants of the solution such that this part is as small as possible.

In Section 3.2 we find interior solutions to the solution of Kerr with $F(r) \neq r^2$ (Case B). For arbitrary $F(r)$ we calculate the non vanishing components of the Ricci tensor $R_{\mu\nu}$, the scalars R and R^2 the eigenvalues of the Ricci tensor R^ν_μ, the quantities $V_1(r, x)$ and $V_2(r, x)$ which determine the eigenvalues B_t and B_ϕ, the energy density μ and the quantities $\mu + P_r$, $\mu + P_\theta$ and $\mu + P_\phi$. We want to find regular solutions which satisfy the WEC or violate these conditions as little as possible. We shall use numerical computer calculations, graphs of interesting quantities and estimation of the maximum violation of WEC. We could not find regular solutions which satisfy the WEC. We found however regular solutions which violate slightly these conditions. Assuming a scaling behavior of $F(r)$ and $H(r)$ we find that

14

$V_1(r,x)$, $V_2(r,x)$, $k^2\mu$, k^2P_r, k^2P_θ and k^2P_ϕ are independent of k. Also we find that in our model with $F(r) \neq r^2$ there is no perfect fluid solution interior to the solution of Kerr. It has been argued that perfect fluid solutions interior to the solution of Kerr do exist [40]. In addition we find that the matching occurs outside or on the outer horizon of the exterior solution of Kerr or inside or on the inner horizon of Kerr.

We present three regular interior solutions to the solution of Kerr in Example 3.2.1, Example 3.2.2 and Example 3.2.3. To calculate maximum and minimum values of various expressions of these Examples we used a program of Mathematica. Calculating with this program the maximum of $V_1(r,x)$ and the minimum of $V_2(r,x)$ we found that the above three solutions have in the interior region $0 \leq r \leq k$ and $0 \leq x \leq 1$ non positive $V_1(r,x)$ and non negative $V_2(r,x)$. Therefore for the three solutions we have $B_1 = B_t$ and $B_2 = B_\phi$. Also we calculated with the help of the program for the three solutions the minimum of $k^2\mu$, $k^2(\mu + P_r)$, $k^2(\mu + P_\theta)$ and $k^2(\mu + P_\phi)$ and found that $k^2\mu$, $k^2(\mu + P_\theta)$ and $k^2(\mu + P_\phi)$ are non negative in the whole interior region, while this does not happen for the quantity $k^2(\mu + P_r)$. Therefore the three solutions do not satisfy the WEC. We have chosen the constants of these solutions such that the violation of the WEC is the smallest we could find. Also for the three solutions we give the graphs of $k^2\mu$, k^2P_r, k^2P_θ, k^2P_ϕ, $k^2(\mu + P_r)$, $k^2(\mu + P_\theta)$ and $k^2(\mu + P_\phi)$ for the values of the constants we have chosen. Finally the line elements of the three solutions for arbitrary values of their constants are given.

2 Interior Solutions to Schwarzschild's Solution

2.1 The General Case

We want to find regular solutions which satisfy the WEC and which match to the solution of Schwarzschild. Their line element is taken of the form

$$ds^2 = -(1 - \frac{2Mh(r)}{f(r)})dt^2 + (1 - \frac{2Mh(r)}{f(r)})^{-1}dr^2 + f(r)(d\theta^2 + \sin^2\theta d\phi^2) \quad (1)$$

where M is a constant. According to our arguments at the beginning of Section 3 of this paper the solution (1) matches to Schwarzschild's solution with mass M

$$ds^2 = -(1 - \frac{2M}{r})dt^2 + (1 - \frac{2M}{r})^{-1}dr^2 + r^2(d\theta^2 + \sin^2\theta d\phi^2) \quad (2)$$

at the matching surface $r = k$ according to the matching conditions of Darmois and also according to the matching conditions of Lichnerowicz if at this surface the functions $f(r)$ and $h(r)$ satisfy the relations

$$f(k) = k^2, \quad h(k) = k \quad (3)$$

and their derivative with respect to r the relations

$$f'(k) = 2k, \quad h'(k) = 1 \quad (4)$$

In the whole paper prime means derivative with respect to r, with some obvious exemptions.

The non-zero components of the Ricci tensor $R_{\mu\nu}$ coming from the metric of Eq (1) are

$$R_{tt} = \frac{M(2Mh(r) - f(r))}{f(r)^4}$$

$$(f(r)(f(r)h''(r) - f'(r)h'(r)) + h(r)(f'(r)^2 - f(r)f''(r))) \quad (5)$$

$$R_{rr} = \frac{1}{2f(r)^2 - 4Mf(r)h(r)}$$

$$(2Mh(r)f''(r) - 2f(r)f''(r) - 2Mf'(r)h'(r) + f'(r)^2 + 2Mf(r)h''(r)) \quad (6)$$

$$R_{\theta\theta} = \frac{R_{\phi\phi}}{\sin^2\theta} = -\frac{1}{2f(r)^2}$$

$$(f(r)^2(f''(r) - 2) + 2Mh(r)f'(r)^2 - 2Mf(r)(h(r)f''(r) + f'(r)h'(r))) \quad (7)$$

the Ricci scalar R of this metric is

$$R = \frac{1}{2f(r)^3}(f(r)^2(-4f''(r) + 4Mh''(r) + 4) - 2Mh(r)f'(r)^2 + f(r)$$

$$(4Mh(r)f''(r) + f'(r)^2)) \quad (8)$$

16

and the second order curvature invariant $R^2 = R_{\mu\nu\rho\sigma}R^{\mu\nu\rho\sigma}$ of this metric is given by the relation

$$R^2 = \frac{1}{4f(r)^6}(8f(r)^4(f''(r)^2 + 2M^2h''(r)^2 + 2) + 108M^2h(r)^2$$
$$f'(r)^4 - 4Mf(r)h(r)f'(r)^2(32Mh(r)f''(r) + 44Mf'(r)h'(r) +$$
$$5f'(r)^2) + f(r)^2(48M^2h(r)^2f''(r)^2 + f'(r)^2(8Mf'(r)h'(r) +$$
$$3f'(r)^2 + 80M^2h'(r)^2) + 16Mh(r)f'(r)(6Mf''(r)h'(r) + f'(r)$$
$$(3f''(r) + 4Mh''(r) + 1))) - 8f(r)^3(4Mh(r)f''(r)(f''(r) +$$
$$Mh''(r)) + 2Mf'(r)h'(r)(f''(r) + 4Mh''(r)) + f'(r)^2(f''(r) +$$
$$1)))$$
(9)

The computer program of Bonano's was used for the calculation of the above expressions and also for most of the mathematical expressions of the paper [16].

We call a solution regular in the interior region $0 \leq r \leq k$ if the quantities R and R^2 of this solution are regular in this region. From Eqs (8) and (9) we see that this happens if $f(r)$ does not vanish in the interior region and if $f(r)$, $f'(r)$, $f''(r)$, $h(r)$, $h'(r)$, $h''(r)$, are regular in this region. As we shall see below in some cases the condition of non-vanishing of $f(r)$ at $r = 0$ may be replaced by the condition $h(r) \sim r^p$, for proper value of p. In all solutions we shall find the functions $f(r)$, $h(r)$ and their first and second derivatives with respect to r are non-singular in the interior region for the values of the constants we shall chose.

We can calculate the eigenvalues B_i and W_i $i = t, r, \theta, \phi$ of the matrices R^ν_μ and $R^\nu_\mu - \frac{R}{2}\delta^\nu_\mu = 8\pi T^\nu_\mu$ respectively. We get

$$B_t = \frac{M}{f(r)^3}$$

$$(f(r)\,(f(r)h''(r) - f'(r)h'(r)) + h(r)\left(f'(r)^2 - f(r))f''(r)\right)$$
(10)

$$B_r = \frac{1}{2f(r)^2}$$

$$(2Mh(r)f''(r) - 2f(r)f''(r) - 2Mf'(r)h'(r) + f'(r)^2 + 2Mf(r)h''(r))$$
(11)

$$B_\theta = B_\phi = -\frac{1}{2f(r)^3}(2Mh(r)f'(r)^2 + f(r)(f''(r)(f(r) - 2Mh(r))$$
$$-2(Mf'(r)h'(r) + f(r))))$$
(12)

$$W_i = B_i - \frac{R}{2} \tag{13}$$

The energy density μ the redial pressure P_r the tangential pressure $P_\perp$ and the quantities $\mu + P_r$ and $\mu + P_\perp$ are given by the relations

$$\mu = -\frac{W_t}{8\pi} = \frac{1}{32\pi f(r)^3}(-4f(r)^2(f''(r) - 1) - 6Mh(r)f'(r)^2 + f(r)$$
$$(8Mh(r)f''(r) + 4Mf'(r)h'(r) + f'(r)^2)) \tag{14}$$

$$P_r = \frac{W_r}{8\pi} =$$

$$\frac{f(r)f'(r)\left(f'(r) - 4Mh'(r)\right) + 2Mh(r)f'(r)^2 - 4f(r)^2}{32\pi f(r)^3} \tag{15}$$

$$P_\perp = \frac{W_\theta}{8\pi} = \frac{W_\phi}{8\pi} = -\frac{1}{32\pi f(r)^3}(-2f(r)^2(f''(r) - 2Mh''(r)) +$$
$$f(r)f'(r)(f'(r) - 4Mh'(r)) + 2Mh(r)f'(r)^2) \tag{16}$$

$$\mu + P_r = -\frac{(f(r) - 2Mh(r))\left(2f(r)f''(r) - f'(r)^2\right)}{16\pi f(r)^3} \tag{17}$$

$$\mu + P_\perp = -\frac{1}{16\pi f(r)^3}(f(r)^2(f''(r) + 2Mh''(r) - 2) +$$
$$4Mh(r)f'(r)^2 - 4Mf(r)(h(r)f''(r) + f'(r)h'(r))) \tag{18}$$

Since $f(k) = k^2$ and $h(k) = k$ for all non rotating solutions of the model we have

$$\mu(k) + P_r(k) \sim 1 - n \tag{19}$$

where $n = \frac{2M}{k}$

Solving the system of Eqs (14), (16) and (17) for $h(r)$, $h'(r)$ and $h''(r)$ we get

$$h(r) = -\frac{f(r)\left(2f(r)f''(r) - f'(r)^2 + 16\pi f(r)^2(\mu + P_r)\right)}{2M\left(f'(r)^2 - 2f(r)f''(r)\right)} \tag{20}$$

$$h'(r) = \frac{1}{2Mf'(r)\,(f'(r)^2 - 2f(r)f''(r))}(32\pi P_r f(r)^3 f''(r) + f'(r)^4$$
$$-4f(r)^2(2\pi(\mu + 3P_r)f'(r)^2 - f''(r)) - 2f(r)f'(r)^2(f''(r) +$$
$$1)) \tag{21}$$

$$h''(r) = \frac{f''(r) - 16\pi f(r)(P_\perp + P_r) - 2}{2M} \tag{22}$$

If relations (20) - (22) hold Eqs (15) and (18) are satisfied. We shall use the above expressions for $h(r)$, $h'(r)$ and $h''(r)$ to find the equation of state of the solutions with $f(r)$ and $h(r)$ of general form (Subsection 2.3.2).

We get a perfect fluid solution if $B_r - B_\theta = 0$ that is if

$$f''(r) - \frac{2f'(r)(f'(r) - 2Mh'(r))}{f(r)} +$$
$$\frac{f'(r)^2(f(r) - 2Mh(r))}{f(r)^2} - 2Mh''(r) + 2 = 0 \tag{23}$$

This relation can be written in the form

$$z''(r) - 2\frac{f'(r)}{f(r)}z'(r) + \frac{f'(r)^2}{f(r)^2}z(r) + 2 = 0 \tag{24}$$

where

$$z(r) = f(r) - 2Mh(r) \tag{25}$$

From Eq (23) and the matching conditions Eqs (3) and (4) we get at the matching surface $r = k$

$$f''(k) - 2Mh''(k) - 2 = 0 \tag{26}$$

Putting $f(r) = r^2$ in Eq (23) and solving the resulting relation for $h(r)$ we get

$$h(r) = C(1)r + C(2)r^4 \tag{27}$$

The above expression satisfies the matching conditions if $C(1) = 1$ and $C(2) = 0$. But the solution with $f(r) = r^2$ and $h(r) = r$ is the solution of Schwarzschild, which means that in our model perfect fluid solution with $f(r) = r^2$ interior to the solution of Schwarzchild does not exist.

Solutions with $B_r - B_t = \mu + P_r = 0$ are obtained if the right hand side of Eq (17) vanish, that is if $f(r) - 2Mh(r) = 0$ or if $2f(r)f''(r) - f'(r)^2 = 0$.

Functions $f(r)$ and $h(r)$ which satisfy the relation $f(r) - 2Mh(r) = 0$ do not satisfy the matching conditions. The solution of equation $2f(r)f''(r) - f'(r)^2 = 0$ which satisfy the matching conditions is $f(r) = r^2$ and this of course happens of every $h(r)$. Therefore all solutions which satisfy the matching conditions Eqs (3) and (4) if they have the equation of state $\mu + P_r = 0$ they have $f(r) = r^2$ and if they have $f(r) = r^2$ they have the equation of state $\mu + P_r = 0$.

We can show that all solutions with line element of the form of Eq (1) are anisotropic fluid or perfect fluid solutions. To do that we shall calculate the energy-momentum tensor $T_{\mu\nu} = \frac{G_{\mu\nu}}{8\pi} = \frac{1}{8\pi}(R_{\mu\nu} - \frac{R}{2}g_{\mu\nu})$, where $R_{\mu\nu}$ is obtained from the metric of this solution. The normalized eigenvectors $(u_\nu)_\mu$ $\nu, \mu = t, r, \theta, \phi$, are given by the relations

$$(u_t)_\mu = \sqrt{-g_{tt}}\delta_{t\mu} \tag{28}$$

$$(u_r)_\mu = \sqrt{g_{rr}}\delta_{r\mu} \tag{29}$$

$$(u_\theta)_\mu = \sqrt{g_{\theta\theta}}\delta_{\theta\mu} \tag{30}$$

$$(u_\phi)_\mu = \sqrt{g_{\phi\phi}}\delta_{\phi\mu} \tag{31}$$

Using the previous expressions for $g_{\mu\nu}$, $R_{\mu\nu}$, R, μ , P_r, $P_\perp$, $(u_t)_\mu$ and $(u_r)_\mu$ we find that $T_{\mu\nu}$ can written in the form

$$T_{\mu\nu} = \frac{G_{\mu\nu}}{8\pi} = (\mu + P_\perp)(u_t)_\mu(u_t)_\nu + P_\perp g_{\mu\nu} + (P_r - P_\perp)(u_r)_\mu(u_r)_\nu \tag{32}$$

which is the form of the energy momentum tensor of an anisotropic fluid solution, and which becomes the energy momentum tensor of a perfect fluid solution if $P_r = P_\perp$ [22]. Therefore all solutions without rotation of this paper are anisotropic fluid of perfect fluid solutions.

From Eqs (14), (15) and (16) we find that at the matching surface $r = k$ the radial pressure P_r the energy density μ and the tangential pressure $P_\perp$ satisfy the relations

$$P_r(k) = 0 \tag{33}$$

$$\mu(k) = \frac{(2M - k)\,(f''(k) - 2)}{8\pi k^3} \tag{34}$$

$$P_\perp(k) = \frac{f''(k) - 2Mh''(k) - 2}{16\pi k^2} \tag{35}$$

Therefore at the matching surface all non-rotating solutions of the paper satisfy two important relations. At the matching surface their radial pressure vanishes and their energy density also vanishes at this surface if at least one of the relations $2M - k = 0$ and $f''(k) - 2 = 0$ hold. Also if the solution satisfies the WEC we have $(2M - k)(f''(k) - 2) \geq 0$ while if $(2M - k)(f''(k) - 2) < 0$ the solution does not satisfy the WEC.

From Eqs (26) and (35) we find that the tangential pressure $P_\perp$ of all perfect fluid solutions at $r = k$ satisfy the relation

$$P_\perp(k) = 0 \tag{36}$$

This was expected since according to Eq (33) for all solutions of the model we have $P_r(k) = 0$ and for the perfect fluid solutions we get $P_r(r) = P_\perp(r)$.

The horizon of the Schwarzschild's solution is at $r = 2M$. The solution we get after matching has a horizon at this position only if this position is in the exterior region or at the matching surface, which happens only if $k \leq 2M$.

The positions $r = r_{int}$ of the horizons of an interior solution are obtained from the relation

$$g^{rr}(r_{int}) = 1 - \frac{2Mh(r_{int})}{f(r_{int})} = 0 \tag{37}$$

These horizons of the interior solution are horizons of the solution we get after matching only if they are in the interior region or at the matching surface that is if $0 < r_{int} \leq k$. Also from Eqs (3) we find that if $k = 2M$ Eq (37) has the solution $r_{int} = k$. This means that if $k = 2M$ after matching we get a "degenerate" horizon at $r = k = 2M$. Therefore we conclude the following:

(a) If $\frac{2M}{k} > 1$ the solution we get after matching has a horizon at $r = 2M$ of the exterior region and horizons at the solutions r_{int} of Eq (37) for which $0 < r_{int} < k$.

(b) If $\frac{2M}{k} = 1$ we have after matching a "degenerate" horizon at $r = k = 2M$ and also horizons at the solutions r_{int} of Eq (37) for which $0 < r_{int} < k$. If Eq (37) has only the solution $r_{int} = k$ the solution we get after matching has only the "degenerate" horizon.

(c) If $\frac{2M}{k} < 1$ we have after matching horizons at the solutions r_{int} of Eq (37) for which $0 < r_{int} < k$. If Eq (37) does not have such solutions the solution we get after matching does not have a horizon.

The solutions of equation (37) of some examples of the paper cannot be found exactly, with the exception of the solution $r_{int} = k = 2M$. We shall not discuss in the following the horizons of these examples which are in the interior region. Also we shall not discuss in the following the horizons, which are in the interior region, of the examples of which Eq (37) is of fourth degree in r. All solutions without rotation of the paper have for $\frac{2M}{k} = n > 1$ a horizon at $r = 2M$ and for $\frac{2M}{k} = n = 1$ a "degenerate" horizon at $r = k = 2M$.

2.2 Regular Solutions with $f(r) = r^2$ and Regular $\frac{h(r)}{r^2}$ in the Interior Region

If $f(r) = r^2$ and we chose an $h(r)$ which gives a regular expression $\frac{h(r)}{r^2}$ and satisfies the matching conditions (3) (4) we don't get always a regular solution. Therefore for each choice of $h(r)$ we have to check the resulting solution for regularity. The $h(r)$ of the following example gives a regular solution.

2.2.1 Example 2.2.1 : Solution with $f(r)$ and $h(r)$ of Eq (38)

, k-¿1
Consider the solution with

$$f(r) = r^2 \quad \text{and} \quad h(r) = \frac{k}{b}\left(\frac{r}{k}\right)^p \left(-(p-1)(\frac{r}{k})^b + b + \frac{q(r-k)^2}{k^2} + p - 1\right) \ (38)$$

where b, p an q are constants. The above functions $f(r)$ and $h(r)$ satisfy the matching conditions (3) and (4). The non zero components of the Ricci tensor $R_{\mu\nu}$, the Ricci scalar R and the second order curvature invariant R^2 of the interior solution with metric of the form of Eq (1) with the $f(r)$ and $h(r)$ of Eq (38) are given by the relations

$$R_{tt} = \frac{M}{b^2 k^2 r^6}(\frac{r}{k})^p (k^2(p-1)((b+p-2)(b+p-1)(\frac{r}{k})^b + (2-p)$$
$$(b+p+q-1)) + 2k(p-1)pqr - p(p+1)qr^2)(2M(\frac{r}{k})^p(-k^2(b+$$
$$p+q-1) + k^2(p-1)(\frac{r}{k})^b + 2kqr - qr^2) + bkr^2) \quad (39)$$

$$R_{rr} =$$
$$\frac{M}{2Mr^2(\frac{r}{k})^p(k^2(-(p-1)(\frac{r}{k})^b + b + p + q - 1) - 2kqr + qr^2) - bkr^4}$$
$$(\frac{r}{k})^p(k^2(p-1)((b+p-2)(b+p-1)(\frac{r}{k})^b + (2-p)(b+p+q-$$
$$1)) + 2k(p-1)pqr - p(p+1)qr^2) \quad (40)$$

22

$$R_{\theta\theta} = \frac{R_{\phi\phi}}{\sin^2\theta} - \frac{2M}{br^3}(\frac{r}{k})^{p+1}(2kpqr - (p+1)qr^2 + k^2(p-1)$$
$$((b+p-1)(\frac{r}{k})^b - b - p - q + 1)) \tag{41}$$

$$R = -\frac{2M}{br^5}(\frac{r}{k})^{p+1}(k^2(p-1)(p^2((\frac{r}{k})^b - 1) + p(-(\frac{r}{k})^b + b(2(\frac{r}{k})^b -$$
$$1) - q + 1) + (b-1)b(\frac{r}{k})^b) + 2kp(p+1)qr - (p^2 + 3p + 2)qr^2) \tag{42}$$

$$R^2 = \frac{4M^2}{b^2k^2r^8}\left(\frac{r}{k}\right)^{2\,p}(4k^3qr((p-1)(b^2(p-2)(p-1) + b(p-1)(p(2p-$$
$$9) + 14) + p(p((p-8)p + 27) - 40) + 24)(\frac{r}{k})^b + (-p(p((p-8)p+27)$$
$$-40) - 24)(b+p+q-1)) + k^4(b^4(p-1)^2(\frac{r}{k})^{2b} + 2b^3(\frac{r}{k})^b((p-1)^2(2p$$
$$-5)(\frac{r}{k})^b - p^3 + 6p^2 - 11p + 6) + b^2(-2(p-2)(p-1)(p(3p+q-15)$$
$$-3q+22)(\frac{r}{k})^b + (p-1)^2(6(p-5)p + 41)(\frac{r}{k})^{2b} + p^4 - 10p^3 + 41p^2 -$$
$$76p + 56) + 2b((p-2)(p-1)(p(2p-11)+19)(\frac{r}{k})^b - p^4 + 10p^3 - 41p^2$$
$$+76p - 56)((p-1)(\frac{r}{k})^b - p - q + 1) + (p(p((p-10)p+41) - 76) +$$
$$56)(-(p-1)(\frac{r}{k})^b + p + q - 1)^2) + 2k^2qr^2(-(p-1)(p(b+p-2)(b(p-$$
$$1) + (p-4)p + 7) + 4)(\frac{r}{k})^b + bp^4 - 6bp^3 + 15bp^2 - 14bp + 4b + p^5 + 3$$
$$p^4q - 7p^4 - 18p^3q + 21p^3 + 49p^2q - 29p^2 - 54pq + 18p + 28q - 4) - 4k$$
$$((p-1)p((p-3)p+6) + 4)q^2r^3 + (((p-2)p+5)p^2 + 4)q^2r^4) \tag{43}$$

From Eq (42) and (43) we find that R and R^2 are non-singular if $p - 4$, $p + b - 4$ and $2(p-4) + b$ are non-negative and b non-zero. Therefore if $p = 4$ we must have $b > 0$. Our solution for $p = 4$ and $b > 0$ has non-singular R and R^2 and therefore it is regular. From Eqs (10)-(12) and (14)-(18) we obtain the eigenvalues $B_t = B_r$ and $B_\theta = B_\phi$ of the Ricci tensor R^ν_μ, the energy density μ, the radial pressure P_r, the tangential pressure $P_\perp = P_\theta = P_\phi$ and the quantities $\mu + P_r$ and $\mu + P_\perp$. We get

$$B_t = B_r = -\frac{M}{br^5}(\frac{r}{k})^{p+1}(k^2(p-1)(b^2(\frac{r}{k})^b + (p-2)(p((\frac{r}{k})^b - 1) -$$

$$(\frac{r}{k})^b - q + 1) + b(p(2(\frac{r}{k})^b - 1) - 3(\frac{r}{k})^b + 2)) + 2k(p-1)pqr - p$$
$$(p+1)qr^2) \tag{44}$$

$$B_\theta = B_\phi = -\frac{2M}{br^5}(\frac{r}{k})^{p+1}(k^2(p-1)((b+p-1)(\frac{r}{k})^b - b - p - q +$$
$$1) + 2kpqr - (p+1)qr^2) \tag{45}$$

$$\mu = -P_r = \frac{M}{4\pi br^5}(\frac{r}{k})^{p+1}(k^2(p-1)(-(b+p-1)(\frac{r}{k})^b + b + p +$$
$$q - 1) - 2kpqr + (p+1)qr^2) \tag{46}$$

$$P_\perp = \frac{M}{8\pi br^5}(\frac{r}{k})^{p+1}(k^2(p-1)((b+p-2)(b+p-1)(\frac{r}{k})^b + (2 -$$
$$p)(b+p+q-1)) + 2k(p-1)pqr - p(p+1)qr^2) \tag{47}$$

$$\mu + P_\perp = \frac{M}{8\pi br^5}(\frac{r}{k})^{p+1}(2k(p-3)pqr + (-p^2 + p + 2)qr^2 +$$
$$k^2(p-1)((b+p-4)(b+p-1)(\frac{r}{k})^b + (4-p)$$
$$(b+p+q-1))) \tag{48}$$

If $b < 0$ we get from Eq (48) as $r \to 0$

$$\mu + P_\perp \to \frac{k^2 M(p-1)(b+p-4)(b+p-1)\left(\frac{r}{k}\right)^{b+p+1}}{8\pi br^5} \tag{49}$$

which since $p - 4 \geq 0$ and $p - 4 + b \geq 0$ is negative. Therefore since we want our solution to satisfy the WEC and since b cannot be zero we must have

$$b > 0 \tag{50}$$

Then from Eqs (46) and (48) we get as $r \to 0$

$$\mu \to \frac{k^2 M(p-1)(b+p+q-1)\left(\frac{r}{k}\right)^{p+1}}{4\pi br^5} \tag{51}$$

$$\mu + P_\perp \to \frac{k^2 M(4-p)(p-1)(b+p+q-1)\left(\frac{r}{k}\right)^{p+1}}{8\pi br^5} \tag{52}$$

24

Therefore the quantities μ and $\mu + P_\perp$ are non-negative as $r \to 0$ if $b + p + q - 1 = 0$ and if $p = 4$ and $b + p + q - 1 \geq 0$.

If $q + p + b - 1 = 0$ the expression of Eq (46) for the energy density takes the form

$$-\frac{M(b+p-1)\left(\frac{r}{k}\right)^{p+1}\left(k^2(p-1)\left(\frac{r}{k}\right)^b - 2kpr + (p+1)r^2\right)}{4\pi br^5} \tag{53}$$

which means that if $b < 1$ becomes negative as $r \to 0$. Also the expression of Eq (48) for $\mu + P_\perp$ becomes for $q + p + b - 1 = 0$

$$\frac{M(b+p-1)}{8\pi br^5}(\frac{r}{k})^{p+1}(k^2(p-1)(b+p-4)(\frac{r}{k})^b - 2k(p-3)pr + (p^2-p-2)r^2) \tag{54}$$

which if $b > 1$ becomes negative as $r \to 0$. Finally if $q + p + b - 1 = 0$ and $b = 1$ the expression of Eq (48) for $\mu + P_\perp$ is negative as $r \to 0$. Therefore if $p - 4 \geq 0$ and $q + p + g - 1 = 0$ the solution does not satisfied we WEC

The line element d^2s of the solution is obtained from Eqs (1) and (38). We get

$$d^2s = -(1 - 2M\frac{k}{br^2}(\frac{r}{k})^p(-1+b+p-(-1+p)(\frac{r}{k})^b + (-k+r)^2$$
$$\frac{q}{k^2}))dt^2 + \frac{d^2r}{1 - 2M\frac{k}{br^2}(\frac{r}{k})^p(-1+b+p-(-1+p)(\frac{r}{k})^b + \frac{q(-k+r)^2}{k^2})}$$
$$+r^2(d\theta^2 + sin^2\theta d\phi^2) \tag{55}$$

As $r \to 0$ the line element (55) takes the form

$$d^2s = -(1 - \frac{2M}{bk^{p-1}}(b+p+q-1)r^{p-2})dt^2 +$$
$$\frac{dr^2}{(1 - \frac{2M}{bk^{p-1}}(b+p+q-1)r^{p-2})} + r^2(d\theta^2 + sin^2\theta d\phi^2) \tag{56}$$

Therefore for $p = 4$ the line element of Eq (55), which is the line element of an interior solution of the solution of Schwarzschild, asymptotically for $r \to 0$ takes the form of the line element of the De Sitter solution.

From Eq (46) we find that the solution has the equation of state

$$\mu = -P_r \tag{57}$$

as expected according to our previous arguments

Example 2.2.1.1 : Solution with $f(r)$ and $h(r)$ of Eq (58)   Consider
the solution with

$$f(r) = r^2 \quad \text{and} \quad h(r) = \frac{r^4}{bk^3}\left(-3\left(\frac{r}{k}\right)^b + b + \frac{q(k-r)^2}{k^2} + 3\right) \quad (58)$$

where b and q are constants. The above function $h(r)$ is obtained from the
$h(r)$ of (38) for $p = 4$. The non zero components of the Ricci tensor $R_{\mu\nu}$, the
Ricci scalar R, the second order curvature invariant R^2 and the eigenvalues
B_i $i = t, r, \theta$ and ϕ of the Ricci tensor R_μ^ν of the interior solution with the
$f(r)$ and $h(r)$ of Eq (58) are given by the relations (39) - (45) for $p = 4$. We
get

$$R_{tt} = \frac{M}{b^2 k^{10}}(3k^2((b+2)(b+3)(\frac{r}{k})^b - 2(b+q+3)) + 24kqr -$$

$$20qr^2)(b(k^5 - 2k^2Mr^2) - 2Mr^2(k^2(-3(\frac{r}{k})^b + q + 3) - 2kqr +$$

$$qr^2)) \quad (59)$$

$$R_{rr} = \frac{M}{b(k^5 - 2k^2Mr^2) - 2Mr^2(k^2(-3(\frac{r}{k})^b + q + 3) - 2kqr + qr^2)}$$
$$(3k^2(2(b+q+3) - (b+2)(b+3)(\frac{r}{k})^b) - 24kqr + 20qr^2) \quad (60)$$

$$R_{\theta\theta} = \frac{R_{\phi\phi}}{sin^2\theta} = -\frac{2Mr^2}{bk^5}(-3k^2(b+q+3)+3(b+3)k^2(\frac{r}{k})^b+8kqr-5qr^2) \quad (61)$$

$$R = \frac{6k^2M\left(4(b+q+3) - (b+3)(b+4)\left(\frac{r}{k}\right)^b\right) - 80kMqr + 60Mqr^2}{bk^5} \quad (62)$$

$$R^2 = \frac{4M^2}{b^2 k^{10}}(9(b(b(b(b(b+6)+17)+28)+24)k^4(\frac{r}{k})^{2b} - 12k^2(\frac{r}{k})^b$$
$$((b+3)(b+4)k^2(b+q+3) - 2(3b(b+5)+20)kqr) + 2(b(3b+$$
$$13)+15)qr^2) + 4(6k^4(b+q+3)^2 - 40k^3qr(b+q+3) + 2k^2qr^2$$
$$(15b+53q+45) - 124kq^2r^3 + 53q^2r^4)) \quad (63)$$

$$B_t = B_r = \frac{M}{bk^5}(3k^2\left(2(b+q+3) - (b+2)(b+3)\left(\frac{r}{k}\right)^b\right) -$$

$$24kqr + 20qr^2) \quad (64)$$

$$B_\theta = B_\phi = -\frac{2M}{bk^5}(-3k^2(b+q+3)+3(b+3)k^2\left(\frac{r}{k}\right)^b + 8kqr -$$

$$5qr^2) \tag{65}$$

The energy density μ, the tangential pressure $P_\perp$ and the quantity $\mu + P_\perp$ are obtained from Eqs (46) - (48) for $p = 4$. We get

$$\mu = -\frac{M}{4\pi bk^5}(-3k^2(b+q+3)+3(b+3)k^2\left(\frac{r}{k}\right)^b + 8kqr - 5qr^2) \tag{66}$$

$$P_\perp = \frac{M}{8\pi bk^5}\left(3k^2\left((b+2)(b+3)\left(\frac{r}{k}\right)^b - 2(b+q+3)\right)+24kqr-20qr^2\right) \tag{67}$$

$$\mu + P_\perp = \frac{M}{8\pi bk^5}(3b(b+3)k^2\left(\frac{r}{k}\right)^b + 8kqr - 10qr^2) \tag{68}$$

Numerically with the help of the computer we can find the values or the range of values of the constants b and q for which μ and $\mu + P_\perp$ are non-negative in the interior region $0 \le r \le k$. We find the following: For $b \le 6$ and $q > 0$ we have $\mu \ge 0$ and $\mu + P_\perp \ge 0$ if

$$q \le \frac{3b(3+b)}{2} \tag{69}$$

For $b > 6$ and $q > 0$ we can find separately for each b the values of q for which $\mu \ge 0$ and $\mu + P_\perp \ge 0$ in the interior region. For example for $b = 8$ we get $\mu \ge 0$ if $q \le 113.83$ and $\mu + P_\perp \ge 0$ if $q \le 122.1$ For $q = 0$ we have $\mu \ge 0$ and $\mu + P_\perp \ge 0$ for all b. For $q < 0$ and $b > 1$ we have $\mu \ge 0$ for $q \le -3 - b$, but $\mu + P_\perp$ cannot be non-negative. Also we can find values $q < 0$ and $b \le 1$ of which $\mu \ge 0$ and $\mu + P_\perp \ge 0$ in the interior region. For example for $b = 0.5$ we get $\mu \ge 0$ if $q \le -3.118$ and $\mu + P_\perp \ge 0$ if $0 > q \ge -1.09$

The line element, which is obtained from Eqs (55) for $p = 4$ is the following:

$$ds^2 = -(1 - \frac{2Mr^2(-3(\frac{r}{k})^b + b + \frac{q(k-r)^2}{k^2} + 3)}{bk^3})dt^2 +$$

$$(1 - \frac{2Mr^2(-3(\frac{r}{k})^b + b + \frac{q(k-r)^2}{k^2} + 3)}{bk^3})^{-1}dr^2 + r^2(d\theta^2 +$$

$$\sin^2\theta d\phi^2) \tag{70}$$

If $b = 1$ we get from Eqs (66) and (68)

$$\mu = \frac{M(k - r)}{4\pi k^4}(12 + q(3 - 5\frac{r}{k})) \qquad (71)$$

$$\mu + P_\perp = \frac{Mr}{4\pi k^4}(6 + q(4 - 5\frac{r}{k})) \qquad (72)$$

If $q = 0$ the energy density μ is non-negative in the interior region, while if $q > 0$ it takes its minimum value for $r = k$ and this value is non-negative if $q \leq 6$. Also if $q < 0$ it takes its minimum value if $r = 0$ and this value is non-negative if $q \geq -4$. Therefore μ is non-negative in the interior region if

$$6 \geq q \geq -4 \qquad (73)$$

In a similar way we find that $\mu + P_\perp$ is non-negative in the interior region if

$$6 \geq q \geq -\frac{3}{2} \qquad (74)$$

Therefore the solution for $p = 4$ and $b = 1$ satisfies the WEC if the above relations holds.

According to Eq (66) the solution has the equation of state

$$\mu = -P_r \qquad (75)$$

Example 2.2.1.1.1 : Solution with $f(r)$ and $h(r)$ of Eq (76)
Consider the solution with

$$f(r) = r^2 \quad \text{and} \quad h(r) = \frac{r^4(4k - 3r)}{k^4} \qquad (76)$$

The above function $h(r)$ is obtained from the $h(r)$ of (58) for $b = 1$ and $q = 0$. From Eqs (1) and (76) we get the line element [41]

$$ds^2 = -(1 - \frac{8Mr^2}{k^3} + \frac{6Mr^3}{k^4})dt^2 + (1 - \frac{8Mr^2}{k^3} + \frac{6Mr^3}{k^4})^{-1}dr^2 +$$
$$r^2(d\theta^2 + sin^2\theta d\phi^2) \qquad (77)$$

The non zero components of the Ricci tensor $R_{\mu\nu}$, the Ricci scalar R and the second order curvature invariant R^2 of the solution with the above line element are the following:

$$R_{tt} = -\frac{12M(2k - 3r)(k^4 - 8kMr^2 + 6Mr^3)}{k^8} \qquad (78)$$

$$R_{rr} = \frac{12M(2k - 3r)}{k^4 - 8kMr^2 + 6Mr^3)} \tag{79}$$

$$R_{\theta\theta} = \frac{R_{\phi\phi}}{sin^2\theta} = \frac{24M(k - r)r^2}{k^4} \tag{80}$$

$$\tilde{R} = \frac{24M(4k - 5r)}{k^4} \tag{81}$$

$$R^2 = \frac{48M^2}{k^8}(32k^2 - 80kr + 57r^2) \tag{82}$$

Eqs (81) and (82) imply that the solution is regular. Also we can calculate the eigenvalues B_i and W_i $i = t, r, \theta, \phi$ of the matrices R_μ^ν and $R_\mu^\nu - \frac{R}{2}\delta_\mu^\nu = 8\pi T_\mu^\nu$ respectively, the energy density μ, the radial pressure P_r, the tangential pressure $P_\perp$ and the quantity $\mu + P_\perp$. We get

$$B_t = B_r = \frac{12M(2k - 3r)}{k^4} \tag{83}$$

$$B_\theta = B_\phi = \frac{24M(k - r)}{k^4} \tag{84}$$

$$\mu = -\frac{W_t}{8\pi} = \frac{3M(k - r)}{\pi k^4} \tag{85}$$

$$P_r = \frac{W_r}{8\pi} = -\frac{3M(k - r)}{\pi k^4} = -\mu \tag{86}$$

$$P_\perp = \frac{W_\perp}{8\pi} = \frac{3M(3r - 2k)}{2\pi k^4} \tag{87}$$

$$\mu + P_\perp = \frac{3Mr}{2\pi k^4} \tag{88}$$

From Eqs (85), (86) and (88) we find that the solution satisfies the WEC as expected. An equation of state of the form $\mu + P_r = 0$ was introduced originally by Sakharov as an equation of state of a superdense fluid [17]. Gliner [18] called the matter with this equation of state $\mu - $ vacuum. He argues that the meaning of a negative pressure is that the internal volume forces in the matter are not forces of repulsion but forces of attraction and also that an object with this equation of state might be formed in gravitational collapse. This equation arises in Grand Unified Theories at very high densities and it is used in the cosmological inflationary senario [37]. Also it is the equation of state in the de Sitter interior of the gravastar (gravitational vacuum star) model [20] [21]. It appears in many papers, in which regular black hole solutions are constructed [2]. It is argued that the Einstein tensor $G_{\mu\nu}$ of a metric of the form $ds^2 = -F(r)dt^2 + \frac{1}{F(r)}dr^2 + r^2(d\theta^2 + \sin^2\theta d\phi^2)$, where $F(r)$ has the asymptotic behavior $F(r) \sim 1 - \frac{r^2}{l^2}$ as $r \to 0$, has the cosmological-constant form

$$G_{\mu\nu} \sim -\Lambda g_{\mu\nu} \quad \text{as} \quad r \to 0 \quad \text{with} \quad \Lambda = \frac{3}{l^2} \tag{89}$$

which means that we have an effective cosmological constant at small distances with Hubble length l [6]. Since from Eqs (86)-(88) we get $\mu + P_\perp \sim 0$ and $P_r - P_\perp \sim 0$ as $r \to 0$ we find from Eq. (32) that the above relation is satisfied for the metric of Eq. (77) with $\Lambda = \frac{24M}{k^3}$. The same result for Λ was found in Ref. [3], since $8\pi\mu \sim \frac{24M}{k^3}$. From Eq. (85) we find that the energy density μ vanishes at the boundary $r = k$ and decreases monotonically as we move from the center to the boundary. Also $P_\perp$ and μ satisfy the relation

$$P_\perp + \mu = -\frac{r}{2}\frac{d\mu}{dr} \tag{90}$$

The horizons of the solution with the metric (77) are obtained from the relation $g^{rr} = 0$, from which we get

$$y^3 - \frac{4}{3}y^2 + w = 0, \quad \text{where} \quad y = \frac{r}{k} \quad \text{and} \quad w = \frac{k}{6M} \tag{91}$$

If y_i are the real and positive roots of Eq. (91) the horizons r_{ih} are at $r_{ih} = ky_i = 6Mwy_i$. Also Schwarzschild's solution has horizon at $r_S = 2M$, while the matching surface r_M is at $r_M = k = 6Mw$. Combining these expressions we get

$$r_M = 3wr_S = \frac{r_{ih}}{y_i} \tag{92}$$

Consider the cubic equation $y^3 + a_2y^2 + a_1y + a_0 = 0$ and define q and p by the relations $q = \frac{1}{9}(3a_1 - a_2^2)$ and $p = \frac{1}{6}(a_1a_2 - 3a_0) - \frac{1}{27}a_2^3$. Then if $q^3 + p^2 > 0$ the solution has one real and two complex roots, if $q^3 + p^2 = 0$ all roots are real and at least two of them are equal and if $q^3 + p^2 < 0$ all roots are real [42]. In our case $w = \frac{256}{729} = w_0$ is the value of w for which $q^3 + p^2 = 0$. Then we get $q^3 + p^2 > 0$ if $w > w_0$ and $q^3 + p^2 < 0$ if $w < w_0$. The solution $y = 1$ of Eq. (91) is obtained for $w = 1/3$. We consider the cases:

(1) $w > w_0$, which means that $k > \frac{1536}{729} M$: Since in this case two of the solutions are complex and the real solution is negative the regular solution we have found does not have an event horizon. Also from Eqs (92) we get

$$r_M > r_S \qquad (93)$$

Therefore the event horizon of Schwarzschild's solution is inside the matching surface. The combination of Schwarzschild's solution with its interior does not lead to the formation of a black hole as the end product of gravitational collapse. It leads to the formation of a regular object with de Sitter center, a gravitational soliton, a G-lump, which is held by its gravitational self inter-action. G-lumps are model independent gravastar and can be responsible for local effects related to dark matter in a way similar to primordial black holes [43]. The criterion of G-lump stability under extremal polar perturbations is given by [43]

$$\mu + (\mu + P_\perp) - r\frac{d(\mu + P_\perp)}{dr} \geq 0 \qquad (94)$$

The solution we have found satisfies the above expression in the interior region since $\mu + P_\perp = \frac{3Mr}{2\pi k^4}$ and $\mu \geq 0$ in this region. Since in all cases which follow one of the real solutions is negative this solution will be ignored and for the other two solutions y_1 and y_2 we shall make the choice $y_1 \geq y_2$.

(2) $w = w_0$: In this case we have $y_1 = y_2 = 8/9$ and we conclude that we have a " degenerate" event horizon at $r_{1h} = r_{2h} = \frac{4096}{2187} M$. Also from Eqs (92) we find that $r_M > r_S > r_{1h}$.

(3) $w_0 > w > \frac{1}{3}$: In this case we have $r_M > r_S > r_{1h} > r_{2h}$

(4) $w < \frac{1}{3}$: For these values of w we get $r_S > r_{1h} > r_M > r_{2h}$.

In cases (2)-(4) regular black hole appears in the final state of the collapse. We do not consider the case $w = \frac{1}{3}$, which corresponds to $k = 2M$, since we shall assume that $k \neq 2M$. We do that because for $k = 2M$ at the matching surface $r = k$ the metrics inside and outside have a coordinate singularity.

2.3   Solutions with non vanishing $f(r)$ in the Interior Region

A general method of getting regular interior solutions is based in the use of functions $f(r)$ which do not vanish in the interior region and which together with other functions $h(r)$ satisfy the matching conditions (3) and (4). Also

31

$f(r)$, $h(r)$ and their first and the second order derivative with respect to r are non singular in the interior region. We shall give a list of such functions

$$h(r) = k\left(\frac{bk}{(b+1)k - r}\right)^b \tag{95}$$

$$h(r) = \frac{k^{1-b}}{b}\left((b-1)k^b + r^b\right) \tag{96}$$

$$h(r) = bke^{\frac{r-k}{bk}} - bk + k \tag{97}$$

$$h(r) = \frac{k(br - k)}{(b-2)k + r} \tag{98}$$

$$h(r) = \frac{k\left(k^q(p(q-1) - q) + pr^q\right)}{k^q((p-1)q - 1) + r^q} \tag{99}$$

$$h(r) = (1 - b)ke^{\frac{r-k}{k}} + br \tag{100}$$

$$h(r) = \frac{k^{1-pq}}{(pq)^q}(pqk^p - q^p + r^p)^q \tag{101}$$

$$h(r) = r \tag{102}$$

$$f(r) = (h(r))^2 \tag{103}$$

$$f(r) = h(r)h_1(r) \text{ where } h_1(r) \neq h(r) \tag{104}$$

$$f(r) = h_1(r)h_2(r) \text{ where } h_1(r) \neq h_2(r) \neq h(r) \tag{105}$$

$$f(r) = b^{-b}k^{2-b}((b-2)k + 2r)^b \tag{106}$$

$$f(r) = \frac{k^{2-b}}{b}((b-2)k^b + 2r^b)) \tag{107}$$

$$f(r) = bk^2e^{\frac{2(r-k)}{bk}} - bk^2 + k^2 \tag{108}$$

$$f(r) = \frac{k(br^2 - k^2)}{(b-3)k + 2r} \tag{109}$$

$$f(r) = \frac{kq\left(k^{q+1}(p(q-1) - q - 1) + 2pr^{q+1}\right)}{(q+1)\left(k^q((p-1)q - 2) + 2r^q\right)} \tag{110}$$

$$f(r) = (1 - b)k^2e^{\frac{2(r-k)}{k}} + br^2 \tag{111}$$

$$f(r) = \frac{k^{2-pq}}{(pq)^q}\left(pqk^q + 2\left(r^p - k^p\right)\right)^q \tag{112}$$

32

If $h_1(r)$, $h_2(r)$,... $h_v(r)$ and $f_1(r)$, $f_2(r)$, ...$f_n(r)$ are acceptable functions $h(r)$ and $f(r)$ then the expressions

$$p_1 h_1(r) + p_2 h_2(r) + ... + p_{v-1} h_{v-1}(r) + (1 - p_1 - p_2 - ... - p_{v-1}) h_v(r) \quad (113)$$

and

$$q_1 f_1(r) + q_2 f_2(r) + ... + q_{n-1} f_{n-1}(r) + (1 - q_1 - q_2 - ... - q_{n-1}) f_n(r) \quad (114)$$

where the expression of Eq (114) does not vanish in the interior region, satisfy the matching conditions and are acceptable functions $h(r)$ and $f(r)$. Also if $F(r)$ and $H(r)$ are the fuctions of an interior solution to the solution of Kerr, as descibed in Section 3 of the paper and $F(r)$ does not vanish in the interior region we can take $f(r) = F(r)$ and $h(r) = -\frac{H(r)}{2M}$.

2.3.1 Solutions with $f(r) = (h(r))^2$

For this choice of $f(r)$ the non vanishing components of the Ricci tensor $R_{\mu\nu}$ the Ricci scalar R and the second order curvature invariant R^2 are the following

$$R_{tt} = -\frac{M(2M - h(r))h''(r)}{h(r)^3} \quad (115)$$

$$R_{rr} = \frac{(2h(r) - 3M)h''(r)}{h(r)(2M - h(r))} \quad (116)$$

$$R_{\theta\theta} = \frac{R_{\phi\phi}}{\sin^2 \theta} = -(h(r) - 2M)h''(r) - h'(r)^2 + 1 \quad (117)$$

$$R = \frac{(6M - 4h(r))h''(r) - 2h'(r)^2 + 2}{h(r)^2} \quad (118)$$

$$R^2 = \frac{4}{h(r)^6}(-8Mh(r)^3 h''(r)^2 + 2h(r)^4 h''(r)^2 +$$
$$12M^2 h'(r)^4 - 4Mh(r)h'(r)^2 \left(3Mh''(r) + h'(r)^2 - 1\right)$$
$$h(r)^2 \left(9M^2 h''(r)^2 + h'(r)^4 + h'(r)^2 (4Mh''(r) - 2) + 1\right)) \quad (119)$$

The eigenvalues B_i and W_i $i = t, r, \theta, \phi$ of the matrices R_μ^ν and $R_\mu^\nu - \frac{R}{2}\delta_\mu^\nu = 8\pi T_\mu^\nu$ respectively, the energy density μ, the radial pressure P_r, the tangential pressure $P_\perp$ and the quantities $\mu + P_r$ and $\mu + P_\perp$ are easily calculated. We get

$$B_t = -M\frac{h''(r)}{h(r)^2} \tag{120}$$

$$B_r = \frac{(3M - 2h(r))h''(r)}{h(r)^2} \tag{121}$$

$$B_\theta = B_\phi = \frac{(2M - h(r))h''(r) - h'(r)^2 + 1}{h(r)^2} \tag{122}$$

$$\mu = -\frac{W_t}{8\pi} = \frac{(4M - 2h(r))h''(r) - h'(r)^2 + 1}{8\pi h(r)^2} \tag{123}$$

$$P_r = \frac{W_r}{8\pi} = \frac{h'(r)^2 - 1}{8\pi h(r)^2} \tag{124}$$

$$P_\perp = \frac{W_\perp}{8\pi} = \frac{(h(r) - M)h''(r)}{8\pi h(r)^2} \tag{125}$$

$$\mu + P_r = \frac{(2M - h(r))h''(r)}{4\pi h(r)^2} \tag{126}$$

$$\mu + P_\perp = \frac{(3M - h(r))h''(r) - h'(r)^2 + 1}{8\pi h(r)^2} \tag{127}$$

Since at the matching surface $r = k$ we have $h(k) = k$ and $h'(k) = 1$ we get at this surface $P_r = 0$ and if in edition $M = \frac{k}{2}$ we get $\mu = \mu + P_r = 0$ as expected according to Eqs (33) and (34). Also from Eq (124) we find that if $f(r) = (h(r))^2$ the radial pressure P_r is independent of M and therefore independent of $n = \frac{2M}{k}$.

If we solve Eqs (124) - (126) for $h(r)$, $h'(r)^2$ and $h''(r)$ we get

$$h(r) = \frac{\mu M + 4MP_\perp + MP_r}{\mu + 2P_\perp + P_r} \tag{128}$$

$$h'(r)^2 = \frac{8\pi M^2 P_r(\mu + 4P_\perp + P_r)^2}{(\mu + 2P_\perp + P_r)^2} + 1 \tag{129}$$

$$h''(r) = \frac{4\pi M(\mu + 4P_\perp + P_r)^2}{\mu + 2P_\perp + P_r} \tag{130}$$

For these expressions of $h(r)$, $h'(r)^2$ and $h''(r)$ Eqs (123) - (127) are satisfied. We shall use Eqs (128) - (130) to find the equation of state of the solutions with $f(r) = (h(r))^2$.

The line element d^2s of this solution is obtained from Eq (1) and the relation $f(r) = (h(r))^2$. We get

$$d^2s = -(1 - \frac{2M}{h(r)})d^2t + \frac{1}{1 - \frac{2M}{h(r)}}d^2r + h(r)^2(d^2\theta + + \sin^2\theta d^2\varphi) \qquad (131)$$

From Eqs (121) and (122) we ge

$$B_r - B_\theta = B_r - B_\phi = \frac{(M - h(r))h''(r) + h'(r)^2 - 1}{h(r)^2} \qquad (132)$$

If the above expression vanish the solution is a perfect fluid solution. This happens if

$$h(r)_{\pm} = M \pm C(1)\sinh\left(\frac{C(2) + r}{C(1)}\right) \qquad (133)$$

where $C(1)$ and $C(2)$ are arbitrary constants. Then the matching conditions (3) and (4) are not satisfied from the $h(r)_-$, while they are satisfied from the $h(r)_+$ only if $M = k$ and $C(2) = -k$. Making these replacements in $h(r)_+$ and substituting the resulting expression in Eq (123) we get

$$\mu = -\frac{\sinh\left(\frac{k-r}{C(1)}\right)\left(3C(1)\sinh\left(\frac{k-r}{C(1)}\right) + 2k\right)}{C(1)h(r)^2} \qquad (134)$$

which is always negative. Therefore there is no perfect fluid solution with $f(r) = (h(r))^2$ which satisfy the WEC. We shall present explicitly some examples.

Example 2.3.1.1 : Solution with $f(r) = (h(r))^2$ and $h(r)$ of Eq (135)
Consider the solution with $f(r) = (h(r))^2$ and

$$h(r) = k(\frac{bk}{(b+1)k - r})^b \qquad (135)$$

In the above expression b is a real constant which satisfy the relations

$$b > 0 \quad \text{or} \quad b < -1 \qquad (136)$$

since for these values of b the function $f(r)$ does not vanish in the interior region $0 \le r \le k$. For this choice of $h(r)$ the g_{tt} of the metric is for $b = 1$ linear in r, for $b = 2$ quadratic in r, for $b = 3$ cubic in r and so on.

From Eqs (115) - (119) and (135) we get the following expressions for the non vanishing components of the Ricci tensor $R_{\mu\nu}$, the Ricci scalar R and the second order curvature invariant R^2

$$R_{tt} = \frac{b(b+1)MN^{-2b}\left(kN^b - 2M\right)}{k^2(bk+k-r)^2} \tag{137}$$

$$R_{rr} = -\frac{b(b+1)\left(2kN^b - 3M\right)}{(bk+k-r)^2\left(kN^b - 2M\right)} \tag{138}$$

$$R_{\theta\theta} = \frac{R_{\phi\phi}}{sin^2\theta} =$$
$$-\frac{k^2\left(b^2\left(2N^{2b}-1\right) + b\left(N^{2b}-2\right) - 1\right) - 2(b+1)k\left(bMN^b - r\right) - r^2}{(bk+k-r)^2} \tag{139}$$

$$R = \frac{2N^{-2b}}{k^2(bk+k-r)^2}(k^2(b^2(1-3N^{2b}) -$$
$$2b(N^{2b}-1)+1) + (b+1)k(3bMN^b - 2r) + r^2) \tag{140}$$

$$R^2 = \frac{4N^{-4b}}{k^4(bk+k-r)^4}(b^2(b(3b+4)+2)k^4N^{4b} - 4b^2(b(2b+3) +$$
$$2)k^3MN^{3b} - b^2k^2N^{2b}(2(b+1)^2k^2 - 4(b+1)kr - 3(b(3b+2) +$$
$$3)M^2 + 2r^2) + 4b^2kMN^b(bk+k-r)^2 + (bk+k-r)^4) \tag{141}$$

where N is defined by the relation

$$N = \frac{bk}{bk+k-r} \tag{142}$$

We see that the invariants R and R^2 are regular in the interior region, which means that the interior solution is regular in this region. From Eqs (120) - (127) and (135) we get the following expressions for the eigenvalues B_i $i =$

t, r, θ and ϕ the energy density μ, the radial pressure P_r, the tangential pressure $P_\perp$ and the quantities $\mu + P_r$ and $\mu + P_\perp$

$$B_t = -\frac{b(1+b)M}{k((1+b)k - r)^2 N^b} \tag{143}$$

$$B_r = \frac{b(b+1)\left(3M - 2kN^b\right)}{k(bk + k - r)^2 N^b} \tag{144}$$

$$B_\theta = B_\phi = -\frac{\left(b(2b+1)Mk^2N^{2b} - 2b(b+1)kMN^b - (bk+k-r)^2\right)}{k^2(bk+k-r)^2 N^{2b}} \tag{145}$$

$$\mu = \frac{1}{8\pi k^2(bk+k-r)^2 N^{2b}}((k^2(b^2(1-3N^{2b}) - 2b(N^{2b}-1)$$
$$+1) + 2(b+1)k(2bMN^b - r) + r^2)) \tag{146}$$

$$P_r = \frac{\left(b^2k^2N^{2b} - b^2k^2 - 2bk^2 + 2bkr - k^2 + 2kr - r^2\right)}{8\pi k^2(bk+k-r)^2 N^{2b}} \tag{147}$$

$$P_\perp = \frac{b(b+1)\left(kN^b - M\right)}{8\pi k(bk+k-r)^2 N^b} \tag{148}$$

$$\mu + P_r = -\frac{b(b+1)\left(kN^b - 2M\right)}{4\pi k(bk+k-r)^2 N^b} \tag{149}$$

$$\mu + P_\perp = \frac{1}{8\pi k^2(bk+k-r)^2 N^{2b}}((k^2(b^2(1-2N^{2b}) - b(N^{2b}-2)$$
$$+1) + (b+1)k(3bMN^b - 2r) + r^2)) \tag{150}$$

To find the equation of state of the solution we shall use Eqs (128), (130) and (135) . We get from Eq (135)

$$h''(r) = \frac{b+1}{bk}\left(\frac{bk}{bk+k-r}\right)^{b+2} \tag{151}$$

or

$$h''(r) = \frac{b+1}{bk}\left(\frac{h(r)}{k}\right)^{\frac{b+2}{b}} \qquad (152)$$

Substituting in the above equation the expressions for $h(r)$ and $h''(r)$ of Eqs (128) and (130) we get

$$\mu = -2P_\perp - P_r + 2^{-b}\left(\frac{b}{b+1}\right)^{-b/2}\pi^{-b/2}Mk^{-b-1}(\mu + 4P_\perp + P_r)^{\frac{2-b}{2}} \qquad (153)$$

which is the equation of state of the solution.

To find the values of b for which the solution satisfies the WEC we shall use Eqs (123), (126) (127) and (135). We have

$$h'(r) = \left(\frac{bk}{bk+k-r}\right)^{b+1} \qquad (154)$$

and since for $b > 0$ and $0 \le r \le k$ we have $\frac{bk}{(b+1)k-r} \le 1$ we get

$$h(r) \le k, \quad h'(r) \le 1 \text{ and } h''(r) > 0 \qquad (155)$$

Therefore if in addition we have $2M - r \ge 0$ we get from Eqs (123), (126) (127)

$$\mu \ge 0, \quad \mu + P_r \ge 0 \text{ and } \mu + P_\perp \ge 0 \qquad (156)$$

Also for $b < -1$ and $0 \le r \le k$ we get $\frac{bk}{(b+1)k-r} \ge 1$ and again relations (155) hold. This means that if in addition the relation $2M - k \ge 0$ is valid the relations (156) hold. Therefore the solution satisfies the WEC if $2M - k \ge 0$ and $b > 0$ or $b < -1$.

The line element d^2s of the solution is obtained from Eqs (131) and (135). We get

$$d^2s = -(1 - \frac{2M}{k}(\frac{(1+b)k-r}{bk})^b)d^2t +$$

$$\frac{1}{1 - \frac{2M}{k}(\frac{(1+b)k-r}{bk})^b}d^2r + k^2(\frac{bk}{(1+b)k-r})^{2b}(d^2\theta + \sin^2\theta d^2\varphi) \qquad (157)$$

After matching the solution has for $\frac{2M}{k} = n > 1$ a horizon at $r = 2M$ and for $\frac{2M}{k} = n = 1$ a "degenerate" horizon at $r = k = 2M$. To find the horizons which are in the interior region we solving equation $g^{rr}(r_{int}) = 0$ in which case we get

$$r_{int} = k(1 + b(1 - (\frac{k}{2M})^{1/b})) \tag{158}$$

To each r_{int} for which

$$0 < r_{int} = k(1 + b(1 - (\frac{k}{2M})^{1/b})) < k \tag{159}$$

a horizon corresponds. Eq (159) is equivalent to the relation

$$1 < (k/2M)^{1/b} < 1 + 1/b \tag{160}$$

if $b > 0$ and to the relation

$$1 > (k/2M)^{1/b} > 1 + 1/b \tag{161}$$

if $b < 0$. Therefore if k, M and $b > 0$ satisfy the relation (160) or if k, M and $b < -1$ satisfy the relation (161) the solution we get after matching has a horizon at the position r_{int} of the interior region given by Eq (158).

We shall study further the solutions we get for $b = 1$, 2 and -2.

Example 2.3.1.1.1 : Solution with $f(r) = (h(r))^2$ and $h(r)$ of Eq (162) Consider the solution with $f(r) = (h(r))^2$ and

$$h(r) = \frac{k^2}{2k - r} \tag{162}$$

which is obtained from Eq (135) for $b = 1$. The very simple line element d^2s of this solution, which is obtained from Eq (157) for $b = 1$ is the following:

$$d^2s = -(1 - \frac{4M}{k} + \frac{2Mr}{k^2})d^2t + \frac{1}{1 - \frac{4M}{k} + \frac{2Mr}{k^2}}d^2r + \frac{k^4}{(2k - r)^2}$$
$$(d^2\theta + \sin^2\theta d^2\varphi) \tag{163}$$

For this solution we can calculate the non-vanishing components of the Ricci tensor $R_{\mu\nu}$, the Ricci scalar R, the second order curvature invariant R^2 and subsequently the eigenvalues B_i, $i = t, r, \theta, and \phi$ of the Ricci tensor R^ν_μ. These expressions are obtained from Eqs (137) - (145) for $b = 1$. We get

$$R_{tt} = \frac{2M(k^2 - 4kM + 2Mr)}{k^4(2k - r)} \tag{164}$$

$$R_{rr} = \frac{-4k(k - 3M) - 6Mr}{(r - 2k)^2 (k^2 - 4kM + 2Mr)} \qquad (165)$$

$$R_{\theta\theta} = \frac{R_{\phi\phi}}{sin^2\theta} = \frac{13k^4 + 8k^3(M - 4r) - 4k^2r(M - 6r) - 8kr^3 + r^4}{(r - 2k)^4} \qquad (166)$$

$$R = \frac{2\left(11k^4 + 12k^3M - 32k^3r - 6k^2Mr + 24k^2r^2 - 8kr^3 + r^4\right)}{k^4(2k - r)^2} \qquad (167)$$

$$R^2 = \frac{36}{(r - 2k)^4} + \frac{112M}{k^2(r - 2k)^3} + \frac{96M^2}{k^4(r - 2k)^2} +$$
$$\frac{1}{k^8}\left(14k^4 + 8k^3(M - 4r) + 4k^2r(6r - M) - 8kr^3 + r^4\right) \qquad (168)$$

$$B_t = -\frac{2M}{k^2(2k - r)} \qquad (169)$$

$$B_r = \frac{-4k(k - 3M) - 6Mr}{k^2(r - 2k)^2} \qquad (170)$$

$$B_\theta = B_\phi = \frac{13k^4 + 8k^3(M - 4r) - 4k^2r(M - 6r) - 8kr^3 + r^4}{k^4(r - 2k)^2} \qquad (171)$$

Also the energy density μ, the radial pressure P_r, the tangential pressure $P_\perp$ and the quantities $\mu + P_r$ and $\mu + P_\perp$ are obtained from Eqs (146) - (150) for $b = 1$. If we write

$$\frac{2M}{k} = n \quad \text{and} \quad \frac{r}{k} = y \qquad (172)$$

we get

$$\mu = \frac{-4n(y - 2) + y^4 - 8y^3 + 24y^2 - 32y + 11}{8\pi k^2(y - 2)^2} \qquad (173)$$

$$P_r = -\frac{y^4 - 8y^3 + 24y^2 - 32y + 15}{8\pi k^2(y - 2)^2} \qquad (174)$$

$$P_\perp = \frac{n(y - 2) + 2}{8\pi k^2(y - 2)^2} \qquad (175)$$

$$\mu + P_r = -\frac{n(y-2)+1}{2\pi k^2(y-2)^2} \tag{176}$$

$$\mu + P_\perp = \frac{-3n(y-2)+y^4-8y^3+24y^2-32y+13}{8\pi k^2(y-2)^2} \tag{177}$$

The equation of state of the solution, which is obtained from Eq (153) if we make the substitution $b = 1$ and then solve for μ , is the following:

$$\mu = \frac{1}{4\pi k^4}(-8\pi k^4 P_\perp - 4\pi k^4 P_r + M^2 - M\sqrt{16\pi k^4 P_\perp + M^2}) \tag{178}$$

If in the above equation we eliminate P_r and $P_\perp$ using Eqs (174) and (175) we get Eqs (173).

In Figures 1 - 6 we present the graphs of $k^2\mu$, $k^2(\mu + P_r)$ and $k^2(\mu + P_\perp)$ of Eqs. (173), (176) and (177) for $n = 1$ and $n = 2$. From these graphs we find that the solution for these values of n satisfies the WEC. Also in Figure 7 we present the graph of $k^2 P_r$ of Eq (174) in the interior region. The radial pressure is independent of n. Finally in Figures 8 and 9 we present the graphs of $k^2 P_\perp$ of Eq (175) for $n = 1$ and $n = 2$.

The solution we get for $(b,n) = (b, \frac{2M}{k}) = (1,1)$ has the "degenerate" horizon at $r = k = 2M$. This is its only horizon since for $(b, \frac{2M}{k}) = (1,1)$ the relation (160) is not satisfied.

The solution we get for $(b,n) = (b, \frac{2M}{k}) = (1,2)$ has a horizon at $r = 2M$. This is its only horizon since for $(b, \frac{2M}{k}) = (1,2)$ the relation (160) is not satisfied.

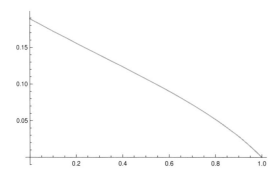

Figure 1: $k^2\mu$ of expression (173) for $n = 1$

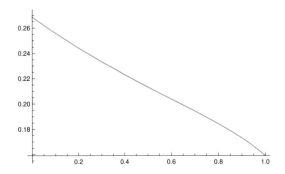

Figure 2: $k^2\mu$ of expression (173) for $n = 2$

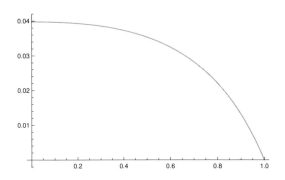

Figure 3: $k^2(\mu + P_r)$ of expression (176) for $n = 1$

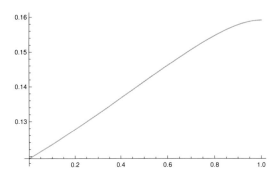

Figure 4: $k^2(\mu + P_r)$ of expression (176) for $n = 2$

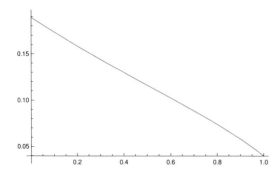

Figure 5: $k^2(\mu + P_\perp)$ of expression (177) for $n = 1$

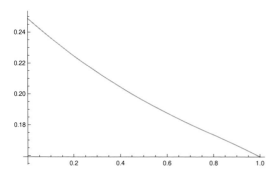

Figure 6: $k^2(\mu + P_\perp)$ of expression (177) for $n = 2$

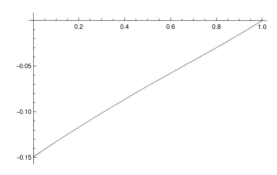

Figure 7: $k^2 P_r$ of expression (174)

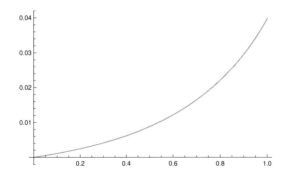

Figure 8: $k^2 P_\perp$ of expression (175) for $n = 1$

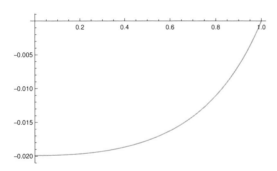

Figure 9: $k^2 P_\perp$ of expression (175) for $n = 2$

Example 2.3.1.1.2 : Solution with $f(r) = (h(r))^2$ and $h(r)$ of Eq (179) Consider the solution with $f(r) = (h(r))^2$ and

$$h(r) = \frac{4k^3}{(3k - r)^2} \tag{179}$$

which is obtained from Eq (135) for $b = 2$. From Eq (157) we get for $b = 2$ the line element

$$d^2 s = -(1 - \frac{M(r - 3k)^2}{2k^3})d^2 t + \frac{1}{1 - \frac{M(r-3k)^2}{2k^3}}d^2 r + \frac{16k^6}{(3k - r)^4}$$
$$(d^2\theta + sin^2\theta d^2\phi) \tag{180}$$

In this case the non-vanishing components of the Ricci tensor $R_{\mu\nu}$, the Ricci scalar R and the second order curvature invariant R^2, which are obtained from Eqs (137) - (142) for $b = 2$, are the following

$$R_{tt} = \frac{3M\left(2k^3 - 9k^2M + 6kMr - Mr^2\right)}{4k^6} \tag{181}$$

$$R_{rr} = \frac{3M}{-2k^3 + 9k^2M - 6kMr + Mr^2} - \frac{12}{(r-3k)^2} \tag{182}$$

$$R_{\theta\theta} = \frac{R_{\phi\phi}}{sin^2\theta} = \frac{1}{(3k-r)^6}(569k^6 + 432k^5M-$$

$$1458k^5r - 288k^4Mr + 1215k^4r^2 + 48k^3Mr^2 - 540k^3r^3 + 135k^2r^4 - 18kr^5 + r^6) \tag{183}$$

$$R = \frac{81k^4 + 36k^3(2M - 3r) + 54k^2r^2 - 12kr^3 + r^4}{8k^6} - \frac{32}{(r-3k)^2} \tag{184}$$

$$R^2 = \frac{352}{(r-3k)^4} - \frac{256M}{k^3(r-3k)^2} + \frac{1}{64k^{12}}(5409k^8 + 24k^7(216M - 697r) +$$

$$4k^6\left(912M^2 - 1728Mr + 5071r^2\right) + 216k^5r^2(16M - 63r) + 6k^4r^3(945r -$$

$$128M) + 8k^3r^4(8M - 189r) + 252k^2r^6 - 24kr^7 + r^8) \tag{185}$$

Also the eigenvalues B_i, $i = t$, r, θ and ϕ of the Ricci tensor R^ν_μ, which are obtained from Eqs (143 - (145) for $b = 2$, are the following

$$B_t = -\frac{3M}{2k^3} \tag{186}$$

$$B_r = \frac{9M}{2k^3} - \frac{12}{(r-3k)^2} \tag{187}$$

$$B_\theta = B_\phi = \frac{81k^4 + 12k^3(4M - 9r) + 54k^2r^2 - 12kr^3 + r^4}{16k^6} - \frac{10}{(r-3k)^2} \tag{188}$$

From Eqs (146) - (150) for $b = 2$ and the relations (172) we get the following expressions for the energy density μ, the radial pressure P_r, the tangential pressure $P_\perp$ and the quantities $\mu + P_r$ and $\mu + P_\perp$

$$\mu = \frac{48n(y-3)^2 + (y((y-9)y + 27) - 43)(y((y-9)y + 27) - 11)}{128\pi k^2 (y-3)^2} \tag{189}$$

$$P_r = -\frac{(y-5)(y-1)((y-8)y + 19)((y-4)y + 7)}{128\pi k^2 (y-3)^2} \tag{190}$$

$$P_\perp = \frac{3\left(n(y-3)^2 - 8\right)}{32\pi k^2 (y-3)^2} \tag{191}$$

$$\mu + P_r = \frac{3\left(n(y-3)^2 - 4\right)}{8\pi k^2 (y-3)^2} \tag{192}$$

$$\mu + P_\perp = \frac{36n(y-3)^2 + y^6 - 18y^5 + 135y^4 - 540y^3 + 1215y^2 - 1458y + 569}{128\pi k^2 (y-3)^2} \tag{193}$$

The equation of state of the solution, which is obtained from Eq (153) for $b = 2$, is given by the relation

$$\mu = \frac{3M}{8\pi k^3} - P_r - 2P_\perp \tag{194}$$

We can show that this relation is satisfied if μ, P_r and $P_\perp$ are given by Eqs (189), (190) and (191) respectively and $M = kn/2$

In Figures 10 - 15 we present the graphs of $k^2\mu$, $k^2(\mu + P_r)$ and $k^2(\mu + P_\perp)$ of Eqs (189) (192) and (193) for $n = 1$ and $n = 2$. It is obvious from these graphs that the solution for these values of n satisfies the WEC. Also in Figure 16 we present the graph of $k^2 P_r$ of Eq (190) in the interior region. The radial pressure P_r is independent of n. In addition in Figures 17 and 18 we present the graphs of $k^2 P_\perp$ of Eq (191) for $n = 1$ and $n = 2$.

The solution we get for $(b, n) = (b, \frac{2M}{k}) = (2, 1)$ has the "degenerate" horizon at $r = k = 2M$, which is the only horizon of the solution since for $(b, \frac{2M}{k}) = (2, 1)$ the relation (160) is not satisfied.

The solution we get for $(b, n) = (b, \frac{2M}{k}) = (2, 2)$ has a horizon at $r = 2M$, which is its only horizon since for $(b, \frac{2M}{k}) = (2, 2)$ the relation (160) is not satisfied.

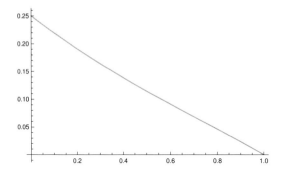

Figure 10: $k^2\mu$ of expression (189) for $n = 1$

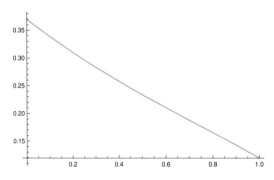

Figure 11: $k^2\mu$ of expression (189) for $n = 2$

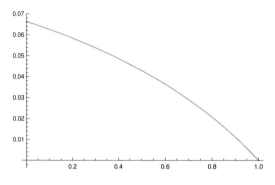

Figure 12: $k^2(\mu + P_r)$ of expression (192) for $n = 1$

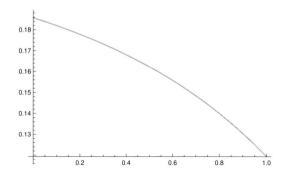

Figure 13: $k^2(\mu + P_r)$ of expression (192) for $n = 2$

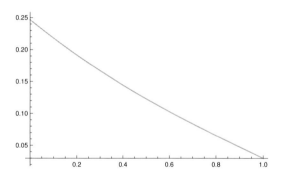

Figure 14: $k^2(\mu + P_\perp)$ of expression (193) for $n = 1$

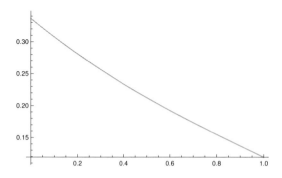

Figure 15: $k^2(\mu + P_\perp)$ of expression (193) for $n = 2$

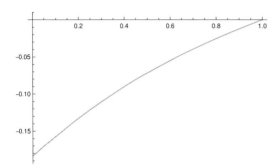

Figure 16: $k^2 P_r$ of expression (190)

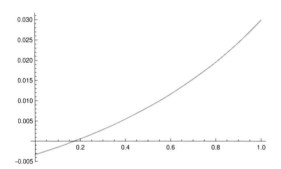

Figure 17: $k^2 P_\perp$ of expression (191) for $n = 1$

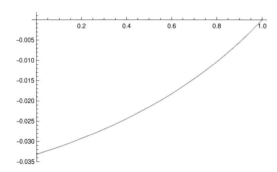

Figure 18: $k^2 P_\perp$ of expression (191) for $n = 2$

Example 2.3.1.1.3 : Solution with $f(r) = (h(r))^2$ and $h(r)$ of Eq (195) Consider the solution with $f(r) = (h(r))^2$ and

$$h(r) = \frac{(r+k)^2}{4k} \tag{195}$$

which is obtained from Eq (135) for $b = -2$. From Eq (157) we get for $b = -2$ the line element

$$d^2s = -(1 - \frac{8kM}{(r+k)^2})d^2t + \frac{1}{1 - \frac{8kM}{(r+k)^2}}d^2r + \frac{(r+k)^4}{16k^2}(d^2\theta + sin^2\theta d^2\phi) \tag{196}$$

The non-vanishing components of the Ricci tensor $R_{\mu\nu}$, the Ricci scalar R, the second order curvature invariant R^2 and the eigenvalues B_i, $i = t$, r, θ and ϕ of the Ricci tensor R^ν_μ of this solution are obtained from Eqs (137) - (145) for $b = -2$. We get

$$R_{tt} = \frac{8kM\left(k^2 + 2k(r - 4M) + r^2\right)}{(k+r)^6} \tag{197}$$

$$R_{rr} = -\frac{4\left(k^2 - 6kM + 2kr + r^2\right)}{(k+r)^2\left(k^2 - 8kM + 2kr + r^2\right)} \tag{198}$$

$$R_{\theta\theta} = \frac{R_{\phi\phi}}{sin^2\theta} = \frac{5k^2 + 8kM - 6kr - 3r^2}{8k^2} \tag{199}$$

$$R = \frac{16\left(k^2 + 3kM - 2kr - r^2\right)}{(k+r)^4} \tag{200}$$

$$R^2 =$$

$$\frac{32\left(8k^2\left(4k^2 + 16kM + 33M^2\right) - 16k(k + 2M)(k+r)^2 + 3(k+r)^4\right)}{(k+r)^8} \tag{201}$$

$$B_t = -\frac{8kM}{(k+r)^4} \tag{202}$$

$$B_r = \frac{24kM}{(k+r)^4} - \frac{4}{(k+r)^2} \tag{203}$$

$$B_\theta = B_\phi = \frac{16k(k+M)}{(k+r)^4} - \frac{6}{(k+r)^2} \tag{204}$$

50

Also if we use Eqs (146) - (150) for $b = -2$ and the relations (172) we get the following expressions for the the energy density μ, the radial pressure P_r, the tangential pressure $P_\perp$ and the quantities $\mu + P_r$ and $\mu + P_\perp$

$$\mu = \frac{2n - y^2 - 2y + 1}{\pi k^2 (y+1)^4} \tag{205}$$

$$P_r = \frac{y^2 + 2y - 3}{2\pi k^2 (y+1)^4} \tag{206}$$

$$P_\perp = \frac{(y+1)^2 - 2n}{4\pi k^2 (y+1)^4} \tag{207}$$

$$\mu + P_r = -\frac{(y+1)^2 - 4n}{2\pi k^2 (y+1)^4} \tag{208}$$

$$\mu + P_\perp = \frac{6n - 3y^2 - 6y + 5}{4\pi k^2 (y+1)^4} \tag{209}$$

The equation of state of the solution, which is obtained from Eq (153) for $b = -2$, is given by the relation

$$\mu = \frac{1}{8\pi k^2 n}(1 - 8\pi k^2 n(4P_\perp + \mathrm{Pr}) - \sqrt{1 - 32\pi k^2 n P_\perp}) \tag{210}$$

Eliminating P_r and $P_\perp$ from the above equation with the help of Eqs (206) and (207) we get Eq (205) as we expected.

In Figures 19 - 24 we present the graphs of $k^2\mu$, $k^2(\mu + P_r)$ and $k^2(\mu + P_\perp)$ of Eqs (205), (208) and (209) for $n = 1$ and $n = 2$. We realize immediately from these graphs that the solution for these values of n satisfies the WEC. Also in Figure 25 we present the graph of $k^2 P_r$ of Eq (206) which is independent of n. Finally in in Figures 26 and 27 we present the graph of $k^2 P_\perp$ of Eq (207) for $n = 1$ and $n = 2$.

The solution we get for $(b, n) = (b, \frac{2M}{k}) = (-2, 1)$ has the "degenerate" horizon at $r = k = 2M$, which is its only horizon since for $(b, \frac{2M}{k}) = (-2, 1)$ the relation (161) is not satisfied.

The solution we get for $(b, n) = (b, \frac{2M}{k}) = (-2, 2)$ has a horizon at $r = 2M$, which is the only horizon of the solution since for $(b, \frac{2M}{k}) = (-2, 2)$ the relation (161) is not satisfied.

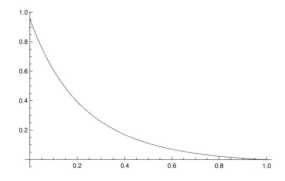

Figure 19: $k^2\mu$ of expression (205) for $n = 1$

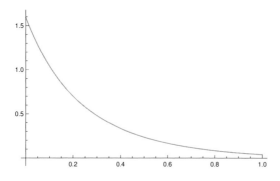

Figure 20: $k^2\mu$ of expression (205) for $n = 2$

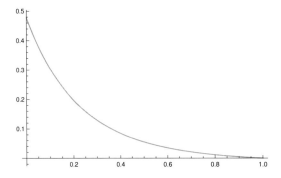

Figure 21: $k^2(\mu + P_r)$ of expression (208) for $n = 1$

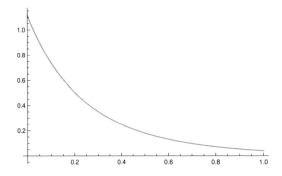

Figure 22: $k^2(\mu + P_r)$ of expression (208) for $n = 2$

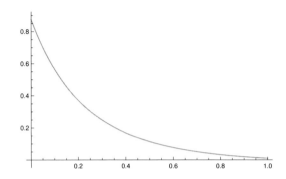

Figure 23: $k^2(\mu + P_\perp)$ of expression (209) for $n = 1$

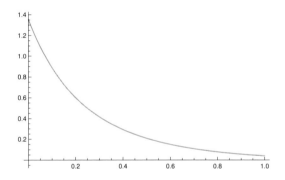

Figure 24: $k^2(\mu + P_\perp)$ of expression (209) for $n = 2$

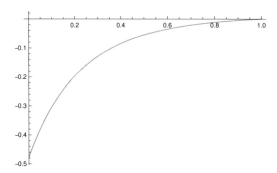

Figure 25: $k^2 P_r$ of expression (206)

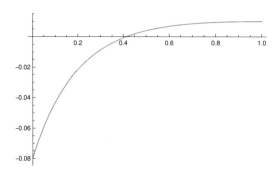

Figure 26: $k^2 P_\perp$ of expression (207) for $n = 1$

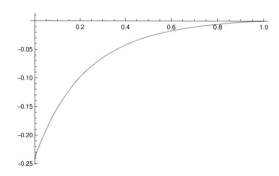

Figure 27: $k^2 P_\perp$ of expression (207) for $n = 2$

Example 2.3.1.2 : Solution with $f(r) = (h(r))^2$ and $h(r)$ of Eq (211)
Consider the solution with $f(r) = (h(r))^2$ and

$$h(r) = \frac{k^{1-b}}{b}(r^b + (b-1)k^b) \tag{211}$$

Since in the interior region $f(r)$ must be regular and non-vanishing we must have $b > 1$. The non-vanishing components of the Ricci tensor $R_{\mu\nu}$, the Ricci scalar R, the second order curvature invariant R^2 and the eigenvalues B_i, $i = t, r, \theta, and \ \phi$ of the Ricci tensor R^ν_μ of this solution are obtained from Eqs (115) - (122) and (211). We get

$$R_{tt} = \frac{(b-1)b^2 M k^{b-2} r^{b-2} \left(k^b((b-1)k - 2bM) + kr^b\right)}{((b-1)k^b + r^b)^3} \tag{212}$$

$$R_{rr} = \frac{1}{2}(b-1)br^{b-2}\left(-\frac{k}{k^b((b-1)k - 2bM) + kr^b} - \frac{3}{(b-1)k^b + r^b}\right) \tag{213}$$

$$R_{\theta\theta} = \frac{R_{\phi\phi}}{sin^2\theta} = -\frac{k^{-2b}}{br^2}((b-1)k^{b+1}r^b((b-1)k - 2bM) - $$
$$br^2 k^{2b} + (2b-1)k^2 r^{2b} \tag{214}$$

$$R = \frac{2b\left(-(b-1)k^{b+1}r^b(2(b-1)k - 3bM) + br^2 k^{2b} - (3b-2)k^2 r^{2b}\right)}{k^2 r^2 \left((b-1)k^b + r^b\right)^2} \tag{215}$$

$$R^2 = \frac{1}{k^4 r^4 ((b-1)k^b + r^b)^6} 4b^2 (2(b-1)b^2 k^{5b} r^{b+4} + (b-1)^2 b^2 r^4$$
$k^{6b} + 2k^{3b+1}r^{3b}((b-1)^2 k(3(b-3)b^2 M^2 + 4(b-1)^3 k^2 - 2b(5b - 6)(b-1)kM) + 2b^2 r^2(-bk + bM + k)) + k^{2b+2}r^{4b}(b^2((9b^2 - 6b + 9)M^2 - 2r^2) + (b-1)^2(b(13b - 24) + 12)k^2 - 4(b-1)(5(b-2)b +6)bkM) + k^{4b}r^{2b}((b-1)^4 k^2(9b^2 M^2 + 2(b-1)^2 k^2 - 8(b-1)bk M) - 2b^2(b-1)kr^2((b-1)k - 2bM) + b^2 r^4) + 2k^{b+3}r^{5b}((b-1)(b(5b-8)+4)k - 2b(b(2b-3)+2)M) + (b(3b-4)+2)k^4 r^{6b}) \tag{216}$

$$B_t = -\frac{(b-1)b^2 M k^{b-1} r^{b-2}}{\left((b-1)k^b + r^b\right)^2} \tag{217}$$

$$B_r = -\frac{(b-1)br^{b-2}\left(2(b-1)k^{b+1} - 3bMk^b + 2kr^b\right)}{k\left((b-1)k^b + r^b\right)^2} \tag{218}$$

$$B_\theta = B_\phi = -\frac{b}{k^2 r^2 ((b-1)k^b + r^b)^2}(((b-1)k^{b+1}r^b((b-1)k - 2b$$
$$M) - br^2 k^{2b} + (2b-1)k^2 r^{2b})) \tag{219}$$

From Eqs (215) and (216) we find that the Ricci scalar R and the second order curvature invariant are regular if $b \geq 2$. Therefore the solution is regular if

$$b \geq 2 \tag{220}$$

The energy density μ, the radial pressure P_r, the tangential pressure $P_\perp$ and the quantities $\mu + P_r$ and $\mu + P_\perp$ of the solution are obtained from Eqs (123) - (127) and (211). We get

$$\mu = \frac{b\left(-2(b-1)k^{b+1}r^b((b-1)k - 2bM) + br^2 k^{2b} - (3b-2)k^2 r^{2b}\right)}{8\pi k^2 r^2 \left((b-1)k^b + r^b\right)^2} \tag{221}$$

$$P_r = \frac{b^2\left(k^2 r^{2b} - r^2 k^{2b}\right)}{8\pi k^2 r^2 \left((b-1)k^b + r^b\right)^2} \tag{222}$$

$$P_\perp = \frac{(b-1)br^{b-2}\left((b-1)k^{b+1} - bMk^b + kr^b\right)}{8\pi k \left((b-1)k^b + r^b\right)^2} \tag{223}$$

$$\mu + P_r = -\frac{(b-1)br^{b-2}\left((b-1)k^{b+1} - 2bMk^b + kr^b\right)}{4\pi k \left((b-1)k^b + r^b\right)^2} \tag{224}$$

$$\mu + P_\perp = -\frac{b}{8\pi k^2 r^2 ((b-1)k^b + r^b)^2}$$
$$(b^2 k^{b+1} r^b (k - 3M) + b(3Mk^{b+1}r^b - 2k^{b+2}r^b -$$
$$r^2 k^{2b} + 2k^2 r^{2b}) + k^2 r^b (k^b - r^b)) \tag{225}$$

To find the equation of state we shall consider separately the cases $b = 2$ and $b \neq 2$. For $b = 2$ calculating $h''(r)$ from Eq (211) and then using Eq (130) we get

$$h''(r) = \frac{1}{k} = \frac{4\pi M(\mu + 4P_\perp + P_r r)^2}{\mu + 2P_\perp + P_r} \tag{226}$$

Solving the above equation for μ we get the solution

$$\mu = \frac{1 - 32\pi k M P_\perp - 8\pi k M P_r - \sqrt{1 - 32\pi k M P_\perp}}{8\pi k M} \tag{227}$$

and a second solution.Eliminating P_r and $P_\perp$ from the above relation using Eqs (222) and (223) with $b = 2$ we get Eq (221) for $b = 2$. This does not happen for the second solution. Therefore Eq (227) is the equation of state of the solution with the $h(r)$ of Eq (211) if $b = 2$.

To find the equation of state if $b \neq 2$ we proceed in an analogous fashion. Solving for r the expression $h''(r)$, which is obtained from Eq (211), we get

$$r = (-\frac{k^{1-b} - bk^{1-b}}{h''(r)})^{\frac{1}{2-b}} \tag{228}$$

Using the above expression for r to eliminate r from $h(r)$ of Eq (211) and eliminating $h(r)$ and $h''(r)$ from the resulting equation using Eqs (128) and (130) we get the relation

$$1 - b - k^{-b} \left(\frac{(b-1)k^{1-b}(\mu + 2P_\perp + \mathrm{Pr})}{4\pi M(\mu + 4P_\perp + \mathrm{Pr})^2} \right)^{\frac{b}{2-b}} + \frac{bM(\mu + 4P_\perp + \mathrm{Pr})}{k(\mu + 2P_\perp + \mathrm{Pr})} = 0 \tag{229}$$

The above equation is satisfied if μ, P_r and $P_\perp$ are replaced by the expressions (221), (222) and (223). Expression (229) is the equation of state of the solutions with the $h(r)$ of Eq (211) and $b \neq 2$.

To find the conditions under which the solution satisfies the WEC we shall use Eqs (123), (126), (127) and (211). We get in the interior region $0 < r < k$ for $b \geq 2$

$$1 - (h'(r))^2 = 1 - (\frac{r}{k})^{2b-2} \geq 0 \tag{230}$$

$$h''(r) = \frac{b-1}{k}(\frac{r}{k})^{b-2} > 0 \tag{231}$$

,

$$2M - h(r) = 2M - k + \frac{k}{b}(1 - (\frac{r}{k})^b) \geq 2M - k \qquad (232)$$

Therefore the energy density μ and the quantities $\mu + P_r$ and $\mu + P_\perp$ are non-negative if $2M - k \geq 0$ which means that the solution satisfy the WEC if

$$2M - k \geq 0 \qquad (233)$$

The line element of the solution is obtained from Eqs (131) and (211). We get

$$d^2s = -(1 - \frac{2M}{\frac{k^{1-b}}{b}(r^b + (b-1)k^b)})d^2t+$$

$$\frac{1}{1 - \frac{2M}{\frac{k^{1-b}}{b}(r^b+(b-1)k^b)}}d^2r + (\frac{k^{1-b}}{b}(r^b + (b-1)k^b))^2(d^2\theta + sin^2\theta d^2\phi) \qquad (234)$$

After matching the solution has for $\frac{2M}{k} = n > 1$ a horizon at $r = 2M$ and for $\frac{2M}{k} = n = 1$ a "degenerate" horizon at $r = k = 2M$. To find the horizons which are in the interior region we solving equation $g^{rr}(r_{int}) = 0$ in which case we get

$$r_{int} = k(1 - b(1 - \frac{2M}{k}))^{\frac{1}{b}} \qquad (235)$$

To each r_{int} which is inside the interior region, that is to each r_{int} for which

$$0 < r_{int} = k(1 - b(1 - \frac{2M}{k}))^{\frac{1}{b}} < k \qquad (236)$$

a horizon corresponds. For $b \geq 2$ Eq (236) is equivalent to the relation

$$1 > \frac{2M}{k} > 1 - 1/b \qquad (237)$$

Therefore if k, M and b satisfy the relation (237) the solution we get after matching has a horizon at the position r_{int} given by Eq (236). If $\frac{2M}{k} \leq 1 - 1/b$ with $b \geq 2$ after matching the solution does not have a horizon.

In the following we shall consider the solution we get for $b = 2$.

Example 2.3.1.2.1 : Solution with $f(r) = (h(r))^2$ and $h(r)$ of Eq (238) Consider the solution with $f(r) = (h(r))^2$ and

$$h(r) = \frac{k^2 + r^2}{2k} \tag{238}$$

which is obtained from the $h(r)$ of Eq (211) for $b = 2$. For $b = 2$ from (234) we get the line element

$$d^2s = -(1 - \frac{4kM}{k^2 + r^2})d^2t + \frac{1}{1 - \frac{4kM}{k^2+r^2}}d^2r + (\frac{k^2 + r^2}{2k})^2(d^2\theta + sin^2\theta d^2\phi) \tag{239}$$

The non-vanishing components of the Ricci tensor $R_{\mu\nu}$, the Ricci scalar R, the second order curvature invariant R^2 and the eigenvalues B_i, $i = t,\, r,\, \theta,\, and\, \phi$ of the Ricci tensor R_μ^ν of this solution which are obtained from Eqs (212)-(219) for $b = 2$ are the following

$$R_{tt} = \frac{4kM\,(k^2 - 4kM + r^2)}{(k^2 + r^2)^3} \tag{240}$$

$$R_{rr} = -\frac{4\,(k^2 - 3kM + r^2)}{(k^2 + r^2)\,(k^2 - 4kM + r^2)} \tag{241}$$

$$R_{\theta\theta} = \frac{R_{\phi\phi}}{sin^2\theta} = \frac{k^2 + 4kM - 3r^2}{2k^2} \tag{242}$$

$$R = \frac{8\,(3kM - 2r^2)}{(k^2 + r^2)^2} \tag{243}$$

$$R^2 = \frac{32}{(k^2 + r^2)^6}(k^6(3k^2 - 8kM + 18M^2)+$$

$$2k^2r^4\left(k^2 - 4kM + 33M^2\right) + 4k^4r^2\left(k^2 - 3M^2\right) + 4kr^6(k-4M) + 3r^8) \tag{244}$$

$$B_t = -\frac{4kM}{(k^2 + r^2)^2} \tag{245}$$

$$B_r = -\frac{4\,(k^2 - 3kM + r^2)}{(k^2 + r^2)^2} \tag{246}$$

$$B_\theta = B_\phi = \frac{2\left(k^2 + 4kM - 3r^2\right)}{\left(k^2 + r^2\right)^2} \tag{247}$$

From Eqs (221) - (225) for $b = 2$ and the relations (172) we get the following expressions for the energy density μ, the radial pressure P_r, the tangential pressure $P_\perp$ and the quantities $\mu + P_r$ and $\mu + P_\perp$

$$\mu = \frac{n - y^2}{\pi k^2 \left(y^2 + 1\right)^2} \tag{248}$$

$$P_r = \frac{y^2 - 1}{2\pi k^2 \left(y^2 + 1\right)^2} \tag{249}$$

$$P_\perp = \frac{-n + y^2 + 1}{4\pi k^2 \left(y^2 + 1\right)^2} \tag{250}$$

$$\mu + P_r = -\frac{-2n + y^2 + 1}{2\pi k^2 \left(y^2 + 1\right)^2} \tag{251}$$

$$\mu + P_\perp = \frac{3n - 3y^2 + 1}{4\pi k^2 \left(y^2 + 1\right)^2} \tag{252}$$

In Figures 28 - 33 we plot in the interior region the graphs of $k^2\mu$, $k^2(\mu + P_r)$ and $k^2(\mu + P_\perp)$ of Eqs (248), (251) and (252) for $n = 1$ and $n = 2$, in Figure 34 we plot $k^2 P_r$ of Eq (249) which is independent of n and in Figures 35 and 36 we plot the graphs of $P_\perp$ of Eq (250) for $n = 1$ and $n = 2$. For these values of n the solution satisfy the WEC.

The equation of state of the solution is given by Eq (227)

The solution we get for $(b, n) = (b, \frac{2M}{k}) = (2, 1)$ has the "degenerate" horizon at $r = k = 2M$. This is the only horizon of the solution since for $(b, \frac{2M}{k}) = (2, 1)$ the relation (237) is not satisfied.

The solution we get for $(b, n) = (b, \frac{2M}{k}) = (2, 2)$ has a horizon at $r = 2M$, which is its only horizon since for $(b, \frac{2M}{k}) = (2, 2)$ the relation (237) is not satisfied.

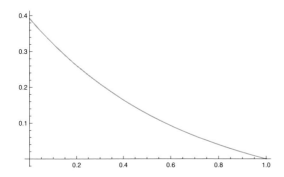

Figure 28: $k^2\mu$ of expression (248) for $n = 1$

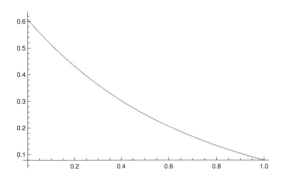

Figure 29: $k^2\mu$ of expression (248) for $n = 2$

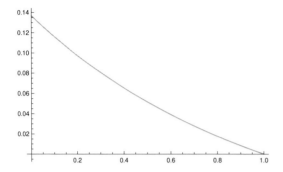

Figure 30: $k^2(\mu + P_r)$ of expression (251) for $n = 1$

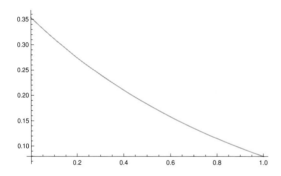

Figure 31: $k^2(\mu + P_r)$ of expression (251) for $n = 2$

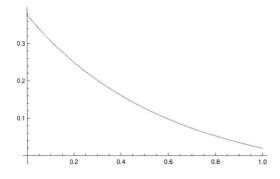

Figure 32: $k^2(\mu + P_\perp)$ of expression (252) for $n = 1$

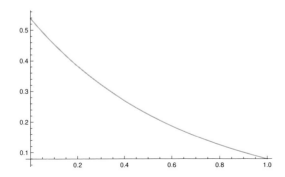

Figure 33: $k^2(\mu + P_\perp)$ of expression (252) for $n = 2$

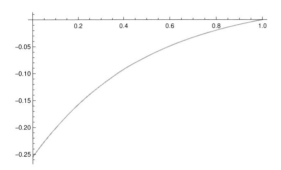

Figure 34: $k^2 P_r$ of expression (249)

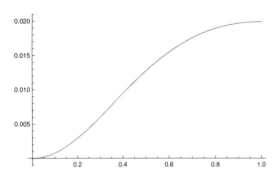

Figure 35: $k^2 P_\perp$ of expression (250) for $n = 1$

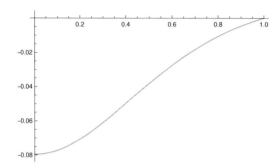

Figure 36: $k^2 P_\perp$ of expression (250) for $n = 2$

Example 2.3.1.3: Solution with $f(r) = (h(r))^2$ and $h(r)$ of Eq (253)
Consider the solution with $f(r) = (h(r))^2$ and

$$h(r) = bk(e^{\frac{r-k}{bk}} - 1) + k \tag{253}$$

which satisfies the matching conditions (3) and (4). A more general case, whose calculations give very long expressions, would be to take an $h(r)$ of the form

$$h(r) = \sum_{i=1}^{n} p_i e^{b_i(r-k)} \tag{254}$$

where the constants b_i and p_i are such that the matching conditions (3) and (4) are satisfied.

Since for $a \geq 0$ we get $e^{-a} + a - 1 \geq 0$ we have in the interior region $0 \leq r \leq k$ if $b > 0$

$$\frac{h(r)}{bk} \geq e^{-\frac{1}{b}} - 1 + \frac{1}{b} > 0 \tag{255}$$

Therefore $h(r)$ does not vanish in the interior region if $b > 0$. If $b < 0$ we have for $r = 0$

$$\frac{h(r)}{bk} = e^{-\frac{1}{b}} - 1 + \frac{1}{b} > 0 \tag{256}$$

while if $r = k$ we have $\frac{h(r)}{bk} = \frac{1}{b} < 0$. Therefore at some r of the interior region $h(r)$ vanish. Since $h(r)$ should not vanish we have to take

$$b > 0 \tag{257}$$

The non-vanishing components of the Ricci tensor $R_{\mu\nu}$, the Ricci scalar R and the second order curvature invariant R^2 of this solution are obtained from Eqs (115) - (119) and (253). If we define N by the relation

$$N = e^{\frac{-k+r}{bk}} \tag{258}$$

we get

$$R_{tt} = \frac{MN(bkN - bk + k - 2M)}{bk^4(bN - b + 1)^3} \tag{259}$$

$$R_{rr} = \frac{N}{2bk}\left(\frac{1}{bk(-N) + bk - k + 2M} - \frac{3}{bkN - bk + k}\right) \tag{260}$$

$$R_{\theta\theta} = \frac{R_{\phi\phi}}{sin^2\theta} = -\frac{N(-bk + k - 2M) + 2bkN^2 - bk}{bk} \tag{261}$$

$$R = \frac{2bk\left(-3N^2 + 2N + 1\right) - 2N(2k - 3M)}{bk^3(b(1 - N) - 1)^2} \tag{262}$$

$$R^2 = \frac{4}{b^2k^6(b(N - 1) + 1)^6}(b(b(bk(N - 1)^2(bk((3N - 4)N^3 + 1) +$$
$$2k(N - 1)(N(5N + 2) + 1) + 4M(1 - 2N)N^2) + k^2(N(13N + 2)$$
$$+1)(N - 1)^2 - 20kMN^2(N - 1)^2 + 3M^2N^2(N(3N - 2) + 3)) +$$
$$2N^2(4k^2(N - 1) + 2kM(6 - 5N) + 3M^2(N - 3))) + N^2(2k^2 -$$
$$8kM + 9M^2)) \tag{263}$$

The invariants R and R^2 are singular at the positions r at which $k(b(1-N) - 1) = -h(r) = 0$, which does not happen if $b > 0$. Therefore the solution is regular if the relation (257) holds.

The eigenvalues B_i, $i = t, r, \theta$, and ϕ of the Ricci tensor R^ν_μ of this solution are obtained from Eqs (120) - (122) and (253). We get

$$B_t = -\frac{MN}{bk^3(b(N - 1) + 1)^2} \tag{264}$$

$$B_r = \frac{N(2bk(1 - N) - 2k + 3M)}{bk^3(b(N - 1) + 1)^2} \tag{265}$$

$$B_\theta = B_\phi = -\frac{N(-bk + k - 2M) + 2bkN^2 - bk}{bk^3(b(1 - N) - 1)^2} \tag{266}$$

The energy density μ, the radial pressure P_r, the tangential pressure $P_\perp$ and the quantities $\mu + P_r$ and $\mu + P_\perp$ are obtained from Eqs (123) - (127) and (253). Using relations (172) we get

$$\mu = \frac{b\left(-3N^2 + 2N + 1\right) + 2(n-1)N}{8\pi bk^2(b(-N)+b-1)^2} \tag{267}$$

$$P_r = \frac{N^2 - 1}{8\pi k^2(b(-N)+b-1)^2} \tag{268}$$

$$\mu + P_r = -\frac{N(bN - b - n + 1)}{4\pi bk^2(b(-N)+b-1)^2} \tag{269}$$

$$P_\perp = \frac{N(2bN - (2b+n-2))}{16\pi bk^2(b(-N)+b-1)^2} \tag{270}$$

$$\mu + P_\perp = \frac{N(-2+3n) + 2b(-2N^2 + N + 1)}{16\pi bk^2(b(-N)+b-1)^2} \tag{271}$$

Since $1 \geq N > 0$ and $k > 0$ from Eqs (267), (269) and (271) for $b > 0$ and $n = \frac{2M}{k} \geq 1$ we get

$$\mu \geq 0, \quad \mu + P_r \geq 0 \quad \text{and} \quad \mu + P_\perp \geq 0 \tag{272}$$

Therefore for $b > 0$ and $n \geq 1$ the solution satisfies the WEC . Also from Eqs (267) and (268) we find that for $n = 1$ at $r = k$ we get $\mu = P_r = 0$ as expected.

The line element of the solution is obtained from Eqs (131) and (253) We get

$$d^2s = -(1 - \frac{2M}{bk(e^{\frac{r-k}{bk}} - 1) + k})d^2t +$$

$$\frac{1}{1 - \frac{2M}{bk(e^{\frac{r-k}{bk}} - 1) + k}} d^2r + (bk(e^{\frac{r-k}{bk}} - 1) + k)^2(d^2\theta + \sin^2\theta d^2\phi) \tag{273}$$

To find the equation of state we solve for $e^{\frac{-k+r}{bk}}$ the expression for $h''(r)$ which we get from Eq (253) We find

$$e^{\frac{r-k}{bk}} = bkh''(r) \tag{274}$$

Using Eq (274) to eliminating $e^{\frac{r-k}{bk}}$ from the $h(r)$ of Eq (253) we get a relation which contains $h(r)$, $h''(r)$ and constants. Eliminating $h(r)$ and $h''(r)$ from this relation using Eqs (128) and (130) and then solving the resulting equation for μ we get two solutions the solution

$$\mu = \frac{1}{8\pi b^2 k^2 M}(M + k\left(-8\pi b^2 kM(4P_\perp + P_r) + b - 1\right) + \sqrt{((b-1)k + M)^2 - 32\pi(b-1)b^2 k^3 M P_\perp)}$$
(275)

and one more. Eliminating P_r, $P_\perp$ and M from the two solution using Eqs (268), (270) and (172) respectively only from the solution (275) we get the expression (267) for the energy density. Therefore the equation of state of this class of solutions is given by relation (275).

After matching the solution has for $\frac{2M}{k} = n > 1$ a horizon at $r = 2M$ and for $\frac{2M}{k} = n = 1$ a "degenerate" horizon at $r = k = 2M$. To find the horizons which are in the interior region we solve equation $g^{rr}(r_{int}) = 0$ in which case we get

$$r_{int} = k(1 + b\, ln(1 + \frac{2M - k}{bk}))$$
(276)

To each r_{int} which is inside the interior region, that is to each r_{int} for which

$$0 < r_{int} = k(1 + b\, ln(1 + \frac{2M - k}{bk})) < k$$
(277)

a horizon corresponds. For $b > 0$ Eq (277) is equivalent to the relation

$$-\frac{1}{b} < ln\,(1 + \frac{2M - k}{bk}) < 0$$
(278)

Therefore if k, M and b satisfy the relation (278) the solution we get after matching has a horizon at the position r_{int} given by Eq (276). If $-\frac{1}{b} > ln\,(1 + \frac{2M-k}{bk})$ after matching the solution does not have a horizon.

We shall study the solutions we get for $b = 1$ and $b = 2$.

Example 2.3.1.3.1: Solution with $f(r) = (h(r))^2$ and $h(r)$ of Eq (279) Consider the solution with $f(r) = (h(r))^2$ and

$$h(r) = ke^{\frac{r-k}{k}}$$
(279)

which is obtained from Eq (253) for $b = 1$. The line element d^2s of the solution, which is obtained from Eq (273) for $b = 1$ is

$$d^2s = -(1 - \frac{2M}{k}e^{\frac{k-r}{k}})d^2t + \frac{1}{1 - \frac{2M}{k}e^{\frac{k-r}{k}}}d^2r + k^2 e^{\frac{2(r-k)}{k}}(d^2\theta + sin^2\theta d^2\phi) \quad (280)$$

The non-vanishing components of the Ricci tensor $R_{\mu\nu}$, the invariants R and R^2 and the eigenvalues B_i, $i = t, r, \theta$, and ϕ of the Ricci tensor are obtained from Eqs (258) - (266) for $b = 1$. We get

$$R_{tt} = \frac{Me^{\frac{k-r}{k}}\left(k - 2Me^{\frac{k-r}{k}}\right)}{k^4} \quad (281)$$

$$R_{rr} = -\frac{2}{k^2} - \frac{M}{k^2\left(2M - ke^{\frac{r-k}{k}}\right)} \quad (282)$$

$$R_{\theta\theta} = \frac{R_{\phi\phi}}{sin^2\theta} = -\frac{2Me^{\frac{r-k}{k}} - 2ke^{\frac{2(r-k)}{k}} + k}{k} \quad (283)$$

$$R = \frac{2\left(3Me^{\frac{k-r}{k}} + k\left(e^{\frac{2(k-r)}{k}} - 3\right)\right)}{k^3} \quad (284)$$

$$R^2 = \frac{4}{k^6}(((9M^2 - 2k^2)e^{\frac{2(k-r)}{k}} + k^2 e^{\frac{4(k-r)}{k}} + 3k^2 - 8kMe^{\frac{k-r}{k}} + 4kMe^{\frac{3(k-r)}{k}})) \quad (285)$$

$$B_t = -\frac{Me^{\frac{k-r}{k}}}{k^3} \quad (286)$$

$$B_r = \frac{3Me^{\frac{k-r}{k}} - 2k}{k^3} \quad (287)$$

$$B_\theta = B_\phi = \frac{2Me^{\frac{k-r}{k}} + k\left(e^{\frac{2(k-r)}{k}} - 2\right)}{k^3} \quad (288)$$

Also the energy density μ, the radial pressure P_r, the tangential pressure $P_\perp$ and the quantities $\mu + P_r$ and $\mu + P_\perp$ are obtained from Eqs (267) - (271) for $b = 1$. We get

$$\mu = -\frac{-2ne^{1-y} - e^{2-2y} + 3}{8\pi k^2} \quad (289)$$

$$P_r = -\frac{e^{2-2y} - 1}{8\pi k^2} \tag{290}$$

$$P_\perp = \frac{2 - ne^{1-y}}{16\pi k^2} \tag{291}$$

$$\mu + P_r = -\frac{1 - ne^{1-y}}{4\pi k^2} \tag{292}$$

$$\mu + P_\perp = -\frac{-3ne^{1-y} - 2e^{2-2y} + 4}{16\pi k^2} \tag{293}$$

In Figures 37 - 42 we present the graphs of $k^2\mu$, $k^2(\mu + P_\perp)$ and $k^2(\mu + P_\perp)$ of Eqs (289), (292) and (293) for $n = 1$ and 2 . From these graphs we find that the solution for $n = 1$ and 2 satisfies the WEC as expected. Also in Figure 43 we present the graph of $k^2 P_r$ of Eq (290). Finally in Figures 44 and 45 we present the graph of $k^2 P_\perp$ of Eq (291) for $n = 1$ and $n = 2$.

From Eq (275) for $b = 1$ we get the relation

$$\mu = -P_r - 4P_\perp + \frac{1}{4\pi k^2} \tag{294}$$

which is the equation of state of the solution.

The solution we get for $(b, n) = (b, \frac{2M}{k}) = (1, 1)$ has the "degenerate" horizon at $r = k = 2M$, which is its only horizon since for $(b, \frac{2M}{k}) = (1, 1)$ the relation (278) is not satisfied.

The solution we get for $(b, n) = (b, \frac{2M}{k}) = (1, 2)$ has a horizon at $r = 2M$. This is the only horizon of the solution since for $(b, \frac{2M}{k}) = (1, 2)$ the relation (278) is not satisfied.

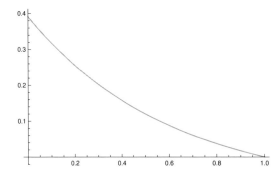

Figure 37: $k^2\mu$ of expression (289) for $n = 1$

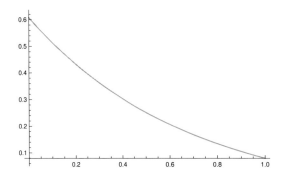

Figure 38: $k^2\mu$ of expression (289) for $n = 2$

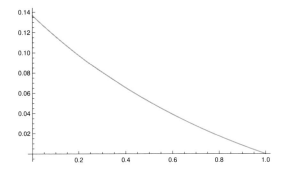

Figure 39: $k^2(\mu + P_r)$ of expression (292) for $n = 1$

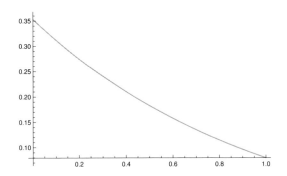

Figure 40: $k^2(\mu + P_r)$ of expression (292) for $n = 2$

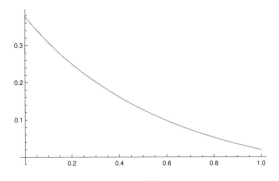

Figure 41: $k^2(\mu + P_\perp)$ of expression (293) for $n = 1$

72

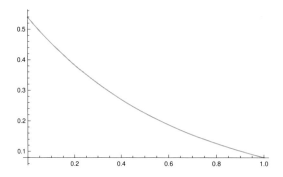

Figure 42: $k^2(\mu + P_\perp)$ of expression (293) for $n = 2$

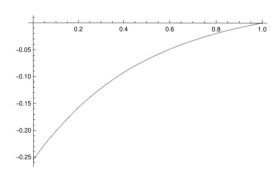

Figure 43: $k^2 P_r$ of expression (290)

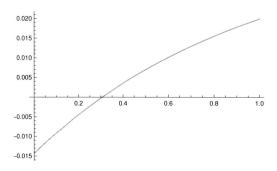

Figure 44: $k^2 P_\perp$ of expression (291) for $n = 1$

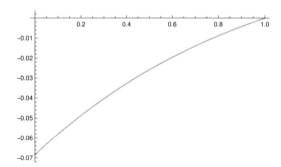

Example 2.3.1.3.2: Solution with $f(r) = (h(r))^2$ and $h(r)$ of Eq (295) Consider the solution with $f(r) = (h(r))^2$ and

$$h(r) = k(2e^{\frac{-k+r}{2k}} - 1) \tag{295}$$

which is obtained from Eq (253) for $b = 2$.

The line element d^2s of the solution, which is obtained from Eq (273) for $b = 2$ is

$$d^2s = -(1 - \frac{2M}{k(2e^{\frac{-k+r}{2k}} - 1)})d^2t + \frac{1}{1 - \frac{2M}{k(2e^{\frac{-k+r}{2k}} - 1)}}d^2r +$$
$$(k(2e^{\frac{-k+r}{2k}} - 1))^2(d^2\theta + sin^2\theta d^2\phi) \tag{296}$$

The non-vanishing components of the Ricci tensor $R_{\mu\nu}$, the Ricci scalar R, the second order curvature invariant R^2 and the eigenvalues B_i, $i = t, r, \theta, and \phi$ of the Ricci tensor R^ν_μ of this solution are obtained from Eqs (258) - (266) for $b = 2$. We get

$$R_{tt} = \frac{M(k + 2M)e^{\frac{r-k}{2k}} - 2kMe^{\frac{r-k}{k}}}{2k^4 \left(1 - 2e^{\frac{r-k}{2k}}\right)^3} \tag{297}$$

$$R_{rr} = \frac{(2k + 3M)e^{\frac{r-k}{2k}} - 4ke^{\frac{r-k}{k}}}{2k^2 \left(-4(k + M)e^{\frac{r-k}{2k}} + 4ke^{\frac{r-k}{k}} + k + 2M\right)} \tag{298}$$

$$R_{\theta\theta} = \frac{R_{\phi\phi}}{sin^2\theta} = -\frac{4ke^{\frac{r-k}{k}} - (k + 2M)e^{\frac{r-k}{2k}} - 2k}{2k} \tag{299}$$

$$R = \frac{(2k - 3M)e^{\frac{r-k}{2k}} + 2(5k + 3M)e^{\frac{r-k}{k}} - 12ke^{\frac{3(r-k)}{2k}} - 2k}{k^3 \left(2e^{\frac{r-k}{2k}} - 1\right)^3} \tag{300}$$

$$R^2 = \frac{1}{k^6 \left(1 - 2e^{\frac{r-k}{2k}}\right)^6}(-16k^2 e^{\frac{r-k}{2k}} + 48k^2 e^{\frac{3(r-k)}{k}} + 4k^2 +$$

$$4\left(4k^2 - 2kM - 3M^2\right)e^{\frac{3(r-k)}{2k}} - 16k(5k + 4M)e^{\frac{5(r-k)}{2k}} +$$

$$\left(10k^2 - 8kM + 9M^2\right)e^{\frac{r-k}{k}} + 4\left(5k^2 + 20kM + 9M^2\right)$$

$$e^{\frac{2(r-k)}{k}}) \tag{301}$$

$$B_t = -\frac{Me^{\frac{r-k}{2k}}}{2k^3 \left(1 - 2e^{\frac{r-k}{2k}}\right)^2} \tag{302}$$

$$B_r = \frac{(2k + 3M)e^{\frac{r-k}{2k}} - 4ke^{\frac{r-k}{k}}}{2k^3 \left(1 - 2e^{\frac{r-k}{2k}}\right)^2} \tag{303}$$

$$B_\theta = B_\phi = \frac{(k + 2M)e^{\frac{r-k}{2k}} - 4ke^{\frac{r-k}{k}} + 2k}{2k^3 \left(1 - 2e^{\frac{r-k}{2k}}\right)^2} \tag{304}$$

Also the energy density μ, the radial pressure P_r, the tangential pressure $P_\perp$ and the quantities $\mu + P_r$ and $\mu + P_\perp$ are obtained from Eqs (267) - (271) for $b = 2$. We get

$$\mu = \frac{(n + 1)e^{\frac{y-1}{2}} - 3e^{y-1} + 1}{8\pi k^2 \left(1 - 2e^{\frac{y-1}{2}}\right)^2} \tag{305}$$

$$P_r = \frac{e^{y-1} - 1}{8\pi k^2 \left(1 - 2e^{\frac{y-1}{2}}\right)^2} \tag{306}$$

$$P_\perp = \frac{e^{\frac{y-1}{2}}\left(-n + 4e^{\frac{y-1}{2}} - 2\right)}{32\pi k^2 \left(1 - 2e^{\frac{y-1}{2}}\right)^2} \tag{307}$$

$$\mu + P_r = \frac{e^{\frac{y-1}{2}}\left(n - 2e^{\frac{y-1}{2}} + 1\right)}{8\pi k^2 \left(1 - 2e^{\frac{y-1}{2}}\right)^2} \tag{308}$$

$$\mu + P_\perp = \frac{(3n+2)e^{\frac{y-1}{2}} - 8e^{y-1} + 4}{32\pi k^2 \left(1 - 2e^{\frac{y-1}{2}}\right)^2} \tag{309}$$

In Figures 46 - 51 we present the graphs of $k^2\mu$, $k^2(\mu+P_\perp)$ and $k^2(\mu+P_\perp)$ of Eqs (305), (308) and (309) for $n = 1$ and 2 . From these graphs we find that the solution for $n = 1$ and 2 satisfies the WEC as expected. Also in Figure 52 we present the graph of k^2P_r of Eq (306). Finally in Figures 53 and 54 we present the graph of $k^2P_\perp$ of Eq (307) for $n = 1$ and $n = 2$.

From Eq (275) for $b = 2$ we get the relation

$$\mu = \frac{M + k(1 - 32\pi kM(P_r + 4P_\perp)) + \sqrt{(k+M)^2 - 128\pi k^3 M P_\perp}}{32\pi k^2 M} \tag{310}$$

which is the equation of state of the solution.

The solution we get for $(b,n) = (b, \frac{2M}{k}) = (2,1)$ has the "degenerate" horizon at $r = k = 2M$, which is its only horizon since for $(b, \frac{2M}{k}) = (2,1)$ the relation (278) is not satisfied.

The solution we get for $(b,n) = (b, \frac{2M}{k}) = (2,2)$ has a horizon at $r = 2M$, which is its only horizon since for $(b, \frac{2M}{k}) = (2,2)$ the relation (278) is not satisfied.

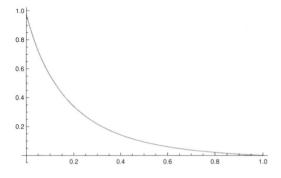

Figure 46: $k^2\mu$ of expression (305) for $n = 1$

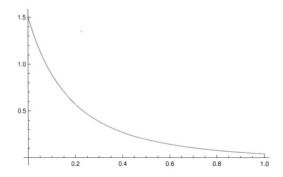

Figure 47: $k^2\mu$ of expression (305) for $n = 2$

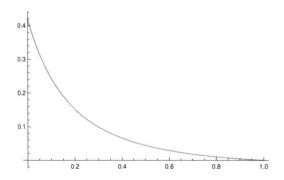

Figure 48: $k^2(\mu + P_r)$ of expression (308) for $n = 1$

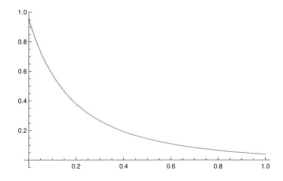

Figure 49: $k^2(\mu + P_r)$ of expression (308) for $n = 2$

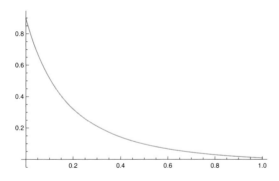

Figure 50: $k^2(\mu + P_\perp)$ of expression (309) for $n = 1$

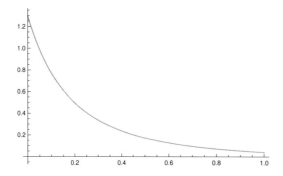

Figure 51: $k^2(\mu + P_\perp)$ of expression (309) for $n = 2$

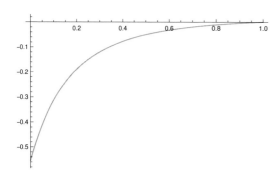

Figure 52: $k^2 P_r$ of expression (306)

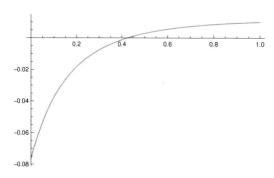

Figure 53: $k^2 P_\perp$ of expression (307) for $n = 1$

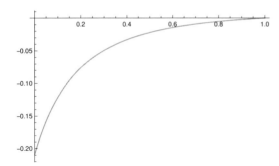

Figure 54: $k^2 P_\perp$ of expression (307) for $n = 2$

Example 2.3.1.4: Solution with $f(r) = (h(r))^2$ and $h(r)$ of Eq (311)
Consider the solution with $f(r) = (h(r))^2$ and

$$h(r) = \frac{k(br - k)}{k(b - 2) + r} \tag{311}$$

which satisfies the matching conditions (3) and (4). Since $h(r)$ should not vanish for $0 \leq r \leq k$ we should have $b > 2$ or $b < 1$ The non-vanishing components of the Ricci tensor $R_{\mu\nu}$, the Ricci scalar R and the second order curvature invariant R^2 are obtained from Eqs (115) - (119) and (311). We get

$$R_{tt} = -\frac{2(b-1)^2 M \left(2(b-2)kM - bkr + k^2 + 2Mr\right)}{k((b-2)k + r)(k - br)^3} \tag{312}$$

$$R_{rr} = -\frac{2(b-1)^2 k \left(3(b-2)kM - 2bkr + 2k^2 + 3Mr\right)}{((b-2)k + r)^2(k - br)\left(2(b-2)kM - bkr + k^2 + 2Mr\right)} \tag{313}$$

$$R_{\theta\theta} = \frac{R_{\phi\phi}}{sin^2\theta} = -\frac{1}{((b-2)k + r)^4}((4b((b-4)b + 6) - 13)k^4 + 2k^3$$
$$(2(b-2)(b-1)^2 M + (b((14 - 3b)b - 25) + 16)r) + 2k^2 r(2(b-1)^2$$
$$M - 3(b-2)^2 r) - 4(b-2)kr^3 - r^4) \tag{314}$$

$$R = \frac{1}{k^2((b-2)k + r)^2(k - br)^2}(2((4b^3 - 14b^2 + 20b - 11)k^4 +$$

$$2k^3 \left(2(-2b^3 + 8b^2 - 13b + 8)r + 3(b-2)(b-1)^2 M \right) + 6k^2 r$$
$$\left((b-1)^2 M - (b-2)^2 r \right) - 4(b-2)kr^3 - r^4)) \tag{315}$$

$$R^2 = \frac{A}{k^4 ((b-2)k + r)^4 (k - br)^6} \tag{316}$$

where A is a polynomial of r, M, b and k. From Eqs (315) and (316) we find that the invariants are regular for $b < 1$ but not for $b > 2$. Therefore the solution is regular for

$$b < 1 \tag{317}$$

The eigenvalues B_i, $i = t, r, \theta$, and ϕ of the Ricci tensor R^ν_μ of this solution are obtained from Eqs (120) - (122) and (311). We get

$$B_t = \frac{2(b-1)^2 M}{((b-2)k + r)(k - br)^2} \tag{318}$$

$$B_r = -\frac{2(b-1)^2 \left(3(b-2)kM - 2bkr + 2k^2 + 3Mr \right)}{((b-2)k + r)^2 (k - br)^2} \tag{319}$$

$$B_\theta = B_\phi = \frac{1}{k^2((b-2)k+r)^2(k-br)^2} ((13 - 4b((b-4)b + 6))k^4$$
$$+ 2k^3 ((b(b(3b - 14) + 25) - 16)r - 2(b-2)(b-1)^2 M) + 2k^2 r(3$$
$$(b-2)^2 r - 2(b-1)^2 M) + 4(b-2)kr^3 + r^4) \tag{320}$$

Also from Eqs (123) - (127) and (311) we can find the energy density μ the radial pressure P_r, the tangential pressure $P_\perp$ and the quantities $\mu + P_r$ and $\mu + P_\perp$. We get in the variables y and n of Eqs (172)

$$\mu = \frac{1}{8\pi k^2 (b+y-2)^2 (by-1)^2} (-4b^3(n - 2y + 1) + b^2(-4n(y-4) +$$
$$6y^2 - 32y + 14) + 4b(n(2y-5) + y^3 - 6y^2 + 13y - 5) - 4n(y-2) +$$
$$y^4 - 8y^3 + 24y^2 - 32y + 11) \tag{321}$$

$$P_r = -\frac{(y-1)}{8\pi k^2 (b+y-2)^2 (by-1)^2} ((4b^3 + 6b^2(y-3) + 4b(y^2 - 5y$$
$$+7) + y^3 - 7y^2 + 17y - 15)) \tag{322}$$

$$P_\perp = \frac{(b-1)^2(n(b+y-2)-2by+2)}{8\pi k^2(b+y-2)^2(by-1)^2} \qquad (323)$$

$$\mu + P_r = -\frac{(b-1)^2(n(b+y-2)-by+1)}{2\pi k^2(b+y-2)^2(by-1)^2} \qquad (324)$$

$$\mu + P_\perp = \frac{1}{8\pi k^2(b+y-2)^2(by-1)^2}(b^3(-3n+6y-4)-b^2(y-4)(3n-6y+4)+b(3n(2y-5)+4y^3-24y^2+50y-24)-3n(y-2)+y^4-8y^3+24y^2-32y+13) \qquad (325)$$

To find the equation of state of the solution we solve for r the relation

$$\frac{k(br-k)}{(b-2)k+r} = \frac{\mu M + 4MP_\perp + MP_r}{\mu + 2P_\perp + Pr} \qquad (326)$$

which is obtained from Eqs (128) and (311). We get

$$r = \frac{k((b-2)M(\mu+4P_\perp+P_r)+k(\mu+2P_\perp+P_r))}{bk(\mu+2P_\perp+P_r)-M(\mu+4P_\perp+P_r)} \qquad (327)$$

Also from Eqs (130) and (311) we find the relation

$$-\frac{2(b-1)^2k^2}{((b-2)k+r)^3} = \frac{4\pi M(\mu+4P_\perp+P_r)^2}{\mu+2P_\perp+Pr} \qquad (328)$$

If we eliminate r from Eq (328) using Eq (327) we find the relation

$$2\pi M(\mu+4P_\perp+P_r)^2 + \frac{(bk(\mu+2P_\perp+P_r)-M(\mu+4P_\perp+P_r))^3}{(b-1)^4k^4(\mu+2P_\perp+P_r)^2} = 0 \quad (329)$$

The above equation is satisfied if we substitute μ, P_r, $P_\perp$ and M by their expressions of Eqs (321), (322), (323) and (172) respectively. Eq (329) is the equation of state for arbitrary b.

The line element d^2s of the solution , which is obtained from Eqs (131) and (311) is the following:

$$d^2s = -(1-\frac{2M(k(b-2)+r)}{k(br-k)})dt^2 + \frac{dr^2}{(1-\frac{2M(k(b-2)+r)}{k(br-k)})} + \frac{k^2(br-k)^2}{(k(b-2)+r)^2}(d^2\theta+sin^2\theta d^2\phi) \qquad (330)$$

To find the conditions under which the solution satisfies the WEC we shall consider the expressions of Eqs (123), (124), (126) and (127) for μ, P_r, $\mu + P_\perp$ and $\mu + P \perp$ together with the $h(r)$ of Eqs (311). We can show that these expressions can be written in the form

$$\mu = \frac{(-b-y+2)^2}{8\pi k^2(1-by)^2}\left(1 - \frac{(1-b)^4}{(-b-y+2)^4} + \frac{(1-b)^2(n-1)}{(-b-y+2)^3} + \frac{6(1-b)^3(1-y)}{(-b-y+2)^4}\right) \tag{331}$$

$$P_r = \frac{(-b-y+2)^2}{8\pi k^2(1-by)^2}\left(-1 + \frac{(1-b)^4}{(-b-y+2)^4}\right) \tag{332}$$

$$\mu + P_r = \frac{(-b-y+2)^2}{2\pi k^2(1-by)^2}\left(\frac{(1-b)^2(n-1)}{(-b-y+2)^3} + \frac{(1-b)^3(1-y)}{(-b-y+2)^4}\right) \tag{333}$$

$$\mu + P_\perp = \frac{(-b-y+2)^2}{8\pi k^2(1-by)^2}\left(1 - \frac{(1-b)^4}{(-b-y+2)^4}\right) + \frac{(b-1)^2}{8\pi k^2(b+y-2)^2(by-1)^2}\left(1 - by + 3(-b-y+2)(n-1) + 3(1-b)(1-y)\right) \tag{334}$$

Since we take $b < 1$ we find from Eqs (331), (333) and (334) that in the interior region $0 \leq y \leq 1$ the energy density μ and the quantities $\mu + P_r$ and $\mu + P_\perp$ are non negative if $n \geq 1$. Therefore the solution is regular and satisfies the WEC if

$$b < 1 \quad \text{and} \quad n \geq 1 \tag{335}$$

Also from Eq (331) we find that for $y = r/k = 1$ we have $\mu = \frac{n-1}{8\pi k^2(1-b)}$, which is negative for $n < 1$. Therefore if $n = 2M/k < 1$ the solution does not satisfy the WEC.

After matching the solution has for $\frac{2M}{k} = n > 1$ a horizon at $r = 2M$, for $\frac{2M}{k} = n = 1$ a "degenerate" horizon at $r = k = 2M$ and if the solution

$$r_{int} = \frac{k^2 - 4kM + 2bkM}{bk - 2M} \tag{336}$$

of Eq $g^{rr}(r_{int}) = 0$ satisfies the relation

$$0 < r_{int} = \frac{k^2 - 4kM + 2bkM}{bk - 2M} < k \tag{337}$$

an additional horizon at r_{int} of the interior region. Since we must have $b < 1$ if $bk - 2M > 0$ the relation (337) is not satisfied while if $bk - 2M < 0$ it is satisfied if

$$\frac{1}{2 - b} < \frac{2M}{k} < 1 \tag{338}$$

Therefore the solution has a horizon at the position r_{int} of Eq (336) if relations $bk - 2M < 0$ and (338) are satisfied. If $\frac{1}{2-b} > \frac{2M}{k}$ the solution does not have a horizon.

We shall consider the solutions we get for $b = -1$ and $b = -2$. For $b = 0$ we get the solution of Example 2.3.1.1.1.

Example 2.3.1.4.1: Solution with $f(r) = (h(r))^2$ and $h(r)$ of Eq (339) Consider the solution with $f(r) = (h(r))^2$ and

$$h(r) = \frac{k(k + r)}{3k - r} \tag{339}$$

which is obtained from Eq (311) for $b = -1$. For this $h(r)$ we get from Eq (131) the line element

$$d^2s = -(1 - \frac{2M(3k - r)}{k(k + r)})d^2t + \frac{d^2r}{(1 - \frac{2M(3k-r)}{k(k+r)})} + \frac{k^2(k + r)^2}{(3k - r)^2}$$
$$(d^2\theta + sin^2\theta d^2\phi) \tag{340}$$

The non-vanishing components of the Ricci tensor $R_{\mu\nu}$ and the Ricci scalar R of this solution are obtained from Eqs (312) - (315) for $b = -1$. We get

$$R_{tt} = \frac{8M\,(k^2 + k(r - 6M) + 2Mr)}{k(3k - r)(k + r)^3} \tag{341}$$

$$R_{rr} = -\frac{8k\,(2k^2 - 9kM + 2kr + 3Mr)}{(r - 3k)^2(k + r)\,(k^2 + k(r - 6M) + 2M)} \tag{342}$$

$$R_{\theta\theta} = \frac{R_{\phi\phi}}{sin^2\theta} = \frac{1}{(r-3k)^4}(57k^4 + 4k^3(12M - 29r) + 2k^2r(27r - 8M) - 12kr^3 + r^4) \tag{343}$$

$$R = \frac{2\left(49k^4 + 4k^3(18M - 31r) - 6k^2r(4M - 9r) - 12kr^3 + r^4\right)}{k^2(r-3k)^2(k+r)^2} \tag{344}$$

The second order curvature invariant R^2, which is obtained from Eqs (119) and (311) for $b = -1$ is given by the expression:

$$R^2 = \frac{4}{k^4(r-3k)^4(k+r)^6}(4353k^{10} + 2k^9(6240M - 2539r) +$$
$$k^8(19008M^2 - 13952Mr - 4403r^2) + 8k^7r(-2016M^2 - 1272Mr$$
$$+1327r^2) + 2k^6r^2(4800M^2 + 5504Mr - 999r^2) - 4k^5r^3(960M^2$$
$$+1072Mr + 865r^2) + 2k^4r^4(288M^2 + 448Mr + 1433r^2) - 8k^3r^6$$
$$(8M + 129r) + 205k^2r^8 - 22kr^9 + r^{10}) \tag{345}$$

The eigenvalues B_i, $i = t, r, \theta$, and ϕ of the Ricci tensor R_μ^ν of this solution are obtained from Eqs (318) - (320) for $b = -1$. We get

$$B_t = -\frac{8M}{(3k-r)(k+r)^2} \tag{346}$$

$$B_r = -\frac{8\left(2k^2 - 9kM + 2kr + 3Mr\right)}{(r-3k)^2(k+r)^2} \tag{347}$$

$$B_\theta = B_\phi = \frac{57k^4 + 4k^3(12M - 29r) + 2k^2r(27r - 8M) - 12kr^3 + r^4}{k^2(r-3k)^2(k+r)^2} \tag{348}$$

Also putting $b = -1$ in Eqs (321) - (325) we find the energy density μ, the radial pressure P_r, the tangential pressure $P_\perp$ and the quantities $\mu + P_r$ and $\mu + P_\perp$ of the solution in the variables y and n of Eqs (172). We get

$$\mu = \frac{-16n(y-3) + y^4 - 12y^3 + 54y^2 - 124y + 49}{8\pi k^2(y-3)^2(y+1)^2} \tag{349}$$

$$P_r = -\frac{y^4 - 12y^3 + 54y^2 - 108y + 65}{8\pi k^2 (y-3)^2 (y+1)^2} \tag{350}$$

$$P_\perp = \frac{n(y-3) + 2(y+1)}{2\pi k^2 (y-3)^2 (y+1)^2} \tag{351}$$

$$\mu + P_r = -\frac{2(n(y-3) + y + 1)}{\pi k^2 (y-3)^2 (y+1)^2} \tag{352}$$

$$\mu + P_\perp = \frac{-12n(y-3) + y^4 - 12y^3 + 54y^2 - 116y + 57}{8\pi k^2 (y-3)^2 (y+1)^2} \tag{353}$$

From Eq (329) for $b = -1$ we get the relation

$$2\pi M (\mu + 4P_\perp + P_r)^2 - \frac{(k(\mu + 2P_\perp + P_r) + M(\mu + 4P_\perp + P_r))^3}{16k^4(\mu + 2P_\perp + P_r)^2} = 0 \tag{354}$$

which is the equation of state of the solution.

In Figures 55 - 60 we present the graphs of $k^2\mu$, $k^2(\mu+P_\perp)$ and $k^2(\mu+P_\perp)$ of Eqs (349), (352) and (353) for $n = 1$ and 2 . From these graphs we find that the solution for $n = 1$ and 2 satisfies the WEC as expected. Also in Figure 61 we present the graph of $k^2 P_r$ of Eq (350). Finally in Figures 62 and 63 we present the graph of $k^2 P_\perp$ of Eq (351) for $n = 1$ and $n = 2$.

The solution we get for $(b, n) = (b, \frac{2M}{k}) = (-1, 1)$ has the "degenerate" horizon at $r = k = 2M$. This is the only horizon of the solution since for $(b, \frac{2M}{k}) = (-1, 1)$ the relation (338) is not satisfied.

The solution we get for $(b, n) = (b, \frac{2M}{k}) = (-1, 2)$ has a horizon at $r = 2M$. This is the only horizon of the solution since for $(b, \frac{2M}{k}) = (-1, 2)$ the relation (338) is not satisfied.

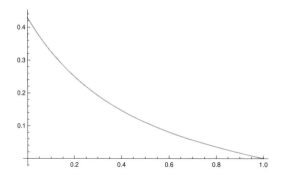

Figure 55: $k^2\mu$ of expression (349) for $n = 1$

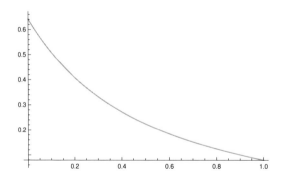

Figure 56: $k^2\mu$ of expression (349) for $n = 2$

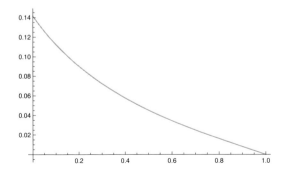

Figure 57: $k^2(\mu + P_r)$ of expression (352) for $n = 1$

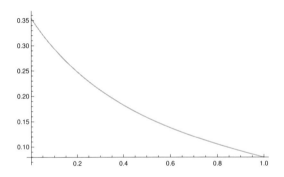

Figure 58: $k^2(\mu + P_r)$ of expression (352) for $n = 2$

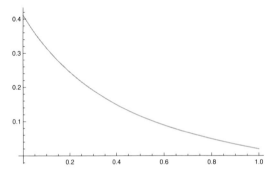

Figure 59: $k^2(\mu + P_\perp)$ of expression (353) for $n = 1$

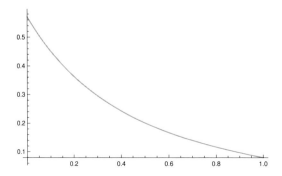

Figure 60: $k^2(\mu + P_\perp)$ of expression (353) for $n = 2$

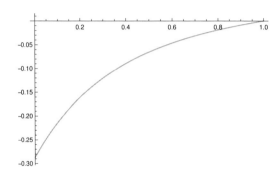

Figure 61: $k^2 P_r$ of expression (350)

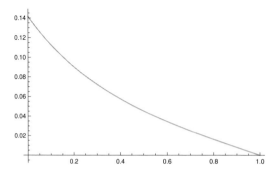

Figure 62: $k^2 P_\perp$ of expression (351) for $n = 1$

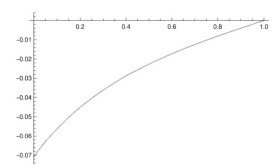

Figure 63: $k^2 P_\perp$ of expression (351) for $n = 2$

Example 2.3.1.4.2: Solution with $f(r) = (h(r))^2$ and $h(r)$ of Eq (355) Consider the solution with $f(r) = (h(r))^2$ and

$$h(r) = \frac{k(k + 2r)}{4k - r} \tag{355}$$

which is obtained from Eq (311) for $b = -2$. For this $h(r)$ we get from Eq (131) the line element

$$d^2 s = -(1 - \frac{2M(4k - r)}{k(k + 2r)})d^2 t + \frac{d^2 r}{(1 - \frac{2M(4k-r)}{k(k+2r)})} + \frac{k^2(k + 2r)^2}{(4k - r)^2}$$
$$(d^2\theta + sin^2\theta d^2\phi) \tag{356}$$

The non-vanishing components of the Ricci tensor $R_{\mu\nu}$ and the Ricci scalar R of this solution are obtained from Eqs (312) - (315) for $b = -2$. We get

$$R_{tt} = \frac{18M(2r(k + M) + k(k - 8M))}{k(4k - r)(k + 2r)^3} \tag{357}$$

$$R_{rr} = -\frac{18k\,(2k^2 + 4k(r - 3M) + 3Mr)}{(r - 4k)^2(k + 2r)(2r(k + M) + k(k - 8M))} \tag{358}$$

$$R_{\theta\theta} = \frac{R_{\phi\phi}}{sin^2\theta} = \frac{1}{(r - 4k)^4}(157k^4 + 4k^3(36M - 73r) + 12k^2 r(8r - 3M) - 16kr^3 + r^4) \tag{359}$$

$$R = \frac{2\left(139k^4 + 8k^3(27M - 41r) + 6k^2r(16r - 9M) - 16kr^3 + r^4\right)}{k^2(r - 4k)^2(k + 2r)^2} \tag{360}$$

The second order curvature invariant R^2 of the solution, which is obtained from Eqs (119) and (311) for $b = -2$, is the following :

$$R^2 = \frac{4}{k^4(r - 4k)^4(k + 2r)^6}(31273k^{10} + 4k^9(59940M + 9521r) + 36k^8$$
$$(28512M^2 + 2583Mr - 3367r^2) + 24k^7r(-36936M^2 - 25353Mr + 172$$
$$r^2) + 6k^6r^2(72900M^2 + 47952Mr + 34277r^2) - 72k^5r^3(1620M^2 + 1062$$
$$Mr + 2105r^2) + 12k^4r^4(972M^2 + 1053Mr + 4762r^2) - 24k^3r^6(27M +$$
$$524r) + 1665k^2r^8 - 124kr^9 + 4r^{10}) \tag{361}$$

The eigenvalues B_i, $i = t, r, \theta$, and ϕ of the Ricci tensor R^ν_μ of this solution, which are obtained from Eqs (318) - (320) for $b = -2$, are the following:

$$B_t = -\frac{18M}{(4k - r)(k + 2r)^2} \tag{362}$$

$$B_r = -\frac{18\left(2k^2 + 4k(r - 3M) + 3Mr\right)}{(r - 4k)^2(k + 2r)^2} \tag{363}$$

$$R_\theta = R_\phi = \frac{157k^4 + 4k^3(36M - 73r) + 12k^2r(8r - 3M) - 16kr^3 + r^4}{k^2(r - 4k)^2(k + 2r)^2} \tag{364}$$

Also the energy density μ, the radial pressure P_r , the tangential pressure $P_\perp$ and the quantities $\mu + P_r$ and $\mu + P_\perp$ of the solution in the variables y and n of Eqs (172), which are obtained from Eqs (321) - (325) for $b = -2$ are given by the relations

$$\mu = \frac{-36n(y - 4) + y^4 - 16y^3 + 96y^2 - 328y + 139}{8\pi k^2(y - 4)^2(2y + 1)^2} \tag{365}$$

$$P_r = -\frac{y^4 - 16y^3 + 96y^2 - 256y + 175}{8\pi k^2(y - 4)^2(2y + 1)^2} \tag{366}$$

$$P_\perp = \frac{9(n(y-4)+4y+2)}{8\pi k^2(y-4)^2(2y+1)^2} \tag{367}$$

$$\mu + Pr = \frac{9(n(y-4)+2y+1)}{2\pi k^2(y-4)^2(2y+1)^2} \tag{368}$$

$$\mu + P_\perp = \frac{-27n(y-4)+y^4-16y^3+96y^2-292y+157}{8\pi k^2(y-4)^2(2y+1)^2} \tag{369}$$

In Figures 64 - 69 we present the graphs of $k^2\mu$, $k^2(\mu+P_\perp)$ and $k^2(\mu+P_\perp)$ of Eqs (365), (368) and (369) for $n=1$ and 2 . From these graphs we find that the solution for $n=1$ and 2 satisfies the WEC as expected. Also in Figure 70 we present the graph of $k^2 P_r$ of Eq (366). Finally in Figures 71 and 72 we present the graph of $k^2 P_\perp$ of Eq (367) for $n=1$ and $n=2$.

The equation of state of the solution, which is obtained from Eq (329) for $b=-2$, is the following:

$$2\pi M(\mu+4P_\perp+P_r)^2 - \frac{(2k(\mu+2P_\perp+P_r)+M(\mu+4P_\perp+P_r))^3}{(81k^4(\mu+2P_\perp+P_r)^2} = 0 \tag{370}$$

The solution we get for $(b,n)=(b,\frac{2M}{k})=(-2,1)$ has the "degenerate" horizon at $r=k=2M$, which is the only horizon of the solution since for $(b,\frac{2M}{k})=(-2,1)$ the relation (338) is not satisfied.

The solution we get for $(b,n)=(b,\frac{2M}{k})=(-2,2)$ has a horizon at $r=2M$, which is the only horizon of the solution since for $(b,\frac{2M}{k})=(-2,2)$ the relation (338) is not satisfied.

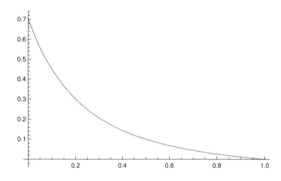

Figure 64: $k^2\mu$ of expression (365) for $n=1$

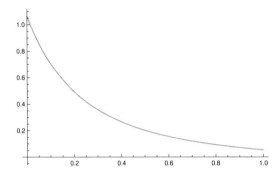

Figure 65: $k^2\mu$ of expression (365) for $n = 2$

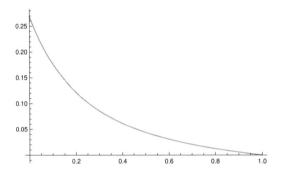

Figure 66: $k^2(\mu + P_r)$ of expression (368) for $n = 1$

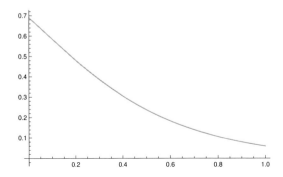

Figure 67: $k^2(\mu + P_r)$ of expression (368) for $n = 2$

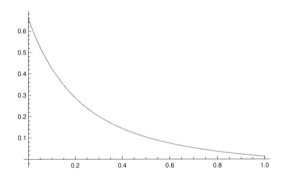

Figure 68: $k^2(\mu + P_\perp)$ of expression (369) for $n = 1$

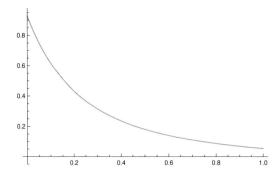

Figure 69: $k^2(\mu + P_\perp)$ of expression (369) for $n = 2$

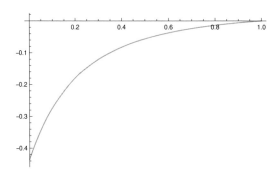

Figure 70: $k^2 P_r$ of expression (366)

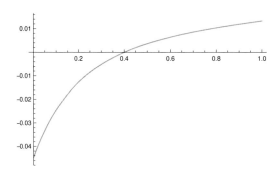

Figure 71: $k^2 P_\perp$ of expression (367) for $n = 1$

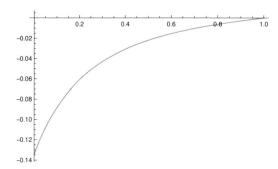

Figure 72: $k^2 P_\perp$ of expression (367) for $n = 2$

Example 2.3.1.5: Solution with $f(r) = (h(r))^2$ and $h(r)$ of Eq (371)
Consider the solution with $f(r) = (h(r))^2$ and

$$h(r) = \frac{k\left(k^q(p(q-1) - q) + pr^q\right)}{k^q((p-1)q - 1) + r^q} \tag{371}$$

which satisfies the matching conditions (3) and (4). The above $h(r)$ depends on three constants, the constant k, which gives the matching surface and the constants p and q, which obey certain conditions, such that the solution is regular and satisfy the WEC but are otherwise arbitrary. The non-vanishing components of the Ricci tensor $R_{\mu\nu}$, the Ricci scalar R and the second order curvature invariant R^2, which are obtained from Eqs (115) - (119) and (371), are the following:

$$R_{tt} = \frac{M(p-1)^2 q^2 k^{q-2} r^{q-2}}{(k^q((p-1)q-1) + r^q)(k^q(p(q-1) - q) + pr^q)^3}((q-1)k^q$$
$$((p-1)q - 1) - (q+1)r^q)(k^q((p-1)q(k-2M) - kp + 2M) +$$
$$r^q(kp - 2M)) \tag{372}$$

$$R_{rr} = -\frac{k^q(-1+p)^2 q^2 r^{-2+q}}{(k^q(-1 + (-1+p)q) + r^q)^2}$$
$$\frac{k^q((p-1)q(2k - 3M) - 2kp + 3M) + r^q(2kp - 3M)}{k^q(p(q-1) - q) + pr^q}$$
$$\frac{(q-1)k^q((p-1)q - 1) - (q+1)r^q}{k^q((p-1)q(k-2M) - kp + 2M) + r^q(kp - 2M)} \tag{373}$$

$$R_{\theta\theta} = \frac{R_{\phi\phi}}{sin^2\theta} = -\frac{1}{(k^q((p-1)q-1)+r^q)^4}((p-1)^4q^4k^{2q+2}r^{2q-2} -$$
$$(k^q((p-1)q-1)+r^q)^4 + (p-1)^2q^2k^{q+1}r^{q-2}((q-1)k^q((p-1)q$$
$$-1)-(q+1)r^q)(k^q((p-1)q(k-2M)-kp+2M)+r^q(kp-$$
$$2M)))$$

$$(374)$$

$$R = \frac{1}{k^2\left(k^q((p-1)q-1)+r^q\right)^2\left(k^q(p(q-1)-q)+pr^q\right)^2}(2(-(p$$
$$-1)^4q^4k^{2q+2}r^{2q-2} + (k^q((p-1)q-1)+r^q)^4 + 3M(p-1)^2q^2k^{q+1}$$
$$r^{q-2}(k^q((p-1)q-1)+r^q)((q-1)k^q((p-1)q-1)-(q+1)r^q) -$$
$$2(p-1)^2q^2k^{q+2}r^{q-2}(k^q(p(q-1)-q)+pr^q)((q-1)k^q((p-1)q-$$
$$1)-(q+1)r^q)))$$

$$(375)$$

$$R^2 = \frac{1}{k^4(k^q((p-1)q-1)+r^q)^4(k^q(p(q-1)-q)+pr^q)^6}(4(12M^2$$
$$(p-1)^8q^8k^{4q+2}r^{4q-4}(k^q((p-1)q-1)+r^q)^2 + (k^q(p(q-1)-q)+$$
$$pr^q)^2((p-1)^8q^8k^{4q+4}r^{4q-4} + (k^q((p-1)q-1)+r^q)^8 + 9M^2(p-$$
$$1)^4q^4k^{2q+2}r^{2q-4}(k^q((p-1)q-1)+r^q)^2((q-1)k^q((p-1)q-1) -$$
$$(q+1)r^q)^2 - 2(p-1)^4q^4k^{2q+2}r^{2q-2}(k^q((p-1)q-1)+r^q)((k^q((p$$
$$-1)q-1)+r^q)^3 + 2M(p-1)^2q^2k^{q+1}r^{q-2}((q+1)r^q-(q-1)k^q$$
$$((p-1)q-1)))) - 8M(p-1)^4q^4k^{2q+3}r^{2q-4}(k^q((p-1)q-1)$$
$$r^q)(k^q(p(q-1)-q)+pr^q)^3((q-1)k^q((p-1)q-1)-(q+1)r^q)^2$$
$$+4M(p-1)^4q^4k^{2q+1}r^{2q-2}(k^q((p-1)q-1)+r^q)(k^q(p(q-1)-q)$$
$$+pr^q)(-(p-1)^4q^4k^{2q+2}r^{2q-2} + (k^q((p-1)q-1+r^q)^4 - 3M(p$$
$$-1)^2q^2k^{q+1}r^{q-2}(k^q((p-1)q-1)+r^q)((q-1)k^q((p-1)q-1) -$$
$$(q+1)r^q)) + 2(p-1)^4q^4k^{2q+4}r^{2q-4}(k^q(p(q-1)-q)+pr^q)^4((q-1)k^q$$
$$((p-1)q-1)-(q+1)r^q)^2))$$

$$(376)$$

If we write $r = ky$ we find from the explicit expressions for R and R^2 that if $p \neq 0$ the solution is regular if

97

$$q \geq 2 \quad \text{and} \quad 1 - q + \frac{q}{p} \neq y^q \quad \text{and} \quad 1 + (1 - p)q \neq y^q \tag{377}$$

while if $p = 0$ the solution is regular if $q \geq 2$. Since $0 \leq y \leq 1$ the second of Eqs (377) is satisfied if

$$1 - q + \frac{q}{p} < 0 \tag{378}$$

or if

$$0 < p < 1 \tag{379}$$

Eq (379) is obtained from the relations $1 - q + \frac{q}{p} > 1$ and $q \geq 2$. Also the third of Eqs (377) is satisfied if

$$1 + (1 - p)q < 0 \tag{380}$$

or if

$$p < 1 \tag{381}$$

Eq (381) is obtained from the relations $1 + (1 - p)q > 1$ and $q \geq 2$.

We shall examine under what conditions one of Eqs (378) and (379) and one of Eqs (380) and (381) hold simultaneously. Eq (380) implies that $p > 0$ and we find from Eqs (378) and (380) that $p > \frac{q}{q-1}$. Eqs (379) and (380) cannot hold simultaneously while Eqs (379) and (381) hold simultaneously if $0 < p < 1$ and 378) and (381) hold simultaneously if $p < 0$. Therefore the solution is regular if

$$q \geq 2 \quad \text{and} \quad p > \frac{q}{q - 1} \quad \text{or} \quad p < 1 \tag{382}$$

The eigenvalues B_i, $i = t, r, \theta$ and ϕ of the Ricci tensor R^ν_μ of this solution are obtained from Eqs (120) - (122) and (371). We get

$$B_t = -\frac{M(p-1)^2 q^2 k^{q-1} r^{q-2} \left((q-1)k^q((p-1)q-1) - (q+1)r^q\right)}{(k^q((p-1)q-1) + r^q)\left(k^q(p(q-1)-q) + pr^q\right)^2} \tag{383}$$

$$B_r = -\frac{(p-1)^2 q^2 k^{q-1} r^{q-2}}{(k^q((p-1)q-1) + r^q)^2 (k^q(p(q-1)-q) + pr^q)^2}((q-1)$$
$$k^q((p-1)q-1) - (q+1)r^q)(2k^{q+1}(p(q-1)-q) - 3Mk^q((p-1)$$
$$q-1) + 2kpr^q - 3Mr^q) \tag{384}$$

$$B_\theta = B_\phi = \frac{(k^q((p-1)q-1)+r^q)^2}{k^2(k^q(p(q-1)-q)+pr^q)^2}(1-$$

$$\frac{(p-1)^4q^4k^{2q+2}r^{2q-2}}{(k^q((p-1)q-1)+r^q)^4} + \frac{(p-1)^2q^2k^{q+1}r^{q-2}}{(k^q((p-1)q-1)+r^q)^4}((q-1)k^q((p$$

$$-1)q-1)-(q+1)r^q)(k^{q+1}(p(-q)+p+q)+2Mk^q((p-1)q-$$

$$1)-kpr^q+2Mr^q))) \tag{385}$$

Also from Eqs (123) - (127) and (371) we can find the energy density μ, the radial pressure P_r, the tangential pressure $P_\perp$ and the quantities $\mu + P_r$ and $\mu + P_\perp$. We get in the variables y and n of Eqs (172) the following expressions:

$$\mu = \frac{1}{16\pi k^2 \left((p-1)q+y^q-1\right)^2 \left(q-p\left(y^q+q-1\right)\right)^2}(-n(p-1)^2q^2$$

$$y^{q-2}((p-1)q+y^q-1)((q+1)(y^q+q-1)-p(q-1)q)+(p-1)^2$$

$$q^2y^{q-2}((q+1)(y^q+q-1)-p(q-1)q)(4(p(y^q+q-1)-q)-3n$$

$$((p-1)q+y^q-1))-2(p-1)^4q^4y^{2q-2}+2((p-1)q+y^q-$$

$$1)^4) \tag{386}$$

$$P_r = -\frac{1}{8\pi k^2 y^2 \left((p-1)q+y^q-1\right)^2 \left(q-p\left(y^q+q-1\right)\right)^2}(-(p-1)^4$$

$$q^4y^{2q}+4((p-1)q-1)^3y^{q+2}+6((p-1)q-1)^2y^{2q+2}+4((p-1)$$

$$q-1)y^{3q+2}+y^2(-pq+q+1)^4+y^{4q+2}) \tag{387}$$

$$P_\perp = -\frac{(p-1)^2q^2y^{q-2}\left((q+1)\left(y^q+q-1\right)-p(q-1)q\right)}{16\pi k^2 \left((p-1)q+y^q-1\right)^2 \left(q-p\left(y^q+q-1\right)\right)^2}(n(-pq-$$

$$y^q+q+1)+2(p(y^q+q-1)-q)) \tag{388}$$

$$\mu + P_r = \frac{-(p-1)^2q^2k^{2q-3}y^{q-2}}{4\pi \left(k^q((p-1)q-1)+k^qy^q\right)^2 \left(pk^qy^q+k^q(p(q-1)-q)\right)^2}$$

$$((q-1)k^q((p-1)q-1)-(q+1)k^qy^q)(-nk^{q+1}((p-1)q-1)+$$

$$n(-k^{q+1})y^q+pk^{q+1}y^q+k^{q+1}(p(q-1)-q)) \tag{389}$$

$$\mu + P_\perp = -\frac{n(p-1)^2 q^2 y^{q-2}((q+1)(y^q + q - 1) - p(q-1)q)}{16\pi k^2((p-1)q + y^q - 1)(q - p(y^q + q - 1))^2} +$$

$$\frac{((p-1)q + y^q - 1)^2}{8\pi k^2(q - p(y^q + q - 1))^2}\left(1 - \frac{(p-1)^4 q^4 y^{2q-2}}{((p-1)q + y^q - 1)^4} + \right.$$

$$\frac{(p-1)^2 q^2 y^{q-2}(n(-pq - y^q + q + 1) + p(y^q + q - 1) - q)}{((p-1)q + y^q - 1)^4}((q+1)$$

$$(y^q + q - 1) - p(q-1)q)) \tag{390}$$

To find the equation of state of the solution we shall use Eqs (128), (130) and (371). From Eqs (128) and (371) we get the relation

$$\frac{k(k^q(p(q-1) - q) + pr^q)}{k^q((p-1)q - 1) + r^q} = \frac{\mu M + 4MP_\perp + MP_r}{\mu + 2P_\perp + P_r} \tag{391}$$

whose solution with respect to r is

$$r = k(k(p(q-1) - q)(\mu + 2P_\perp + P_r) - M((p-1)q - 1)(\mu + 4P_\perp + P_r))^{\frac{1}{q}}(M(\mu + 4P_\perp + P_r) - kp(\mu + 2P_\perp + P_r))^{-\frac{1}{q}} \tag{392}$$

Also calculating $h''(r)$ from Eq (371) and using Eq (130) we get

$$\frac{(p-1)^2 q^2 k^{q+1} r^{q-2}((q-1)k^q((p-1)q - 1) - (q+1)r^q)}{(k^q((p-1)q - 1) + r^q)^3} =$$

$$\frac{4\pi M(\mu + 4P_\perp + P_r)^2}{\mu + 2P_\perp + P_r} \tag{393}$$

If we eliminate r from the above expression using Eq (392) we obtain the equation of state of the solution. From this expression, which is very long, we get for $q = 2$ the relation

$$(\mu + 4P_\perp + \text{Pr})^2 - \frac{1}{4\pi k^4 M(p-1)^4(\mu + 2P_\perp + P_r)^2}((kp(\mu + 2P_\perp + P_r) - M(\mu + 4P_\perp + P_r))^2(k(p^2 - 3)(\mu + 2P_\perp + P_r) - 2M(2p - 3)(\mu + 4P_\perp + \text{Pr}))) = 0 \tag{394}$$

The above equation is satisfied if we replace μ, P_r and $P_\perp$ by their expressions of Eqs (386), (387) and (388) for $q = 2$, as expected. It is the equation of state for $q = 2$.

The line element of the solution, which is obtained from Eqs (131) and (371) is the following:

$$d^2s = -(1 - \frac{2M(k^q(-1+(-1+p)q) + r^q)}{k(k^q(p(-1+q) - q) + pr^q)})d^2t +$$

$$\frac{d^2r}{1 - \frac{2M(k^q(-1+(-1+p)q)+r^q)}{k(k^q(p(-1+q)-q)+pr^q)}} +$$

$$(\frac{k(k^q(p(-1+q) - q) + pr^q)}{k^q(-1+(-1+p)q) + r^q})^2(d^2\theta + sin^2\theta d^2\phi) \qquad (395)$$

From the function $h(r)$ of Eq (371) we get in the range $0 \leq \frac{r}{k} \leq 1$ for $q \geq 2$ and $p < 1$ or $p \geq \frac{q+1}{q-1}$

$$h(r) = kp + \frac{k(p-1)^2q}{-\left(\frac{r}{k}\right)^q + (1-p)q + 1} \leq kp + \frac{kq(p-1)^2}{(1-p)q} = k \qquad (396)$$

Therefore we find that $2M - h(r) \geq 2M - k$ in the interior region if $q \geq 2$ and $p \leq 1$ or $p \geq \frac{q+1}{q-1}$

Also for $q \geq 2$, $p < 1$ and $0 \leq 1 - (\frac{r}{k})^q \leq 1$ we find from the explicit expressions of $h'(r)$ and $h''(r)$

$$h'(r) = \frac{(1-p)^2q^2(\frac{r}{k})^{q-1}}{(-(\frac{r}{k})^q + (1-p)q + 1)^2} \leq \frac{(1-p)^2q^2(\frac{r}{k})^{q-1}}{(1-p)^2q^2} \leq 1 \qquad (397)$$

$$h''(r) = \frac{(p-1)^2q^2\left(\frac{r}{k}\right)^{q-2}\left((q+1)\left(\frac{r}{k}\right)^q + (q-1)((1-p)q + 1)\right)}{k\left(-\left(\frac{r}{k}\right)^q + (1-p)q + 1\right)^3} > 0 \quad (398)$$

We shall show that relations $h'(r) \leq 1$ and $h''(r) > 0$ also hold if $q \geq 2$ and $p \geq \frac{q+1}{q-1}$. To do that we shall write $y = \frac{r}{k} \leq 1$ and we shall use the relation

$$y^q - 1 + (p-1)q \geq (p-1)qy^{\frac{q-1}{2}} \qquad (399)$$

To prove this relation we shall write it in the form

$$(p-1)q \geq \frac{1 - y^q}{1 - y^{\frac{q-1}{2}}} \qquad (400)$$

If $q \geq 2$ and $p \geq \frac{q+1}{q-1}$ we get $(p-1)q \geq 4$. Also plotting the expression $\frac{1-y^q}{1-y^{\frac{q-1}{2}}}$ for $q \geq 2$ and $0 < y < 1$ we find that $\frac{1-y^q}{1-y^{\frac{q-1}{2}}} \leq 4$, which means that relation (399) holds and therefore relation (397) is satisfied.

From relation (399) we get

$$y^q - 1 + (p-1)q \geq 0 \tag{401}$$

This means that relation (398) is satisfied for $p \geq \frac{q+1}{q-1}$ which implies $1 - p \leq -\frac{2}{q-1}$ since

$$(q+1)y^q + (q-1)((1-p)+1) = (q+1)(y^p - 1) + q((q-1)(1$$
$$-p) + 2) \leq (q+1)(y^q - 1) + q((q-1)\frac{-2}{q-1} + 2) = (q+1)(y^q -$$
$$1) < 0 \tag{402}$$

Therefore we have found that if

$$q \geq 2, \quad p < 1 \quad \text{or} \quad p \geq \frac{q+1}{q-1} \tag{403}$$

we get

$$2M - h(r) \geq 2M - k, \quad h'(r) \leq 1 \quad \text{and} \quad h''(r) > 0 \tag{404}$$

Then from Eqs (123), (126) and (127) we conclude that if $2M - k \geq 0$ and if relations (403), which imply relations (404), hold the solution satisfies the WEC.

After matching the solution has for $\frac{2M}{k} = n > 1$ a horizon at $r = 2M$ and for $\frac{2M}{k} = n = 1$ a "degenerate" horizon at $r = k = 2M$. To find the horizons which are in the interior region we solving equation $g^{rr}(r_{int}) = 0$ in which case we get

$$r_{int} = k \left(\frac{k(p(q-1) - q) + M(2 - 2(p-1)q)}{2M - kp} \right)^{\frac{1}{q}} \tag{405}$$

To each r_{int} which is inside the interior region, that is to each r_{int} for which

$$0 < r_{int} = k \left(\frac{k(p(q-1) - q) + M(2 - 2(p-1)q)}{2M - kp} \right)^{\frac{1}{q}} < k \tag{406}$$

a horizon corresponds. Eq (406) is equivalent to the relation

$$-1 < \frac{(n-1)(1-p)q}{n-p} < 0 \tag{407}$$

If for some values of the constants relation (407) is not satisfied the solution we get after matching does not have a horizonn in the interior region. If for these values of the constants we have $\frac{2M}{k} < 1$ the solution we get after matching does not have a horizon.

We shall consider the solutions we get for (p,q)= (3,2) and for (p,q) (-1,2)

Example 2.3.1.5.1 : Solution with $f(r) = (h(r))^2$ and $h(r)$ of Eq (408)

Consider the solution with $f(r) = (h(r))^2$ and

$$h(r) = \frac{k\left(k^2 + 3r^2\right)}{3k^2 + r^2} \tag{408}$$

which is obtained from the $h(r)$ of Eq (371) for $p = 3$ and $q = 2$.

The line element d^2s of the solution, which is obtained from Eq (395) for $p = 3$ and $q = 2$, is the following:

$$d^2s = -(1 - \frac{2M(3k^2 + r^2)}{k(k^2 + 3r^2)})d^2t + \frac{d^2r}{1 - \frac{2M(3k^2+r^2)}{k(k^2+3r^2)}} + \frac{k^2(k^2 + 3r^2)^2}{(3k^2 + r^2)^2}$$
$$(d^2\theta + sin^2\theta d^2\phi) \tag{409}$$

The non-vanishing components of the Ricci tensor $R_{\mu\nu}$ the Ricci scalar R and the second order curvature invariant R^2, which are obtained from Eqs (372) - (376) for $p = 3$ and $q = 2$, are the following:

$$R_{tt} = \frac{48M(k-r)(k+r)\left(k^2(k-6M) + r^2(3k-2M)\right)}{(3k^2 + r^2)\left(k^2 + 3r^2\right)^3} \tag{410}$$

$$R_{rr} = -\frac{48k^2(k-r)(k+r)\left(2k^3 - 9k^2M + 6kr^2 - 3Mr^2\right)}{(3k^2 + r^2)^2\left(k^2 + 3r^2\right)\left(k^2(k-6M) + r^2(3k-2M)\right)} \tag{411}$$

$$R_{\theta\theta} = \frac{R_{\phi\phi}}{sin^2\theta} = \frac{k^2 - r^2}{(3k^2 + r^2)^4}(33k^6 + 288k^5M - 211k^4r^2 + 96k^3M$$
$$r^2 - 13k^2r^4 - r^6) \tag{412}$$

$$R = -\frac{(2(k^2 - r^2))}{(3k^5 + 10k^3r^2 + 3kr^4)^2}(3k^5(5k - 144M) + k^3r^2(355k -$$
$$144M) + 13k^2r^4 + r^6) \tag{413}$$

$$R^2 = \frac{4}{k^4\left(3k^2 + r^2\right)^4\left(k^2 + 3r^2\right)^6}(24k^5r^{14}(439k + 128M) + 2413k^4$$

$$r^{16} + 222k^2 r^{18} + 9k^{18}(1241k^2 - 6144kM + 20736M^2) + 18k^{16}r^2$$
$$(3415k^2 - 512kM - 25344M^2) + k^{14}r^4(88693k^2 + 479232kM +$$
$$3684096M^2) + 8k^{12}r^6(1173k^2 + 49792kM + 547200M^2) + 6k^{10}$$
$$r^8(-30349k^2 + 130048kM + 548480M^2) - 4k^8 r^{10}(94259k^2 +$$
$$286464kM - 328320M^2) + 2k^6 r^{12}(187617k^2 - 225280kM +$$
$$93312M^2) + 9r^{20})$$
$$(414)$$

The eigenvalues B_i, $i = t, r, \theta$ and ϕ of the Ricci tensor R^ν_μ of this solution are obtained from Eqs (383) - (385) for $p = 3$ and $q = 2$. We get

$$B_t = -\frac{48kM(k-r)(k+r)}{(3k^2 + r^2)(k^2 + 3r^2)^2} \tag{415}$$

$$B_r = -\frac{48k(k-r)(k+r)(2k^3 - 9k^2 M + 6kr^2 - 3Mr^2)}{(3k^2 + r^2)^2 (k^2 + 3r^2)^2} \tag{416}$$

$$B_\theta = B_\phi = \frac{(k^2 - r^2)}{(3k^5 + 10k^3 r^2 + 3kr^4)^2}((3k^5(11k + 96M) + k^3 r^2(96$$
$$M - 211k) - 13k^2 r^4 - r^6)) \tag{417}$$

The energy density μ the radial pressure P_r , the tangential pressure $P_\perp$ and the quantities $\mu + P_r$ and $\mu + P_\perp$, in the variables y and n of Eqs (172), which are obtained from Eqs (386) - (390) for $p = 3$ and $q = 2$, are the following:

$$\mu = \frac{(y-1)(y+1)(-96n(y^2 + 3) + y^6 + 13y^4 + 355y^2 + 15)}{8\pi k^2 (3y^4 + 10y^2 + 3)^2} \tag{418}$$

$$P_r = -\frac{(y^2 - 1)^2 (y^4 + 14y^2 + 81)}{8\pi k^2 (3y^4 + 10y^2 + 3)^2} \tag{419}$$

$$P_\perp = \frac{3(y^2 - 1)(n(y^2 + 3) - 6y^2 - 2)}{\pi k^2 (y^2 + 3)^2 (3y^2 + 1)^2} \tag{420}$$

$$\mu + P_r = -\frac{12(y-1)(y+1)(n(y^2 + 3) - 3y^2 - 1)}{\pi k^2 (y^2 + 3)^2 (3y^2 + 1)^2} \tag{421}$$

$$\mu + P_\perp = \frac{(y-1)(y+1)\left(-72n\left(y^2+3\right)+y^6+13y^4+211y^2-33\right)}{8\pi k^2\left(3y^4+10y^2+3\right)^2} \quad (422)$$

In Figures 73 - 78 we present the graphs of $k^2\mu$, $k^2(\mu+P_\perp)$ and $k^2(\mu+P_\perp)$ of Eqs (418), (421) and (422) for $n=1$ and 2 . From these graphs we find that the solution for $n=1$ and 2 satisfies the WEC as expected. Also in Figure 79 we present the graph of $k^2 P_r$ of Eq (419), which is independent of n. In addition in Figures 80 and 81 we present the graph of $k^2 P_\perp$ of Eq (420) for $n=1$ and $n=2$.

From Eq (394) for $p=3$ we get the relation

$$(\mu+4P_\perp+P_r)^2 - \frac{3}{32\pi k^4 M(\mu+2P_\perp+P_r)^2}(k(\mu+2P_\perp+P_r) -$$
$$M(\mu+4P_\perp+P_r))(M(\mu+4P_\perp+P_r)-3k(\mu+2P_\perp+P_r))^2$$
$$= 0 \quad (423)$$

which is the equation of state of the solution.

The solution we get for $(p,q,n)=(p,q,\frac{2M}{k})=(3,2,1)$ has the "degenerate" horizon at $r=k=2M$. This is the only horizon of the solution since for $(p,q,\frac{2M}{k})=(3,2,1)$ the relation (407) is not satisfied.

The solution we get for $(p,q,n)=(p,q,\frac{2M}{k})=(3,2,2)$ has a horizon at $r=2M$. This is the only horizon of the solution since for $(p,q,\frac{2M}{k})=(3,2,2)$ the relation (407) is not satisfied.

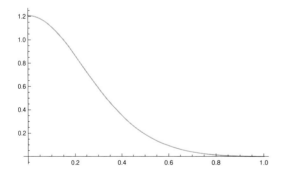

Figure 73: $k^2\mu$ of expression (418) for $n=1$

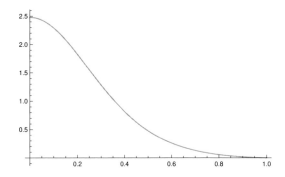

Figure 74: $k^2\mu$ of expression (418) for $n = 2$

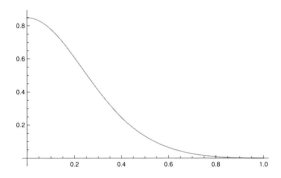

Figure 75: $k^2(\mu + P_r)$ of expression (421) for $n = 1$

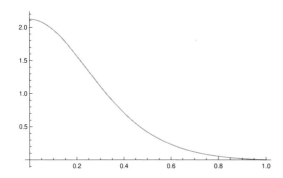

Figure 76: $k^2(\mu + P_r)$ of expression (421) for $n = 2$

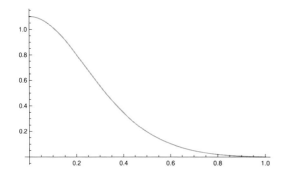

Figure 77: $k^2(\mu + P_\perp)$ of expression (422) for $n = 1$

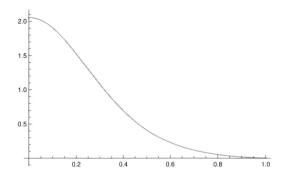

Figure 78: $k^2(\mu + P_\perp)$ of expression (422) for $n = 2$

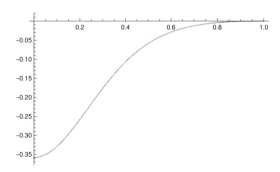

Figure 79: $k^2 P_r$ of expression (419)

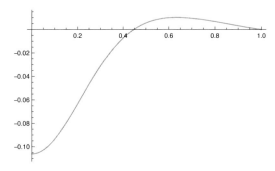

Figure 80: $k^2 P_\perp$ of expression (420) for $n = 1$

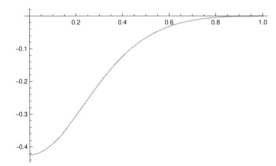

Figure 81: $k^2 P_\perp$ of expression (420) for $n = 2$

Example 2.3.1.5.2 : Solution with $f(r) = (h(r))^2$ and $h(r)$ of Eq (424)

Consider the solution with $f(r) = (h(r))^2$ and

$$h(r) = \frac{k\,(3k^2 + r^2)}{5k^2 - r^2} \tag{424}$$

which is obtained from the $h(r)$ of Eq (371) for $p = -1$ and $q = 2$. The line element d^2s of the solution, which is obtained from Eq (395) for $p = -1$ and $q = 2$ is the following:

$$d^2s = -(1 - \frac{2M(5k^2 - r^2)}{k(3k^2 + r^2)})d^2t + \frac{d^2r}{1 - \frac{2M(5k^2 - r^2)}{k(3k^2 + r^2)}} + \frac{k^2(3k^2 + r^2)^2}{(5k^2 - r^2)^2}$$
$$(d^2\theta + sin^2\theta d^2\phi) \tag{425}$$

Also from Eqs (372) - (376) and (383) - (385) for $p = -1$ and $q = 2$ we get the following expressions for the non-vanishing components of the Ricci tensor $R_{\mu\nu}$, the Ricci scalar R, the second order curvature invariant R^2 and the eigenvalues B_i, $i = t$, r, θ and ϕ of the Ricci tensor R^ν_μ of this solution

$$R_{tt} = \frac{16M\,(5k^2 + 3r^2)\,(k^2(3k - 10M) + r^2(k + 2M))}{(5k^2 - r^2)\,(3k^2 + r^2)^3} \tag{426}$$

$$R_{rr} = -\frac{16k^2\,(5k^2 + 3r^2)\,(3k^2(2k - 5M) + r^2(2k + 3M))}{(r^2 - 5k^2)^2\,(3k^2 + r^2)\,(k^2(3k - 10M) + r^2(k + 2M))} \tag{427}$$

109

$$R_{\theta\theta} = \frac{R_{\phi\phi}}{sin^2\theta} = \frac{1}{(r^2 - 5k^2)^4}(385k^8 + 800k^7M - 980k^6r^2 + 320k^5$$
$$Mr^2 + 102k^4r^4 - 96k^3Mr^4 - 20k^2r^6 + r^8) \tag{428}$$

$$R = \frac{2}{k^2\left(-15k^4 - 2k^2r^2 + r^4\right)^2}(5k^7(29k + 240M) + 4k^5r^2(120M$$
$$-301k) + 18k^3r^4(3k - 8M) - 20k^2r^6 + r^8) \tag{429}$$

$$R^2 = \frac{4}{k^4\left(r^2 - 5k^2\right)^4\left(3k^2 + r^2\right)^6}(-8k^5r^{14}(459k + 128M) + 469k^4$$
$$r^{16} - 34k^2r^{18} + 225k^{18}(20233k^2 - 30720kM + 57600M^2) - 30k^{16}$$
$$r^2(117823k^2 + 17920kM - 19200M^2) + k^{14}r^4(4275277k^2 -$$
$$16445440kM + 17145600M^2) + 8k^{12}r^6(352965k^2 - 228224kM -$$
$$773760M^2) + 2k^{10}r^8(90049k^2 + 304128kM + 407424M^2) + 4k^8$$
$$r^{10}(18797k^2 - 23296kM - 40320M^2) + 2k^6r^{12}(9913k^2 + 20480k$$
$$M + 10368M^2) + r^{20}) \tag{430}$$

$$B_t = -\frac{16kM\left(5k^2 + 3r^2\right)}{\left(5k^2 - r^2\right)\left(3k^2 + r^2\right)^2} \tag{431}$$

$$B_r = -\frac{16k\left(5k^2 + 3r^2\right)\left(6k^3 - 15k^2M + 2kr^2 + 3Mr^2\right)}{\left(-15k^4 - 2k^2r^2 + r^4\right)^2} \tag{432}$$

$$B_\theta = B_\phi = \frac{1}{\left(15k^5 + 2k^3r^2 - kr^4\right)^2}(385k^8 + 800k^7M - 980k^6r^2 +$$
$$320k^5Mr^2 + 102k^4r^4 - 96k^3Mr^4 - 20k^2r^6 + r^8) \tag{433}$$

The energy density μ, the radial pressure P_r, the tangential pressure $P_\perp$ and the quantities $\mu + P_r$ and $\mu + P_\perp$ are obtained from Eqs (386) - (390) for $p = -1$ and $q = 2$. These quantities in the variables y and n of Eqs (172) are the following:

$$\mu = \frac{n\left(-96y^4 + 320y^2 + 800\right) + y^8 - 20y^6 + 54y^4 - 1204y^2 + 145}{8\pi k^2 \left(y^4 - 2y^2 - 15\right)^2} \tag{434}$$

$$P_r = -\frac{y^8 - 20y^6 + 150y^4 - 756y^2 + 625}{8\pi k^2 \left(y^4 - 2y^2 - 15\right)^2} \tag{435}$$

$$P_\perp = \frac{(3y^2 + 5)(n(y^2 - 5) + 2(y^2 + 3))}{\pi k^2 (y^4 - 2y^2 - 15)^2} \tag{436}$$

$$\mu + P_r = -\frac{4\left(3y^2 + 5\right)\left(n\left(y^2 - 5\right) + y^2 + 3\right)}{\pi k^2 \left(y^4 - 2y^2 - 15\right)^2} \tag{437}$$

$$\mu + P_\perp = \frac{1}{8\pi k^2 \left(y^4 - 2y^2 - 15\right)^2}\left(n\left(-72y^4 + 240y^2 + 600\right) + y^8\right.$$
$$\left. -20y^6 + 102y^4 - 980y^2 + 385\right) \tag{438}$$

In Figures 82 - 87 we present the graphs of $k^2\mu$ of $k^2(\mu + P_r)$ and of $k^2(\mu + P_\perp)$ of Eqs (434), (437) and (438) for $n = 1$ and 2. It is obvious from these graphs that the solution satisfies the WEC. Also in Figure 88 we present the graph of $k^2 P_r$ of Eq (435) and in Figures 89 and 90 the graph of $k^2 P_\perp$ of Eq (436) for $n = 1$ and 2.

From Eq (394) for $p = -1$ we get the relation

$$(\mu + 4P_\perp + P_r)^2 + \frac{1}{32\pi k^4 M(\mu + 2P_\perp + P_r)^2}((k(\mu + 2P_\perp + P_r) -$$
$$5M(\mu + 4P_\perp + P_r))(k(\mu + 2P_\perp + P_r) + M(\mu + 4P_\perp +$$
$$P_r))^2) = 0 \tag{439}$$

which is the equation of states of the solution.

The solution we get for $(p, q, n) = (p, q, \frac{2M}{k}) = (-1, 2, 1)$ has the "degenerate" horizon at $r = k = 2M$, which is the only horizon of the solution since for $(p, q, \frac{2M}{k}) = (-1, 2, 1)$ the relation (407) is not satisfied.

The solution we get for $(p, q, n) = (p, q, \frac{2M}{k}) = (-1, 2, 2)$ has a horizon at $r = 2M$. This is the only horizon of the solution since for $(p, q, \frac{2M}{k}) = (-1, 2, 2)$ the relation (407) is not satisfied.

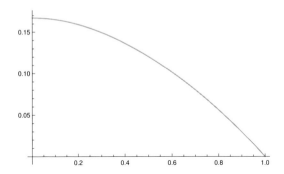

Figure 82: $k^2\mu$ of expression (434) for $n = 1$

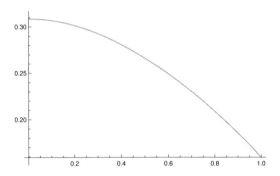

Figure 83: $k^2\mu$ of expression (434) for $n = 2$

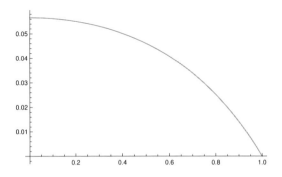

Figure 84: $k^2(\mu + P_r)$ of expression (437) for $n = 1$

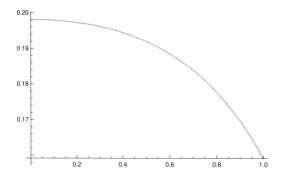

Figure 85: $k^2(\mu + P_r)$ of expression (437) for $n = 2$

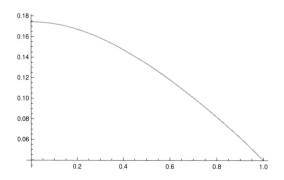

Figure 86: $k^2(\mu + P_\perp)$ of expression (438) for $n = 1$

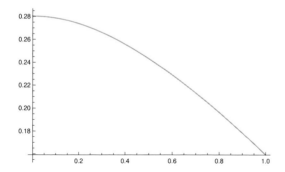

Figure 87: $k^2(\mu + P_\perp)$ of expression (438) for $n = 2$

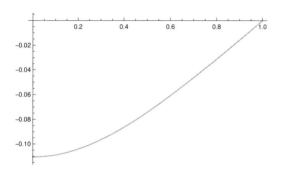

Figure 88: $k^2 P_r$ of expression (435)

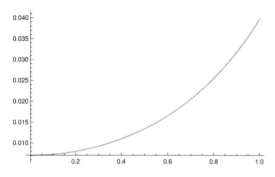

Figure 89: $k^2 P_\perp$ of expression (436) for $n = 1$

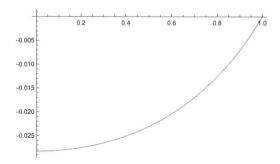

Figure 90: $k^2 P_\perp$ of expression (436) for $n = 2$

Example 2.3.1.6: Solution with $f(r) = (h(r))^2$ and $h(r)$ of Eq (440)

Consider the solution with $f(r) = (h(r))^2$ and

$$h(r) = \frac{b(k+r)^2}{4k} + (1-b)r \qquad (440)$$

which is of the form of Eq (113) and satisfies the matching condition (3) and (4). Since $h(r)$ should not vanish for $0 \le r \le k$ we shall take

$$b > 0 \qquad (441)$$

The non-vanishing components of the Ricci tensor $R_{\mu\nu}$, the Ricci scalar R and the second order curvature invariant R^2 are obtained from Eqs (115) - (119) and (440). We get

$$R_{tt} = \frac{8bkM\left(k^2 b - 2k(4M + (b-2)r) + br^2\right)}{\left(k^2 b - 2k(b-2)r + br^2\right)^3} \qquad (442)$$

$$R_{rr} = b\left(-\frac{1}{k^2 b - 2k(4M + (b-2)r) + br^2} - \frac{3}{k^2 b - 2k(b-2)r + br^2}\right) \qquad (443)$$

$$R_{\theta\theta} = \frac{R_{\phi\phi}}{sin^2\theta} = -\frac{b}{8k^2}(k^2(3b-8) - 2k(4M + 3(b-2)r) + 3br^2) \qquad (444)$$

$$R = -\frac{16b\left(k(k(b-2) - 3M) - 2k(b-2)r + br^2\right)}{\left(k^2 b - 2k(b-2)r + br^2\right)^2} \qquad (445)$$

115

$$R^2 = \frac{32}{(k^2b - 2k(b-2)r + br^2)^6}(6144k^6M^2(b-1)^2 + 8k^2b(4k^2b + $$
$$8kM(3b-1) + 33M^2b)(k^2b - 2k(b-2)r + br^2)^2 - 16kb^2(k + $$
$$2M)(k^2b - 2k(b-2)r + br^2)^3 + 3b^2(k^2b - 2k(b-2)r + br^2)^4 - $$
$$256k^4M(b-1)b(2k + 9M)(k^2b - 2k(b-2)r + br^2)) \tag{446}$$

The expressions R and R^2 of Eqs (445) and (446) are regular if relation (441) is satisfied. Therefore if relation (441) is satisfied the solution is regular.

The eigenvalues B_i, $i = t, r, \theta$ and ϕ of the Ricci tensor R^ν_μ of this solution, which are obtained from Eqs (120) - (122) and (440) are the following:

$$B_t = -\frac{8kMb}{(k^2b - 2k(b-2)r + br^2)^2} \tag{447}$$

$$B_r = -\frac{4b\left(k^2b - 2k(3M + (b-2)r) + br^2\right)}{(k^2b - 2k(b-2)r + br^2)^2} \tag{448}$$

$$B_\theta = B_\phi = \frac{2b\left(k(8(k+M) - 3kb) + 6k(b-2)r - 3br^2\right)}{(k^2b - 2k(b-2)r + br^2)^2} \tag{449}$$

From Eqs (123) - (127) and (440) we find the energy density μ, the radial pressure P_r, the tangential pressure $P_\perp$ and the quantities $\mu + P_r$ and $\mu + P_\perp$. We obtain in the variables y and n of Eqs (172)

$$\mu = -\frac{b\left(-2n + b(y-1)^2 + 4y - 2\right)}{\pi k^2\left(b(y-1)^2 + 4y\right)^2} \tag{450}$$

$$P_r = \frac{b(y-1)(b(y-1) + 4)}{2\pi k^2\left(b(y-1)^2 + 4y\right)^2} \tag{451}$$

$$P_\perp = \frac{b\left(-2n + b(y-1)^2 + 4y\right)}{4\pi k^2\left(b(y-1)^2 + 4y\right)^2} \tag{452}$$

$$\mu + P_r = -\frac{b(-4n + b(y-1)^2 + 4y)}{2\pi k^2(b(y-1)^2 + 4y)^2} \tag{453}$$

$$\mu + P_\perp = -\frac{b(-6n + 3b(y-1)^2 + 12y - 8)}{4\pi k^2(b(y-1)^2 + 4y)^2} \tag{454}$$

To find the equation of state of the solution we solve for r the equation we obtain if in relation (128) we substitute the $h(r)$ of Eq (440), in which

116

case we get two solutions say r_1 and r_2. Repeating the same procedure with Eq (129) we get other two solutions say r_3 and r_4. Then equating each of r_1 and r_2 with each of r_3 and r_4 we get after some calculations the relation

$$b\frac{\mu M + 4MP_\perp + MP_r}{\mu + 2P_\perp + P_r} - bk = k\frac{8\pi M^2 P_r(\mu + 4P_\perp + P_r)^2}{(\mu + 2P_\perp + P_r)^2} \tag{455}$$

Solving the above equation for μ we get the relation

$$\mu = \frac{1}{k(4\pi k^2 n^2 P_r + (2-n)b)}(-4\pi k^3 n^2 P_r(4P_\perp + P_r) + kb((3n -$$

$$4)P_\perp + (n-2)P_r) - \sqrt{-k^2\ n^2 b P_\perp^2(32\pi k^2 P_r - b)}) \tag{456}$$

which is satisfied if its μ, P_r and $P_\perp$ are replaced by expressions (450), (451) and (452) respectively, and another expression for μ which is not satisfied by such replacements. Therefore the expression (456) is the equation of state of the solution.

To find values of the constants for which the WEC are satisfied we shall use relations (123), (126) and (127). From these relations we find that our solution satisfies the WEC if $n = \frac{2M}{k} \geq 1$ and if in the interior region $0 \leq r \leq k$ we have

$$h(r) \leq k, \quad h'(r) < 1 \quad \text{and} \quad h''(r) > 0 \tag{457}$$

Using Eq (440) we get

$$h(r) - k = \frac{k-r}{4k}(b(k-r) - 4k) \tag{458}$$

which means that the first of relations (457) is satisfied if $b \leq 4$. For these values of b we have $h'(r) - 1 = \frac{b}{2k}(r-k) \leq 0$ and $h''(r) = \frac{b}{2k} > 0$. Therefore our solution is regular and satisfies the WEC if

$$n \geq 1 \quad \text{and} \quad 4 \geq b > 0 \tag{459}$$

The line element of the solution, which is obtained from Eqs (131) and (440), is the following:

$$d^2s = -(1 - \frac{2M}{\frac{b(k+r)^2}{4k} + (1-b)r})dt^2 + \frac{dr^2}{1 - \frac{2M}{\frac{b(k+r)^2}{4k} + (1-b)r}} +$$

$$\left(\frac{b(k+r)^2}{4k} + (1-b)r\right)^2 (d^2\theta + sin^2\theta d^2\phi) \tag{460}$$

After matching the solution has for $\frac{2M}{k} = n > 1$ a horizon at $r = 2M$ and for $\frac{2M}{k} = n = 1$ a "degenerate" horizon at $r = k = 2M$. To find the horizons which are in the interior region we solving equation $g^{rr}(r_{int}) = 0$ in which case we get

$$r_{int} = k\left(\frac{b - 2 \pm 2\sqrt{nb - b + 1}}{b}\right) \tag{461}$$

To each r_{int} which is inside the interior region, that is to each r_{int} for which

$$0 < r_{int} = k\left(\frac{b - 2 \pm 2\sqrt{nb - b + 1}}{b}\right) < k \tag{462}$$

a horizon corresponds. Eq (406) since $b > 0$ is equivalent to the relation

$$2 - b < \pm 2\sqrt{nb - b + 1} < 2 \tag{463}$$

If the constants b and n with $n < 1$ do not satisfy relation (462) the solution we get after matching does not have a horizon.

We shall consider the solutions we get for $b = \frac{1}{2}$ and $b = \frac{3}{2}$.

Example 2.3.1.6.1 : Solution with $f(r) = (h(r))^2$ and $h(r)$ of Eq (464)

Consider the solution with $f(r) = (h(r))^2$ and

$$h(r) = \frac{(k + r)^2}{8k} + \frac{r}{2} \tag{464}$$

which is obtained from the $h(r)$ of Eq (440) for $b = \frac{1}{2}$. Also for $b = \frac{1}{2}$ from Eqs (442) - (449) we get the following expressions for the non-vanishing components of the Ricci tensor $R_{\mu\nu}$, the Ricci scalar R, the second order curvature invariant R^2 and the eigenvalues B_i, $i = t, r, \theta$ and ϕ of the Ricci tensor R_μ^ν of this solution:

$$R_{tt} = \frac{16kM\left(k^2 - 16kM + 6kr + r^2\right)}{\left(k^2 + 6kr + r^2\right)^3} \tag{465}$$

$$R_{rr} = -\frac{4\left(k^2 + 6k(r - 2M) + r^2\right)}{\left(k^2 + 6kr + r^2\right)\left(k^2 - 16kM + 6kr + r^2\right)} \tag{466}$$

$$R_{\theta\theta} = \frac{R_{\phi\phi}}{sin^2\theta} = \frac{13k^2 + 2k(8M - 9r) - 3r^2}{32k^2} \tag{467}$$

118

$$R = \frac{16\left(3k(k + 2M) - 6kr - r^2\right)}{\left(k^2 + 6kr + r^2\right)^2} \tag{468}$$

$$R^2 = \frac{32}{\left(k^2 + 6kr + r^2\right)^6}\left(98304k^6 M^2 + 32k^2(4k^2 + 8kM + 33M^2)\right)$$
$$\left(k^2 + 6kr + r^2\right)^2 - 32k(k + 2M)(k^2 + 6kr + r^2)^3 + 3(k^2 + 6kr + r^2)^4 + 2048k^4 M(2k + 9M)(k^2 + 6kr + r^2)) \tag{469}$$

$$B_t = -\frac{16kM}{\left(k^2 + 6kr + r^2\right)^2} \tag{470}$$

$$B_r = -\frac{4(k^2 + 6k(r - 2M) + r^2)}{\left(k^2 + 6kr + r^2\right)^2} \tag{471}$$

$$B_\theta = B_\phi = \frac{26k^2 + 4k(8M - 9r) - 6r^2}{\left(k^2 + 6kr + r^2\right)^2} \tag{472}$$

From Eqs (450) - (454) for $b = \frac{1}{2}$ we obtain the energy density μ, the radial pressure P_r, the tangential pressure $P_\perp$ and the quantities $\mu + P_r$ and $\mu + P_\perp$ of the solution in the variables y and n of Eqs (172). We get:

$$\mu = \frac{4n - y^2 - 6y + 3}{\pi k^2 \left(y^2 + 6y + 1\right)^2} \tag{473}$$

$$P_r = \frac{y^2 + 6y - 7}{2\pi k^2 \left(y^2 + 6y + 1\right)^2} \tag{474}$$

$$P_\perp = \frac{-4n + y^2 + 6y + 1}{4\pi k^2 \left(y^2 + 6y + 1\right)^2} \tag{475}$$

$$\mu + P_r = -\frac{-8n + y^2 + 6y + 1}{2\pi k^2 \left(y^2 + 6y + 1\right)^2} \tag{476}$$

$$\mu + P_\perp = \frac{12n - 3y^2 - 18y + 13}{4\pi k^2 \left(y^2 + 6y + 1\right)^2} \tag{477}$$

In Figures 91 - 96 we present the graphs of $k^2\mu$ of $k^2(\mu + P_r)$ and of $k^2(\mu + P_\perp)$ of Eqs (473), (476) and (477) for $n = 1$ and 2. It is obvious from these graphs that the solution satisfies the WEC. Also in Figure 97 we present the graph of $k^2 P_r$ of Eq (474) and in Figures 98 and 99 the graph of $k^2 P_\perp$ of Eq (475) for $n = 1$ and 2.

The equation of state of the solution, which is obtained from Eq (456) for $b = \frac{1}{2}$, is the following:

$$\mu = \frac{1}{k\,(8\pi k^2 n^2 \Pr -n + 2)}(-8\pi k^3 n^2 \Pr(4P_\perp + \Pr) + k((3n - 4)P_\perp +$$
$$(n - 2)\Pr)) - \sqrt{-k^2 n^2 P^2\ (64\pi k^2 \Pr -1)} \tag{478}$$

The line element of the solution, which is obtained from Eqs (460) and $b = \frac{1}{2}$ is the following:

$$d^2 s = -(1 - \frac{16Mk}{(k + r)^2 + 4kr})dt^2 + \frac{dr^2}{1 - \frac{16Mk}{(k+r)^2+4kr}} +$$
$$\frac{((k + r)^2 + 4kr)^2}{64k^2}(d^2\theta + sin^2\theta d^2\phi) \tag{479}$$

The solution we get for $(b, n) = (b, \frac{2M}{k}) = (\frac{1}{2}, 1)$ has the "degenerate" horizon at $r = k = 2M$. This is the only horizon of the solution since for $(b, \frac{2M}{k}) = (\frac{1}{2}, 1)$ the relation (463) is not satisfied.

The solution we get for $(b, n) = (b, \frac{2M}{k}) = (\frac{1}{2}, 2)$ has a horizon at $r = 2M$. This is the only horizon of the solution since for $(b, \frac{2M}{k}) = (\frac{1}{2}, 2)$ the relation (463) is not satisfied.

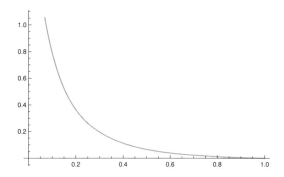

Figure 91: $k^2\mu$ of expression (473) for $n = 1$

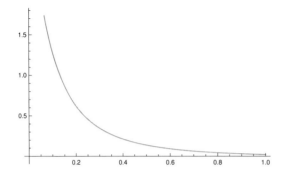

Figure 92: $k^2\mu$ of expression (473) for $n = 2$

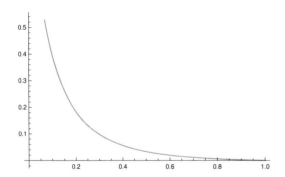

Figure 93: $k^2(\mu + P_r)$ of expression (476) for $n = 1$

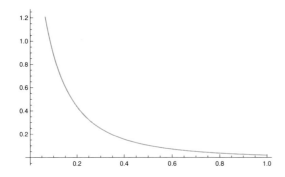

Figure 94: $k^2(\mu + P_r)$ of expression (476) for $n = 2$

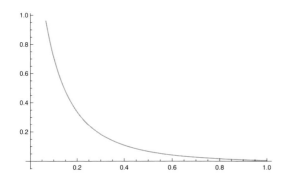

Figure 95: $k^2(\mu + P_\perp)$ of expression (477) for $n = 1$

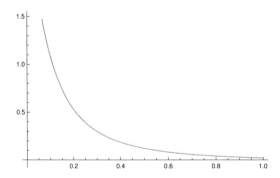

Figure 96: $k^2(\mu + P_\perp)$ of expression (477) for $n = 2$

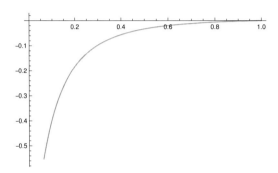

Figure 97: $k^2 P_r$ of expression (474)

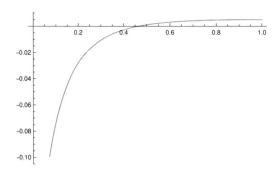

Figure 98: $k^2 P_\perp$ of expression (475) for $n = 1$

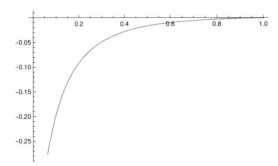

Figure 99: $k^2 P_\perp$ of expression (475) for $n = 2$

Example 2.3.1.6.2 : Solution with $f(r) = (h(r))^2$ and $h(r)$ of Eq (480)

Consider the solution with $f(r) = (h(r))^2$ and

$$h(r) = \frac{3(k+r)^2}{8k} - \frac{r}{2} \tag{480}$$

which is obtained from the $h(r)$ of Eq (440) for $b = \frac{3}{2}$. For $b = \frac{3}{2}$ from Eqs (442) - (449) we get the following expressions for the non-vanishing components of the Ricci tensor $R_{\mu\nu}$, the Ricci scalar R, the second order curvature invariant R^2 and the eigenvalues B_i, $i = t$, r, θ and ϕ of the Ricci tensor R_μ^ν of this solution:

$$R_{tt} = \frac{48kM\left(3k^2 + 2k(r - 8M) + 3r^2\right)}{\left(3k^2 + 2kr + 3r^2\right)^3} \tag{481}$$

$$R_{rr} = -\frac{12\left(3k^2 - 12kM + 2kr + 3r^2\right)}{\left(3k^2 + 2kr + 3r^2\right)\left(3k^2 - 16kM + 2kr + 3r^2\right)} \tag{482}$$

$$R_{\theta\theta} = \frac{R_{\phi\phi}}{\sin^2\theta} = \frac{3\left(7k^2 + 16kM - 6kr - 9r^2\right)}{32k^2} \tag{483}$$

$$R = \frac{48\left(k^2 + 6kM - 2kr - 3r^2\right)}{\left(3k^2 + 2kr + 3r^2\right)^2} \tag{484}$$

$$R^2 = \frac{96}{\left(3k^2 + 2kr + 3r^2\right)^6}\left(32768k^6 M^2 + 32k^2(12k^2 + 56kM + 99\right.$$
$$M^2)(3k^2 + 2kr + 3r^2)^2 - 96k(k + 2M)(3k^2 + 2kr + 3r^2)^3 + 9$$
$$\left.(3k^2 + 2kr + 3r^2)^4 - 2048k^4 M(2k + 9M)(3k^2 + 2kr + 3r^2)\right) \tag{485}$$

$$B_t = -\frac{48kM}{(3k^2 + 2kr + 3r^2)^2} \tag{486}$$

$$B_r = -\frac{12\left(3k^2 + 2k(r - 6M) + 3r^2\right)}{(3k^2 + 2kr + 3r^2)^2} \tag{487}$$

$$B_\theta = B_\phi = \frac{6\left(7k^2 + 16kM - 6kr - 9r^2\right)}{(3k^2 + 2kr + 3r^2)^2} \tag{488}$$

The energy density μ, the radial pressure P_r, the tangential pressure $P_\perp$ and the quantities $\mu + P_r$ and $\mu + P_\perp$ of the solution in the variables y and n of Eqs (172) are obtained from Eqs (450) - (454) for $b = \frac{3}{2}$. We get

$$\mu = \frac{3\left(4n - 3y^2 - 2y + 1\right)}{\pi k^2 \left(3y^2 + 2y + 3\right)^2} \tag{489}$$

$$P_r = \frac{3\left(3y^2 + 2y - 5\right)}{2\pi k^2 \left(3y^2 + 2y + 3\right)^2} \tag{490}$$

$$P_\perp = \frac{3\left(-4n + 3y^2 + 2y + 3\right)}{4\pi k^2 \left(3y^2 + 2y + 3\right)^2} \tag{491}$$

$$\mu + P_r = -\frac{3\left(-8n + 3y^2 + 2y + 3\right)}{2\pi k^2 \left(3y^2 + 2y + 3\right)^2} \tag{492}$$

$$\mu + P_\perp = \frac{3\left(12n - 9y^2 - 6y + 7\right)}{4\pi k^2 \left(3y^2 + 2y + 3\right)^2} \tag{493}$$

We present the graphs of $k^2\mu$ of $k^2(\mu + P_r)$ and of $k^2(\mu + P_\perp)$ of Eqs (489), (492) and (493) for $n = 1$ and 2 in Figures 100 - 105 . It is obvious from these graphs that the solution satisfies the WEC. Also in Figure 106 we present the graph of $k^2 P_r$ of Eq (490) and in Figures 107 and 108 the graph of $k^2 P_\perp$ of Eq (491) for $n = 1$ and 2.

The equation of state of the solution, which can be obtained from Eq (456) for $b = \frac{3}{2}$, is the following:

$$\mu = \frac{1}{k\left(8\pi k^2 n^2 P_r - 3n + 6\right)}(3k((3n - 4)P_\perp + (n - 2)P_r) - 8\pi k^3$$
$$n^2 P_r (4P_\perp + P_r) - \sqrt{3}\sqrt{-k^2 n^2 P_\perp^2 \left(64\pi k^2 P_r - 3\right)}) \tag{494}$$

The line element of the solution, which is obtained from Eqs (460) and $b = \frac{3}{2}$ is the following:

$$d^2s = -(1 - \frac{16Mk}{3(k+r)^2 - 4kr})dt^2 + \frac{dr^2}{1 - \frac{16Mk}{3(k+r)^2-4kr}} +$$

$$\frac{(3(k+r)^2 - 4kr)^2}{64k^2}(d^2\theta + sin^2\theta d^2\phi) \tag{495}$$

The solution we get for $(b, n) = (b, \frac{2M}{k}) = (\frac{3}{2}, 1)$ has the "degenerate" horizon at $r = k = 2M$, which is the only horizon of the solution since or $(b, \frac{2M}{k}) = (\frac{3}{2}, 1)$ the relation (463) is not satisfied.

The solution we get for $(b, n) = (b, \frac{2M}{k}) = (\frac{3}{2}, 2)$ has a horizon at $r = 2M$, which is the only horizon of the solution since for $(b, \frac{2M}{k}) = (\frac{3}{2}, 2)$ the relation (463) is not satisfied.

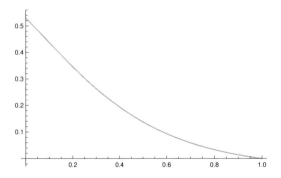

Figure 100: $k^2\mu$ of expression (489) for $n = 1$

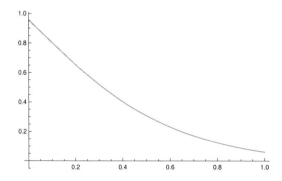

Figure 101: $k^2\mu$ of expression (489) for $n = 2$

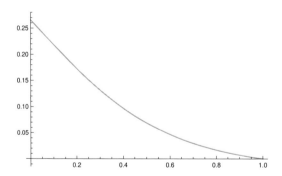

Figure 102: $k^2(\mu + P_r)$ of expression (492) for $n = 1$

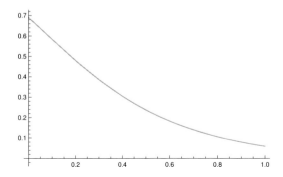

Figure 103: $k^2(\mu + P_r)$ of expression (492) for $n = 2$

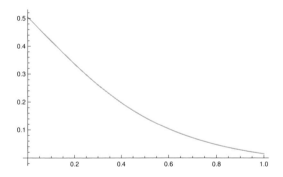

Figure 104: $k^2(\mu + P_\perp)$ of expression (493) for $n = 1$

128

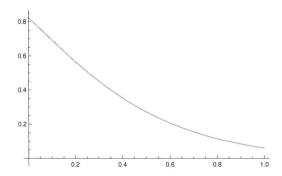

Figure 105: $k^2(\mu + P_\perp)$ of expression (493) for $n = 2$

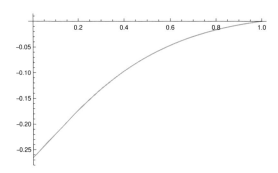

Figure 106: $k^2 P_r$ of expression (490)

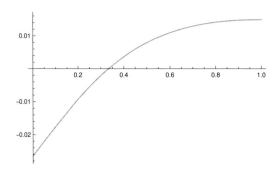

Figure 107: $k^2 P_\perp$ of expression (491) for $n = 1$

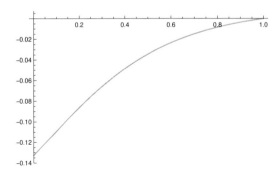

Figure 108: $k^2 P_\perp$ of expression (491) for $n = 2$

Example 2.3.1.7: Solution with $f(r) = (h(r))^2$ and $h(r)$ of Eq (496)

Consider the solution with $f(r) = (h(r))^2$ and

$$h(r) = r + kC(b)(1 - \frac{r}{k})^b \tag{496}$$

where b and $C(b)$ are constants. Since $f(r)$ should not vanish in the interior region $0 \leq r \leq k$ we shall take

$$C(b) > 0 \tag{497}$$

From the $h(r)$ of Eq (496) and Eqs (115) - (122) we get the following expressions for the non-vanishing components of the Ricci tensor $R_{\mu\nu}$, the Ricci scalar R, the second order curvature invariant R^2 and the eigenvalues B_i, $i = t, r, \theta$ and ϕ:

$$R_{tt} = \frac{(b-1)bkMC(b)\left(1 - \frac{r}{k}\right)^b \left(kC(b)\left(1 - \frac{r}{k}\right)^b - 2M + r\right)}{(k-r)^2 \left(kC(b)\left(1 - \frac{r}{k}\right)^b + r\right)^3} \tag{498}$$

$$R_{rr} = \frac{(b-1)bkC(b)\left(1 - \frac{r}{k}\right)^b \left(-2kC(b)\left(1 - \frac{r}{k}\right)^b + 3M - 2r\right)}{(k-r)^2 \left(kC(b)\left(1 - \frac{r}{k}\right)^b + r\right)\left(-kC(b)\left(1 - \frac{r}{k}\right)^b + 2M - r\right)} \tag{499}$$

$$R_{\theta\theta} = \frac{R_{\phi\phi}}{sin^2\theta} = -\frac{bkC(b)\left(1 - \frac{r}{k}\right)^b}{(k-r)^2}((2b-1)kC(b)\left(1 - \frac{r}{k}\right)^b - 2bM + br$$

$$-2k + 2M + r) \tag{500}$$

$$R = -\frac{2bC(b)k^{1-b}(k-r)^{b-2}}{\left(kC(b)\left(1-\frac{r}{k}\right)^b + r\right)^2}(-2k + 3M - 3bM + 2br + (-2+3b)$$
$$k(1-r/k)^bC(b))\tag{501}$$

$$R^2 = \frac{4}{\left(kC(b)\left(1-\frac{r}{k}\right)^b + r\right)^6}(bC(b)k^{1-b}(k-r)^{b-2}(C(b)k^{1-b}(k-r)^{b-2}$$

$$(kC(b)(1-\frac{r}{k})^b(bkC(b)(1-\frac{r}{k})^b((9b^2 - 6b + 9)M^2 + kC(b)(1-\frac{r}{k})^b((b$$

$$(3b-4)+2)kC(b)(1-\frac{r}{k})^b - 2b(4bM - 5br + 2k - 6M + 6r) - 8M +$$

$$8r) + 8(b+1)k(M-r) - 4(b(5b-8)+8)Mr + (b(13b-16)+16)r^2 +$$

$$4k^2) + 2r(3b(b^2+7)M^2 + 4bk^2 + 4(6b+1)kM) - 4r^2(b((b+4)k + (b$$

$$(5b-11)+14)M) + M) - 4kM(4bk + 6b(b+1)M + k) + 4b(b(2b-3)$$

$$+4)r^3) + r^2(4bk^2 - 8(b-5)(b+1)kM + 3(b(b(3b-14)+31)+4)M^2)$$

$$+4k^2M(3(5bM+M)+2k) - 4r^3(2bk + (b(2(b-3)b+7)+4)M) - 4k$$

$$Mr((3b+8)k - 6(b-6)bM + 6M) + 2b((b-2)b+3)r^4) + 4M(r((b-$$

$$3)r - 3(b-5)M) + 2k(r-6M))) + 12M^2(k-r)^2)\tag{502}$$

$$B_t = -\frac{(b-1)bkMC(b)\left(1-\frac{r}{k}\right)^b}{(k-r)^2\left(kC(b)\left(1-\frac{r}{k}\right)^b + r\right)^2}\tag{503}$$

$$B_r = -\frac{(b-1)bkC(b)\left(1-\frac{r}{k}\right)^b\left(2kC(b)\left(1-\frac{r}{k}\right)^b - 3M + 2r\right)}{(k-r)^2\left(kC(b)\left(1-\frac{r}{k}\right)^b + r\right)^2}\tag{504}$$

$$B_\theta = B_\phi = -\frac{bkC(b)\left(1-\frac{r}{k}\right)^b}{(k-r)^2\left(kC(b)\left(1-\frac{r}{k}\right)^b + r\right)^2}((2b-1)kC(b)\left(1-\frac{r}{k}\right)^b -$$

$$2bM + br - 2k + 2M + r)\tag{505}$$

From Eqs (497), (501) and (502) we find that the invariants R and R^2 of the solution are regular if

$$b \geq 2\tag{506}$$

Therefore if relations (497) and (506) are satisfied the solution is regular.

From Eqs (123) - (127) and (496) we find that the energy density μ, the radial pressure P_r, the tangential pressure $P_\perp$ and the quantities $\mu + P_r$ and $\mu + P_\perp$ are the following in the variables y and n of Eqs (172):

$$\mu = -\frac{bC(b)(1-y)^{b-2}\left((3b-2)C(b)(1-y)^b + 2(-bn + by + n - 1)\right)}{8\pi k^2 \left(C(b)(1-y)^b + y\right)^2} \tag{507}$$

$$P_r = \frac{bC(b)(1-y)^{b-2}\left(bC(b)(1-y)^b + 2y - 2\right)}{8\pi k^2 \left(C(b)(1-y)^b + y\right)^2} \tag{508}$$

$$P_\perp = \frac{(b-1)bC(b)(1-y)^{b-2}\left(2C(b)(1-y)^b - n + 2y\right)}{16\pi k^2 \left(C(b)(1-y)^b + y\right)^2} \tag{509}$$

$$\mu + P_r = -\frac{(b-1)bC(b)(1-y)^{b-2}\left(C(b)(1-y)^b - n + y\right)}{4\pi k^2 \left(C(b)(1-y)^b + y\right)^2} \tag{510}$$

$$\mu + P_\perp = -\frac{b(b)(1-y)^{b-2}}{16\pi k^2 \left(C(b)(1-y)^b + y\right)^2}(2(2b-1)C(b)(1-y)^b - 3(b-1)n + 2(by + y - 2)) \tag{511}$$

To find the equation of state of the solution for $b > 2$ we use the relation

$$\frac{4\pi M(\mu + P_r + 4P_\perp)^2}{\mu + P_r + 2P_\perp} = \frac{(b-1)bC(b)\left(1 - \frac{r}{k}\right)^{b-2}}{k} \tag{512}$$

which is obtained from Eqs (130) and (496) and the relation

$$\frac{M(\mu + P_r + 4P_t)}{\mu + P_r + 2P_t} = kC(b)\left(1 - \frac{r}{k}\right)^b + r \tag{513}$$

which is obtained from Eqs (128) and (496). Solving Eq (512) for $1 - \frac{r}{k}$ and substituting the resulting relation in Eq (513) we get

$$(4\pi)^{\frac{b}{b-2}}C(b)\left(\frac{(b-1)bC(b)(\mu + P_r + 2P_t)}{kM(\mu + P_r + 4P_t)^2}\right)^{\frac{b}{2-b}} - (4\pi)^{\frac{1}{b-2}}$$
$$\left(\frac{(b-1)bC(b)(\mu + P_r + 2P_t)}{kM(\mu + P_r + 4P_t)^2}\right)^{\frac{1}{2-b}} - \frac{M(\mu + P_r + 4P_\perp)}{k(\mu + P_r + 2P_\perp)} +$$
$$1 = 0 \tag{514}$$

The above relation is satisfied if we replace μ, P_r and $P_\perp$ by their expressions of Eqs (507), (508) and (509) and M by $nk/2$. Eq (514) is the equation of state of the solution for $b > 2$.

For $b = 2$ from Eqs (130) and (496) we obtain

$$\frac{4\pi M(\mu + \mathrm{Pr} + 4P_\perp)^2}{\mu + P_r + 2P_\perp} = \frac{2C(2)}{k} \tag{515}$$

Solving the above equation for μ we get the relation

$$\mu = \frac{-\sqrt{C(2)^2 - 16\pi C(2)kMP_\perp} + C(2) - 4\pi kMP_r - 16\pi kMP_\perp}{4\pi kM} \tag{516}$$

which is satisfied if we replace μ, P_r and $P_\perp$ by their expressions of Eqs (507), (508) and (509) for $b = 2$ and M by $nk/2$ and one more relation, which however is not satisfied if we make these replacements. Therefore the relation (516) is the equation of state of the solution for $b = 2$.

We shall assume that the solution is regular, which means that Eqs (497) and (506) hold and we shall find the relations the constants of the solution should satisfy so that the solution satisfy the WEC. From Eqs (126), (130) and (496) we find that we have $\mu + P_r \geq 0$ if

$$2M - h(r) = k(n - y - C(b)(1 - y)^b) \geq 0 \tag{517}$$

According to Eqs (128) and (129) if this relation is valid sufficient condition to have $\mu \geq 0$ and $\mu + P_\perp > 0$ is to have

$$1 - (h'(r))^2 = bC(b)(1 - y)^{b-1}(2 - bC(b)(1 - y)^{b-1}) \geq 0 \tag{518}$$

This relation is satisfied if

$$2 \geq bC(b) \tag{519}$$

from which we get since relation (506) holds that $C(b) \leq 1$. Then we get

$$y + C(b)(1 - y)^b \leq (y + C(b)(1 - y)) \leq y + (1 - y) \leq 1 \tag{520}$$

Therefore relation (517) is satisfied if

$$n \geq 1 \tag{521}$$

Therefore the solution is regular and satisfies the WEC if relations (497), (506), (519) and (521) hold.

The line element of the solution, which is obtained from Eqs (131) and (496), is the following:

$$d^2s = -(1 - \frac{2M}{r + k(1 - \frac{r}{k})^bC(b)})dt^2 + \frac{dr^2}{1 - \frac{2M}{r+k(1-\frac{r}{k})^bC(b)}} +$$

$$(r + k(1 - \frac{r}{k})^bC(b))^2(d^2\theta + sin^2\theta d^2\phi) \tag{522}$$

We shall consider the solutions we get for $b = 2$ and $b = 4$.

Example 2.3.1.7.1 : Solution with $f(r) = (h(r))^2$ and $h(r)$ of Eq (523)

Consider the solution with $f(r) = (h(r))^2$ and

$$h(r) = r + kC(2)(1 - \frac{r}{k})^2 \tag{523}$$

which is obtained from the $h(r)$ of Eq (496) for $b = 2$. For this value of b from Eqs (498) - (505) we get the following expressions for the non-vanishing components of the Ricci tensor $R_{\mu\nu}$, the Ricci scalar R, the second order curvature invariant R^2 and the eigenvalues B_i, $i = t, r, \theta$ and ϕ of the Ricci tensor R_μ^ν of this solution:

$$R_{tt} = \frac{2C(2)kM \left(C(2)(k - r)^2 + k(r - 2M)\right)}{\left(C(2)(k - r)^2 + kr\right)^3} \tag{524}$$

$$R_{rr} = \frac{2C(2) \left(k(3M - 2r) - 2C(2)(k - r)^2\right)}{2C(2)k(k - r)^2(r - M) + C(2)^2(k - r)^4 + k^2r(r - 2M)} \tag{525}$$

$$R_{\theta\theta} = \frac{R_{\phi\phi}}{sin^2\theta} = -\frac{2C(2) \left(3C(2)(k - r)^2 - 2k(k + M) + 3kr\right)}{k^2} \tag{526}$$

$$R = -\frac{4C(2) \left((4C(2) - 2) k^2 + k \left(-8C(2)r - 3M + 4r\right) + 4C(2)r^2\right)}{\left(C(2)k^2 + k \left(r - 2C(2)r\right) + C(2)r^2\right)^2} \tag{527}$$

$$R^2 = \frac{16}{\left(C(2)(k - r)^2 + kr\right)^6}(-2C(2)k^5M(12kM - 2kr - 9Mr + r^2) +$$
$$C(2)^4k^2(k - r)^4(4k^2 - 24r(k + 2M) + 24kM + 33M^2 + 36r^2) + C(2)^2$$
$$k^4(r^2(4k^2 + 36kM + 51M^2) + 2k^2M(2k + 33M) - 4r^3(2k + 5M) -$$
$$4kMr(7k + 27M) + 6r^4) + 2C(2)^3k^3(k - r)^2(r(4k^2 + 26kM + 33M^2)$$
$$-r^2(12k + 25M) - 9kM(k + 4M) + 12r^3) - 8C(2)^5k(k - r)^6(k +$$
$$2M - 3r) + 6C(2)^6(k - r)^8 + 3k^6M^2) \tag{528}$$

$$B_t = \frac{2C(2)kM}{(C(2)k^2 + k\,(r - 2C(2)r) + C(2)r^2)^{\,2}} \tag{529}$$

$$B_r = -\frac{2C(2)kM}{(C(2)k^2 + k\,(r - 2C(2)r) + C(2)r^2)^{\,2}} \tag{530}$$

$$B_\theta = B_\phi = -\frac{2C(2)\,(3C(2)(k - r)^2 - 2k(k + M) + 3kr)}{(C(2)k^2 + k\,(r - 2C(2)r) + C(2)r^2)^{\,2}} \tag{531}$$

From Eqs (507) - (511) for $b = 2$ we obtain the energy density μ, the radial pressure P_r, the tangential pressure $P_\perp$ and the quantities $\mu + P_r$ and $\mu + P_\perp$ of the solution in the variables y and n of Eqs (172). We get:

$$\mu = \frac{C(2)\,(-2C(2)(y - 1)^2 + n - 2y + 1)}{2\pi k^2\,(C(2)(y - 1)^2 + y)^{\,2}} \tag{532}$$

$$P_r = \frac{C(2)(y - 1)\,(C(2)(y - 1) + 1)}{2\pi k^2\,(C(2)y^2 - 2C(2)y + C(2) + y)^{\,2}} \tag{533}$$

$$P_\perp = \frac{C(2)(-n + 2(y + C(2) - 2yC(2) + y^2 C(2)))}{8k^2\pi(y + C(2) - 2yC(2) + y^2 C(2))^2} \tag{534}$$

$$\mu + P_r = -\frac{C(2)\,(C(2)y^2 - 2C(2)y + C(2) - n + y)}{2\pi k^2\,(C(2)y^2 - 2C(2)y + C(2) + y)^{\,2}} \tag{535}$$

$$\mu + P_\perp = -\frac{C(2)\,(6C(2)y^2 + (6 - 12C(2))\,y + 6C(2) - 3n - 4)}{8\pi k^2\,(C(2)y^2 - 2C(2)y + C(2) + y)^{\,2}} \tag{536}$$

In Figures 109 - 114 we present the graphs of $k^2\mu$ of $k^2(\mu + P_r)$ and of $k^2(\mu + P_\perp)$ of Eqs (532), (535) and (536) for $C(2) = 0.1$ and $n = 1$ and also for $C(2) = 0.1$ and $n = 2$. It is obvious from these graphs that the solution satisfies the WEC. Also in Figure 115 we present the graph of $k^2 P_r$ of Eq (533) and in Figures 116 and 117 the graphs of $k^2 P_\perp$ of Eq (534) for the same values of their constants $C(2)$ or $C(2)$ and n.

The equation of state of the solution is given by relation (516).

The line element of the solution is obtained from Eqs (131) and (523). We get

$$d^2 s = -(1 - \frac{2M}{r + k(1 - \frac{r}{k})^2 C(2)})dt^2 + \frac{dr^2}{1 - \frac{2M}{r + k(1 - \frac{r}{k})^2 C(2)}} +$$
$$(r + k(1 - \frac{r}{k})^2 C(2))^2 (d^2\theta + sin^2\theta d^2\phi) \tag{537}$$

After matching the solution has for $\frac{2M}{k} = n > 1$ a horizon at $r = 2M$ and for $\frac{2M}{k} = n = 1$ a "degenerate" horizon at $r = k = 2M$. To find the horizons which are inside the interior region we solve equation $g^{rr}(r_{int}) = 0$ in which case we get

$$r_{int} = \frac{k\left(-1 + 2C(2) \pm \sqrt{4C(2)(n-1)+1}\right)}{2C(2)} \tag{538}$$

To each r_{int} which is inside the interior region, that is to each r_{int} for which

$$0 < r_{int} = \frac{k\left(-1 + 2C(2) \pm \sqrt{4C(2)(n-1)+1}\right)}{2C(2)} < k \tag{539}$$

a horizon corresponds. However for $C(2) = 0.1$ and $n = 1$ and also for $C(2) = 0.1$ and $n = 2$ the relations (539) are not satisfied. Therefore the solutions we get for these values of the constants $C(2)$ and n do not have horizons inside the interior region.

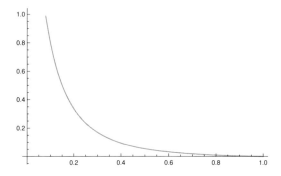

Figure 109: $k^2\mu$ of expression (532) for $C(2) = 0.1$ and $n = 1$

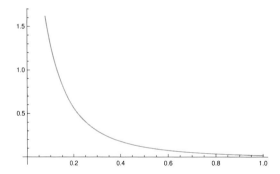

Figure 110: $k^2\mu$ of expression (532) for $C(2) = 0.1$ and $n = 2$

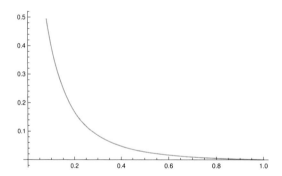

Figure 111: $k^2(\mu + P_r)$ of expression (535) for $C(2) = 0.1$ and $n = 1$

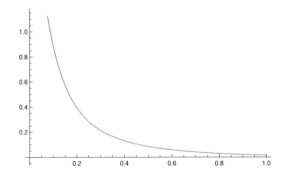

Figure 112: $k^2(\mu + P_r)$ of expression (535) for $C(2) = 0.1$ and $n = 2$

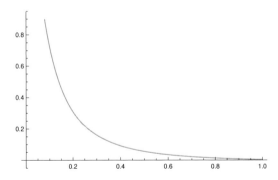

Figure 113: $k^2(\mu + P_\perp)$ of expression (536) for $C(2) = 0.1$ and $n = 1$

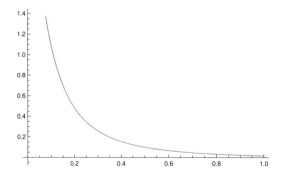

Figure 114: $k^2(\mu + P_\perp)$ of expression (536) for $C(2) = 0.1$ and $n = 2$

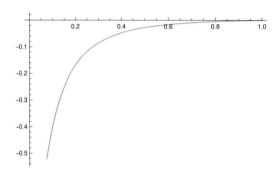

Figure 115: $k^2 P_r$ of expression (533)
for $C(2) = 0.1$

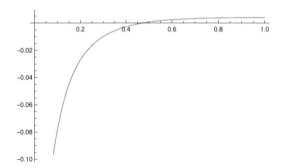

Figure 116: $k^2 P_\perp$ of expression (534) for $C(2) = 0.1$ and $n = 1$

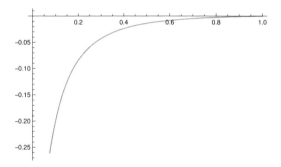

Figure 117: $k^2 P_\perp$ of expression (534) for $C(2) = 0.1$ and $n = 2$

Example 2.3.1.7.2 : Solution with $f(r) = (h(r))^2$ and $h(r)$ of Eq (540)

Consider the solution with $f(r) = (h(r))^2$ and

$$h(r) = r + kC(4)(1 - \frac{r}{k})^4 \qquad (540)$$

which is obtained from the $h(r)$ of Eq (496) for $b = 4$. For this value of b from Eqs (498) - (505) we get the following expressions for the non-vanishing components of the Ricci tensor $R_{\mu\nu}$, the Ricci scalar R, the second order curvature invariant R^2 and the eigenvalues B_i, $i = t$, r, θ and ϕ of the Ricci

140

tensor R_μ^ν of this solution:

$$R_{tt} = \frac{12C(4)k^3M(k-r)^2\left(C(4)(k-r)^4 + k^3(r-2M)\right)}{(C(4)(k-r)^4 + k^3r)^{\,3}} \tag{541}$$

$$R_{rr} = \frac{12C(4)(k-r)^2\left(k^3(3M-2r) - 2C(2)(k-r)^4\right)}{2C(2)k^3(k-r)^4(r-M) + C(4)^2(k-r)^8 + k^6r(r-2M)} \tag{542}$$

$$R_{\theta\theta} = \frac{R_{\phi\phi}}{sin^2\theta} = -\frac{4C(4)(k-r)^2\left(7C(4)(k-r)^4 + k^3(-2k - 6M + 5r)\right)}{k^6} \tag{543}$$

$$R = \frac{8C(4)(k-r)^2\left(k^3(2k + 9M - 8r) - 10C(4)(k-r)^4\right)}{(C(4)(k-r)^4 + k^3r)^{\,2}} \tag{544}$$

$$R^2 = \frac{16}{(C(4)(k-r)^4 + k^3r)^{\,6}}\left(4C(4)k^{15}M(k-r)^2(2k(r-6M) + r(3M\right.$$
$$+r)) - 32C(4)^5k^3(k-r)^{16}(2k + 11M - 15r) + 4C(4)^2k^{12}(k-r)^4(2r^2$$
$$(2k^2 + 5kM + 36M^2) + k^2M(2k + 63M) - 8r^3(k + 8M) - 2kMr(10k$$
$$+27M) + 22r^4) + 4C(4)^3k^9(k-r)^8(2r(4k^2 + 25kM + 69M^2) - r^2(32k$$
$$+201M) - kM(17k + 120M) + 96r^3) + 4C(4)^4k^6(k-r)^{12}(4k^2 + 40k$$
$$(M-r) + 129M^2 - 224Mr + 160r^2) + 136C(4)^6(k-r)^{20} + 3k^{18}$$
$$\left.M^2\right) \tag{545}$$

$$B_t = -\frac{12C(4)k^3M(k-r)^2}{(C(4)(k-r)^4 + k^3r)^{\,2}} \tag{546}$$

$$B_r = \frac{12C(4)(k-r)^2\left(k^3(3M-2r) - 2C(4)(k-r)^4\right)}{(C(4)(k-r)^4 + k^3r)^{\,2}} \tag{547}$$

$$B_\theta = B_\phi = \frac{4C(4)(k-r)^2\left(k^3(2k + 6M - 5r) - 7C(4)(k-r)^4\right)}{(C(4)(k-r)^4 + k^3r)^{\,2}} \tag{548}$$

The energy density μ, the radial pressure P_r, the tangential pressure $P_\perp$ and the quantities $\mu + P_r$ and $\mu + P_\perp$ of the solution in the variables y and n of Eqs (172), which are obtained from Eqs (507) - (511) for $b = 4$ are given by the relations

$$\mu = \frac{C(4)(y-1)^2\left(-5C(4)(y-1)^4 + 3n - 4y + 1\right)}{\pi k^2\left(C(4)(y-1)^4 + y\right)^2} \tag{549}$$

$$P_r = \frac{C(4)(y-1)^3 \left(2C(4)(y-1)^3 + 1\right)}{\pi k^2 \left(C(4)(y-1)^4 + y\right)^2} \tag{550}$$

$$P_\perp = \frac{3C(4)(y-1)^2 \left(2\left(C(4)(y-1)^4 + y\right) - n\right)}{4\pi k^2 \left(C(4)(y-1)^4 + y\right)^2} \tag{551}$$

$$\mu + P_r = \frac{3C(4)(y-1)^2 \left(-C(4)(y-1)^4 + n - y\right)}{\pi k^2 \left(C(4)(y-1)^4 + y\right)^2} \tag{552}$$

$$\mu + P_\perp = \frac{C(4)(y-1)^2 \left(-14C(4)(y-1)^4 + 9n - 10y + 4\right)}{4\pi k^2 \left(C(4)(y-1)^4 + y\right)} \tag{553}$$

In Figures 118 - 123 we present the graphs of $k^2\mu$ of $k^2(\mu + P_r)$ and of $k^2(\mu + P_\perp)$ of Eqs (549), (552) and (553) for $C(4) = 0.1$ and $n = 1$ and also for $C(4) = 0.1$ and $n = 2$. It is obvious from these graphs that the solution satisfies the WEC. Also in Figure 124 we present the graph of $k^2 P_r$ of Eq (550) and in Figures 125 and 126 the graphs of $k^2 P_\perp$ of Eq (551) for the same values of their constants $C(4)$ or $C(4)$ and n.

The equation of state of the solution is obtained from relation (514) for $b = 4$. We get

$$\frac{\pi^2 k^2 M^2 (\mu + 4P_\perp + P_r)^4}{9C(4)(\mu + 2P_\perp + P_r)^2} + \frac{\sqrt{kM\pi}(\mu + 4P_\perp + P_r)}{\sqrt{3C(4)(\mu + 2P_\perp + P_r)}} - \frac{M(\mu + 4P_\perp + P_r)}{k(\mu + 2P_\perp + P_r)}$$
$$+1 = 0 \tag{554}$$

The line element of the solution is obtained from Eq (522) for $b = 4$.

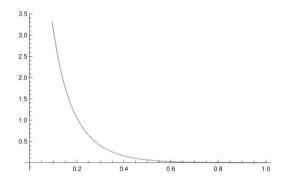

Figure 118: $k^2\mu$ of expression (549) for $C(4) = 0.1$ and $n = 1$

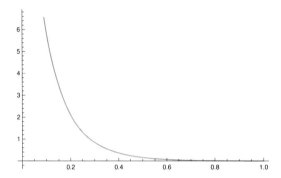

Figure 119: $k^2\mu$ of expression (549) for $C(4) = 0.1$ and $n = 2$

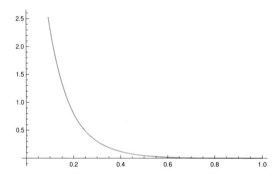

Figure 120: $k^2(\mu + P_r)$ of expression (552) for $C(4) = 0.1$ and $n = 1$

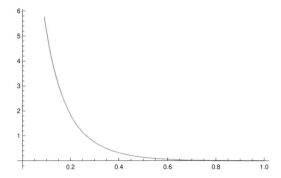

Figure 121: $k^2(\mu + P_r)$ of expression (552) for $C(4) = 0.1$ and $n = 2$

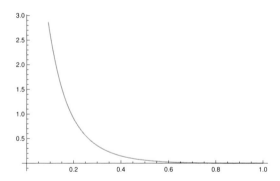

Figure 122: $k^2(\mu + P_\perp)$ of expression (553) for $C(4) = 0.1$ and $n = 1$

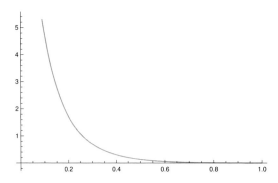

Figure 123: $k^2(\mu + P_\perp)$ of expression (553) for $C(4) = 0.1$ and $n = 2$

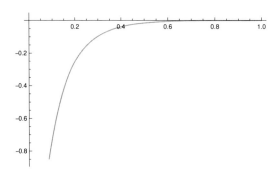

Figure 124: $k^2 P_r$ of expression (550)
for $C(4) = 0.1$

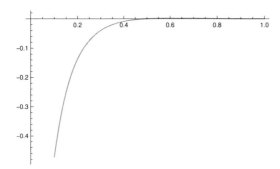

Figure 125: $k^2 P_\perp$ of expression (551) for $C(4) = 0.1$ and $n = 1$

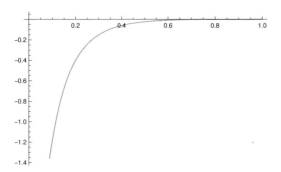

Figure 126: $k^2 P_\perp$ of expression (551) for $C(4) = 0.1$ and $n = 2$

2.3.2 Solutions with $f(r)$ and $h(r)$ of General Form

In this case the functions $f(r)$ and $h(r)$ are not connected by some relation. Of course these functions satisfy the matching conditions (3) and (4), are not singular in the interior region and $f(r)$ does not vanish in this region. Also the first and the second order derivatives with respect to r of $f(r)$ and $h(r)$ are non singular in the interior region. We shall consider some examples.

Example 2.3.2.1 : Solution with the $f(r)$ and the $h(r)$ of Eq (555)

Consider the solution with

$$f(r) = k^2 e^{\frac{2(-k+r)}{k}} \quad \text{and} \quad h(r) = \frac{(r-k+bk)^b}{k^{b-1}b^b} \tag{555}$$

The non-vanishing components of the Ricci tensor $R_{\mu\nu}$, the Ricci scalar R, the second order curvature invariant R^2 and the eigenvalues B_i, $i = t, r, \theta$ and ϕ of the Ricci tensor R^ν_μ of this solution are obtained from Eqs (5) - (12) and (555). We get

$$R_{tt} = b^{1-2b} M k^{-2b-3} e^{\frac{4(k-r)}{k}} ((b-1)k + r)^{b-2}((b-1)k + 2r)$$
$$(b^b k^{b+1} e^{\frac{2(r-k)}{k}} - 2M((b-1)k + r)^b) \tag{556}$$

$$R_{rr} = \frac{1}{k^2((b-1)k+r)^2 \left(b^b k^{b+1} e^{\frac{2(r-k)}{k}} - 2M((b-1)k+r)^b\right)}$$
$$(M((b-1)k+r)^b \left((b-1)(3b-4)k^2 + 2(3b-4)kr + 4r^2\right) -$$
$$2b^b k^{b+1} e^{\frac{2(r-k)}{k}} ((b-1)k+r)^2) \tag{557}$$

$$R_{\theta\theta} = \frac{R_{\phi\phi}}{\sin^2\theta} = 2b^{1-b} M k^{-b}((b-1)k+r)^{b-1} - 2e^{\frac{2(r-k)}{k}} + 1 \tag{558}$$

$$R = \frac{1}{((b-1)k+r)^2} (b^{-b} k^{-b-3} e^{\frac{2(k-r)}{k}} (2M((b-1)k+r)^b((b-1)$$
$$(3b-2)k^2 + 4(b-1)kr + 2r^2) - 2b^b k^{b+1}(3e^{\frac{2(r-k)}{k}} - 1)((b-1)k +$$
$$r)^2)) \tag{559}$$

$$R^2 = \frac{1}{((b-1)k+r)^4} 4b^{-2b} k^{-2(b+3)} e^{-\frac{4(r-k)}{k}} (4b^{b+1} M k^{b+2}(5e^{\frac{2(r-k)}{k}}$$
$$-4)(k-r)^3((b-1)k+r)^b + 12b^{b+2} M k^{b+3}(2 - 3e^{\frac{2(r-k)}{k}})(k-r)^2$$
$$((b-1)k+r)^b + 4b^{b+4} M k^{b+5}(1 - 2e^{\frac{2(r-k)}{k}})((b-1)k+r)^b + 4$$
$$b^{b+3} M k^{b+4}(7e^{\frac{2(r-k)}{k}} - 4)(k-r)((b-1)k+r)^b + b^{2b+4} k^{2b+6}(-2$$

$$e^{\frac{2(r-k)}{k}} + 3e^{\frac{4(r-k)}{k}} + 1) + b^{2b}k^{2b+2}(-2e^{\frac{2(r-k)}{k}} + 3e^{\frac{4(r-k)}{k}} + 1)(k - $$
$$r)^4 - 4b^{2b+1}k^{2b+3}(-2e^{\frac{2(r-k)}{k}} + 3e^{\frac{4(r-k)}{k}} + 1)(k - r)^3 + 6b^{2b+2}$$
$$k^{2b+4}(-2e^{\frac{2(r-k)}{k}} + 3e^{\frac{4(r-k)}{k}} + 1)(k - r)^2 - 4b^{2b+3}k^{2b+5}(-2e^{\frac{2(r-k)}{k}}$$
$$+3e^{\frac{4(r-k)}{k}} + 1)(k - r) + 4b^bMk^{b+1}(1 - e^{\frac{2(r-k)}{k}})(k - r)^4((b - 1)k$$
$$+r)^b + 9b^4k^4M^2((b - 1)k + r)^{2b} - 2b^3k^3M^2(21k - 20r)((b - 1)k$$
$$+r)^{2b} + b^2k^2M^2(85k^2 - 160kr + 76r^2)((b - 1)k + r)^{2b} + 28M^2(k$$
$$-r)^4((b - 1)k + r)^{2b} - 8bkM^2(10k - 9r)(k - r)^2((b - 1)k + $$
$$r)^{2b}) \tag{560}$$

$$B_t = -b^{1-b}Mk^{-b-2}e^{2-\frac{2r}{k}}((b - 1)k + r)^{b-2}((b - 1)k + 2r) \tag{561}$$

$$B_r = \frac{1}{k^3}(b^{-b}Mk^{-b}e^{2-\frac{2r}{k}}((b - 1)k + r)^{b-2}((b - 1)(3b - 4)k^2 + $$
$$2(3b - 4)kr + 4r^2) - 2k) \tag{562}$$

$$B_\theta = B_\phi = -\frac{e^{2-\frac{2r}{k}}}{k^2}(-2b^{1-b}Mk^{-b}((b - 1)k + r)^{b-1} + 2e^{\frac{2r}{k}-2} - 1) \tag{563}$$

From Eqs (559) and (560) we find that for

$$b > 1 \quad \text{and} \quad b = -1, -2, -3, ... \tag{564}$$

the solution is regular, since for these value of b the invariants R and R^2 are regular. We took $b = -1, -2, -3, ...$ and not $b < 0$ in order to avoid imaginary expressions in our calculations.

The energy density μ, the radial pressure P_r, the tangential pressure $P_\perp$ and the quantities $\mu + P_r$ and $\mu + P_\perp$ are obtained from Eqs (14) - (18) and (555). We get in the variables y and n of Eqs (172)

$$\mu = \frac{e^{2-2y}\left(b^{-b}n(2b + y - 1)(b + y - 1)^{b-1} - 3e^{2y-2} + 1\right)}{8\pi k^2} \tag{565}$$

$$P_r = \frac{e^{-2(y-1)}\left(b^{-b}n(y - 1)(b + y - 1)^{b-1} + e^{2(y-1)} - 1\right)}{8\pi k^2} \tag{566}$$

$$P_\perp = \frac{1 - \frac{1}{2}b^{-b}ne^{2-2y}(b + y - 1)^{b-2}\left(b^2 + b(2y - 3) + 2(y - 1)^2\right)}{8\pi k^2} \tag{567}$$

$$\mu + P_r = -\frac{1 - b^{-b}ne^{2-2y}(b + y - 1)^b}{4\pi k^2} \tag{568}$$

$$\mu + P_\perp = \frac{e^{-2(y-1)}}{16\pi k^2}\left((b^{1-b}n(b + y - 1)^{b-2}(3b + 4y - 3) - 2\right.$$
$$\left.(2e^{2(y-1)} - 1))\right) \tag{569}$$

Since we want the solution to satisfy the WEC in the interior region $0 \le y \le 1$ and since for $y = 1$ we have $\mu + P_r = \frac{n-1}{4\pi k^2}$ we must have $n \ge 1$. If in Eq (568), we make the substitution

$$y = 1 - bw \quad \text{which implies} \quad 0 \le w \le \frac{1}{b} \tag{570}$$

we find that since we want to have $\mu + P_r \ge 0$ the function w should satisfies the relation

$$1 - w - n^{-1/b}e^{-2w} \ge 0 \tag{571}$$

If the above equation is satisfied for $n = 1$ and $b > 0$ it is also satisfied for $n > 1$ and $b > 0$. Numerical calculations show that equation $1 - w - e^{-2w} = 0$ is satisfied for $w = 0$ and for $w = 0.7968$ and that for $0 < w < 0.7968$ we have $1 - w - e^{-2w} > 0$. Also the smallest value of b in the range $0 < w < 0.7968$, according to the second of relations (570), is $b = \frac{1}{0.7968} = 1.255$. Therefore we have $\mu + P_r \ge 0$ in the interior region if

$$n \ge 1 \quad \text{and} \quad b \ge 1.255 \tag{572}$$

Also μ and $\mu + P_\perp$ can be written in the form

$$\mu = \frac{1}{8\pi k^2}\left(-2 + e^{2-2y} + \frac{b}{b + y - 1} + 4\pi k^2\left(\frac{b}{b + y - 1} + 1\right)(\mu + P_r)\right) \tag{573}$$

$$\mu + P_\perp = \frac{1}{16\pi k^2}\left(-4 + 2e^{-2(y-1)} + \frac{b(3b + 4y - 3)}{(b + y - 1)^2} + 4\pi bk^2\right.$$
$$\left.\frac{(3b + 4y - 3)}{(b + y - 1)^2}(\mu + P_r)\right) \tag{574}$$

Since in the interior region $0 \leq y \leq 1$ for $b > 0$ we have $\frac{b}{b+y-1} \geq 1$ and $\frac{(3b+4y-3)}{(b+y-1)^2} \geq 3$ from Eqs (573) and (574) we find that $\mu \geq 0$ and $\mu + P_\perp \geq 0$ if $\mu + P_r \geq 0$. . Therefore the solution satisfies the WEC if the relations (572) are satisfied.

With numerical computer calculations we find that the quantity $\mu + P_r$ for $n \geq 1$ and $b = -1, -2, -3, \ldots$ is non negative in the interior region and also the expressions $-2 + e^{2-2y} + \frac{b}{b+y-1}$ and $-4 + 2e^{-2(y-1)} + \frac{b(3b+4y-3)}{(b+y-1)^2}$ are non negative in the interior region for $b = -1, -2, -3, \ldots$. Then using Eqs (573) and (574) we find that the energy density μ and the quantity $\mu + P_\perp$ for $n \geq 1$ and $b = -1, -2, -3, \ldots$ are non negative in the interior region. Therefore the solution for

$$n \geq 1, \ \text{and} \ b = -1, -2, -3, \ldots \tag{575}$$

satisfies the WEC.

To find the equation of state we solve for $ne^{2-2y}\left(\frac{y-1}{b}+1\right)^{b-1}$ and e^{2-2y} the expressions for μ and P_r Eqs (565) and (566). We get

$$ne^{2-2y}\left(\frac{y-1}{b}+1\right)^{b-1} = \frac{b\left(4\pi k^2(\mu+P_r)+1\right)}{b+y-1} \tag{576}$$

$$e^{2-2y} = \frac{-8\pi bk^2\,\mathrm{Pr}+b-2(y-1)\left(2\pi k^2(\mathrm{Pr}-\mu)-1\right)}{b+y-1} \tag{577}$$

Substituting the above expressions in Eq (569) for $\mu + P_\perp$ and solving for y the resulting relation we obtain two solutions but only one of them the solution

$$y = \frac{1}{8\pi k^2(\mu+2P_\perp+P_r)}(b-4\pi k^2((b-2)\mu+4(b-1)P_\perp+(b-$$
$$2)P_r)\sqrt{b\left(4\pi k^2(\mu+4P_\perp+P_r)-1\right)-8\pi k^2(\mu+2P_\perp+P_r)}$$
$$\sqrt{-b\left(4\pi k^2(\mu+P_r)+1\right)}) \tag{578}$$

can be used to get the equation of state. Also from Eqs (576) and (577) we get

$$n\left(\frac{y-1}{b}+1\right)^{b-1} = \frac{b\left(4\pi k^2(\mu+\mathrm{Pr})+1\right)}{-8\pi bk^2\,\mathrm{Pr}+b-2(y-1)\left(2\pi k^2(\mathrm{Pr}-\mu)-1\right)} \tag{579}$$

Substituting y of equation (578) in the above equation we get the relation

$$(8\pi)^{1-b}n\left(\frac{1}{bk^2(\mu+2P_\perp+P_r)}b(4\pi k^2(\mu+P_r)+1)+\sqrt{-b(4\pi k^2(\mu+P_r)+1)}\right.$$
$$\sqrt{b(4\pi k^2(\mu+4P_\perp+P_r)-1)-8\pi k^2(\mu+2P_\perp+P_r)))^{b-1}}+4\pi bk^2$$
$$(4\pi k^2(\mu+P_r)+1)(\mu+2P_\perp+P_r)(-(2\pi k^2(\mu-P_r)+1)$$
$$\sqrt{-b(4\pi k^2(\mu+\Pr)+1)}$$
$$\sqrt{(b(4\pi k^2(\mu+4P_\perp+P_r)-1)-8\pi k^2(\mu+2P_\perp+P_r))}$$
$$+b(4\pi k^2(\mu+P_r)+1)(2\pi k^2(\mu+4P_\perp+3P_r)-1))^{-1}=0 \tag{580}$$

The above relation is satisfied if we replace μ, P_r and $P_\perp$ by their expressions of Eqs (565), (566) and (567) respectively. The relation (580) is the equation of state of the solution.

The line element d^2s of the solution is obtained from Eqs (1) and (555). We get

$$d^2s = -(1-2b^{-b}Mk^{-b-1}e^{\frac{2(k-r)}{k}}(bk-k+r)^b)d^2t +$$
$$\frac{d^2r}{1-2b^{-b}Mk^{-b-1}e^{\frac{2(k-r)}{k}}(bk-k+r)^b}+k^2e^{\frac{2(r-k)}{k}}(d^2\theta +$$
$$sin^2\theta d^2\phi) \tag{581}$$

We shall consider the solutions we get for $b=2$ and $b=3$.

Example 2.3.2.1.1 : Solution with the $f(r)$ and the $h(r)$ of Eq (582)

Consider the solution with

$$f(r)=k^2e^{\frac{2(-k+r)}{k}} \quad \text{and} \quad h(r)=\frac{(r+k)^2}{4k} \tag{582}$$

which are obtained from the $f(r)$ and $h(r)$ of Eq (555) for $b=2$. The line element d^2s of this solution, which is obtained from Eq (581) for $b=2$, is the following:

$$d^2s = -(1-\frac{Me^{-\frac{2(r-k)}{k}}(k+r)^2}{2k^3})d^2t +$$
$$\frac{d^2r}{1-\frac{Me^{-\frac{2(r-k)}{k}}(k+r)^2}{2k^3}}+k^2e^{\frac{2(r-k)}{k}}(d^2\theta+sin^2\theta d^2\phi) \tag{583}$$

Also from Eqs (556) - (563) for $b = 2$ and (582) we get the following expressions for the non-vanishing components of the Ricci tensor $R_{\mu\nu}$, the Ricci scalar R, the second order curvature invariant R^2 and the eigenvalues B_i, $i = t,\ r,\ \theta$ and ϕ of the Ricci tensor R_μ^ν of this solution:

$$R_{tt} = \frac{1}{4k^7}(Me^{\frac{4(k-r)}{k}}(k+2r)\left(2k^3 e^{\frac{2(k+r)}{k}} - M(k+r)^2\right) \tag{584}$$

$$R_{rr} = \frac{M\left(k^2 + 2kr + 2r^2\right) - 4k^3 e^{\frac{2(k+r)}{k}}}{2k^5 e^{\frac{2(k+r)}{k}} - k^2 M(k+r)^2} \tag{585}$$

$$R_{\theta\theta} = \frac{R_{\phi\phi}}{sin^2\theta} = -\frac{1}{k^2}(-2k^2 e^{\frac{2(r-k)}{k}} + k^2 + kM + Mr) \tag{586}$$

$$R = e^{-\frac{2r}{k}+2}\left(\left(2k^3 + 2k^2 M + 2kMr + Mr^2\right) - 6k^3 e^{\frac{2r}{k}-2}\right) \tag{587}$$

$$R^2 = \frac{1}{k^{10}}e^{-\frac{4r}{k}+4}(12k^6\ e^{\frac{4r}{k}-4} - 4k^3 e^{\frac{2r}{k}-2}(2k^3 + 3k^2 M + 4kMr + M$$
$$r^2) + 8k^3 Mr(k+M) + 2k^2 Mr^2(2k+3M) + 4k^4(k^2 + kM$$
$$+M^2) + 8kM^2 r^3 + 7M^2 r^4) \tag{588}$$

$$B_t = -\frac{Me^{2-\frac{2r}{k}}(k+2r)}{2k^4} \tag{589}$$

$$B_r = \frac{1}{2k^5}e^{-\frac{2r}{k}+2}\left(M\left(k^2 + 2kr + 2r^2\right) - 4k^3 e^{\frac{2r}{k}-2}\right) \tag{590}$$

$$B_\theta = B_\phi = \frac{1}{k^4}e^{-\frac{2r}{k}-2}\left(\left(k^2 + kM + Mr\right) - 2k^2 e^{\frac{2r}{k}-2}\right) \tag{591}$$

The energy density μ, the radial pressure P_r, the tangential pressure $P_\perp$ and the quantities $\mu + P_r$ and $\mu + P_\perp$, which are obtained from Eqs (565) - (569) for $b = 2$, are the following :

$$\mu = \frac{e^{-2y+2}\left(n(y+1)(y+3)+4-12e^{2y-2}\right)}{32\pi k^2} \tag{592}$$

$$P_r = \frac{e^{-2y+2}(n(y^2-1)-4)+4e^{2y-2})}{32\pi k^2} \tag{593}$$

$$P_\perp = \frac{4 - ne^{2-2y}y^2}{32\pi k^2} \tag{594}$$

$$\mu + P_r = \frac{e^{-2y+2}(n(y+1)^2 - 4e^{2y-2})}{16\pi k^2} \tag{595}$$

$$\mu + P_\perp = \frac{e^{-2y+2}\left(n(4y+3) + 4 - 8e^{2y-2}\right)}{32\pi k^2} \tag{596}$$

In Figures 127 - 132 we present the graphs of $k^2\mu$ of $k^2(\mu + P_r)$ and of $k^2(\mu + P_\perp)$ of Eqs (592), (595) and (596) for $n = 1$ and 2. It is obvious from these graphs that the solution satisfies the WEC as expected. Also in Figures 133 and 134 we present the graph of $k^2 P_r$ of Eq (593) for $n = 1$ and $n = 2$ and in Figures 135 and 136 the graph of $k^2 P_\perp$ of Eq (594) for $n = 1$ and 2.

The equation of state of the solution is obtained from Eq (580) for $b = 2$. We get

$$\frac{1}{16\pi k^2(\mu + 2P_\perp + P_r)}(2n(\sqrt{(1 - 8\pi k^2 P_\perp)(4\pi k^2(\mu + P_r) + 1)}$$
$$+4\pi k^2(\mu + P_r) + 1) + (128\pi^2 k^4(4\pi k^2(\mu + P_r) + 1)(\mu + 2P_\perp + P_r)^2)$$
$$(2(2\pi k^2(P_r - \mu) - 1)\sqrt{(1 - 8\pi k^2 P_\perp)(4\pi k^2(\mu + P_r) + 1)}$$
$$+2(4\pi k^2(\mu + P_r) + 1)(2\pi k^2(\mu + 4P_\perp + 3P_r) - 1))^{-1}) = 0 \tag{597}$$

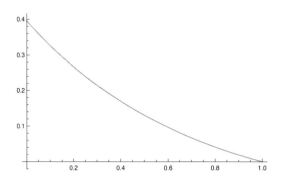

Figure 127: $k^2\mu$ of expression (592) for $n = 1$

153

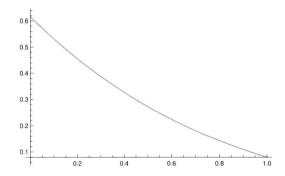

Figure 128: $k^2\mu$ of expression (592) for $n = 2$

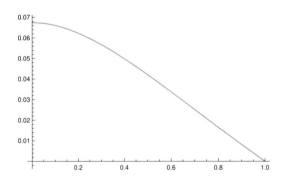

Figure 129: $k^2(\mu + P_r)$ of expression (595) for $n = 1$

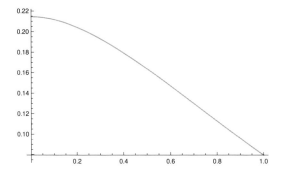

Figure 130: $k^2(\mu + P_r)$ of expression (595) for $n = 2$

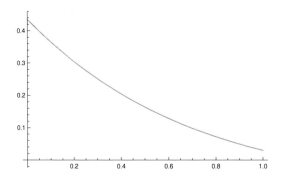

Figure 131: $k^2(\mu + P_\perp)$ of expression (596) for $n = 1$

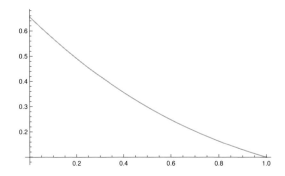

Figure 132: $k^2(\mu + P_\perp)$ of expression (596) for $n = 2$

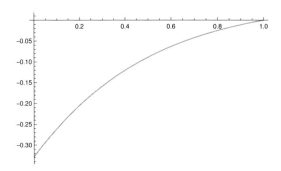

Figure 133: $k^2 P_r$ of expression (593) for $n = 1$

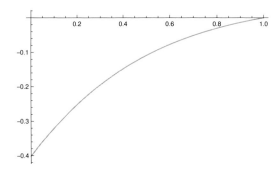

Figure 134: $k^2 P_r$ of expression (593) for $n = 2$

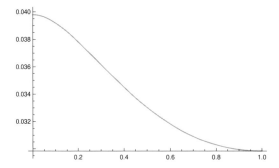

Figure 135: $k^2 P_\perp$ of expression (594) for $n = 1$

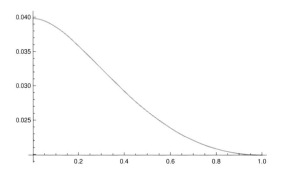

Figure 136: $k^2 P_\perp$ of expression (594) for $n = 2$

Example 2.3.2.1.2 : Solution with the $f(r)$ and the $h(r)$ of Eq (598)

Consider the solution with

$$f(r) = k^2 e^{\frac{2(-k+r)}{k}} \quad \text{and} \quad h(r) = \frac{(r + 2k)^3}{27k^2} \tag{598}$$

which are obtained from the $f(r)$ and $h(r)$ of Eq (555) for $b = 3$. The line element d^2s of this solution, which is obtained from Eq (581) for $b = 3$, is the following:

$$d^2s = -(1 - \frac{2M e^{-\frac{2(r-k)}{k}} (2k + r)^3}{27k^4}) d^2t +$$

157

$$\frac{d^2r}{1 - \frac{2Me^{-\frac{2(r-k)}{k}}(2k+r)^3}{27k^4}} + k^2 e^{\frac{2(r-k)}{k}}(d^2\theta + sin^2\theta d^2\phi) \tag{599}$$

The non-vanishing components of the Ricci tensor $R_{\mu\nu}$, the Ricci scalar R, the second order curvature invariant R^2 and the eigenvalues B_i, $i = t, r, \theta$, and ϕ of the Ricci tensor R^ν_μ of this solution are obtained from Eqs (556) - (563) for $b = 3$. We get

$$R_{tt} = \frac{2Me^{2-\frac{4r}{k}}(k+r)(2k+r)\left(27k^4 e^{\frac{2r}{k}} - 2e^2M(2k+r)^3\right)}{243k^9} \tag{600}$$

$$Rrr = \frac{2M(2k+r)\left(5k^2 + 5kr + 2r^2\right) - 54k^4 e^{\frac{2(r-k)}{k}}}{27k^6 e^{\frac{2(r-k)}{k}} - 2k^2M(2k+r)^3} \tag{601}$$

$$R_{\theta\theta} = \frac{R_{\phi\phi}}{sin^2\theta} = \frac{\left(9k^3 + 8k^2M + 8kMr + 2Mr^2\right) - 18k^3 e^{\frac{2(r-k)}{k}}}{9k^3} \tag{602}$$

$$R = \frac{e^{-\frac{2(r-k)}{k}}\left(54k^4 + 56k^3M + 60k^2Mr + 24kMr^2 + 4Mr^3\right) - 162k^4}{27k^6} \tag{603}$$

$$R^2 = \frac{4}{729k^{12}}e^{\frac{4(k-r)}{k}}(2187k^8 e^{\frac{4(r-k)}{k}} + 729k^8 + 864k^7M + 16k^6M$$
$$(37M + 81r) + 24k^5Mr(62M + 27r) + 36k^4Mr^2(49M + 3r) +$$
$$1360k^3M^2r^3 + 708k^2M^2r^4 - 54k^4 e^{\frac{2(r-k)}{k}}(27k^4 + 40k^3M + 48k^2$$
$$Mr + 18kMr^2 + 2Mr^3) + 216kM^2r^5 + 28M^2r^6) \tag{604}$$

$$B_t = -\frac{2Me^{\frac{2(k-r)}{k}}(k+r)(2k+r)}{9k^5} \tag{605}$$

$$B_r = \frac{2Me^{\frac{2(k-r)}{k}}\left(10k^3 + 15k^2r + 9kr^2 + 2r^3\right) - 54k^4}{27k^6} \tag{606}$$

$$B_\theta = B_\phi = \frac{e^{\frac{2(k-r)}{k}}\left(9k^3 + 8k^2M + 8kMr + 2Mr^2\right) - 18k^3}{9k^5} \tag{607}$$

From Eqs (565) - (569) for $b = 3$ we obtain the energy density μ, the radial pressure P_r, the tangential pressure $P_\perp$ and the quantities $\mu + P_r$ and $\mu + P_\perp$ in the variables y and n of Eqs (172). We get

$$\mu = \frac{e^{2-2y}\left(n(y+5)(y+2)^2 + 27\right) - 81}{216\pi k^2} \tag{608}$$

$$P_r = \frac{e^{2-2y}\left(n(y-1)(y+2)^2 - 27\right) + 27}{216\pi k^2} \tag{609}$$

$$P_\perp = \frac{27 - ne^{2-y}\left(y^3 + 3y^2 + 3y + 2\right)}{216\pi k^2} \tag{610}$$

$$\mu + P_r = \frac{ne^{2-2y}(y+2)^3 - 27}{108\pi k^2} \tag{611}$$

$$\mu + P_\perp = \frac{e^{2-2y}(n(y+2)(2y+3) + 9) - 18}{72\pi k^2} \tag{612}$$

In Figures 137 - 142 we present the graphs of $k^2\mu$ of $k^2(\mu + P_r)$ and of $k^2(\mu + P_\perp)$ of Eqs (608), (611) and (612) for $n = 1$ and 2. From these graphs we find that the solution satisfies the WEC as expected. Also in Figures 143 and 144 we present the graph of $k^2 P_r$ of Eq (609) for $n = 1$ and $n = 2$ and in Figures 145 and 146 the graph of $k^2 P_\perp$ of Eq (610) for $n = 1$ and 2.

The equation of state of the solution is obtained from Eq (580) for $b = 3$. We get

$$\frac{n}{576\pi^2 k^4(\mu + 2P_\perp + P_r)^2}(\sqrt{(-4\pi k^2(\mu + P_r) - 1)(4\pi k^2(\mu + 8P_\perp + P_r) - 3)}$$
$$\sqrt{3} + 12\pi k^2(\mu + P_r) + 3)^2 + 12\pi k^2(4\pi k^2(\mu + P_r) + 1)(\mu + 2P_\perp + P_r)(\sqrt{3}$$
$$\sqrt{(-4\pi k^2(\mu + P_r) - 1)(3(4\pi k^2(\mu + 4P_\perp + P_r) - 1) - 8\pi k^2(\mu + 2P_\perp + P_r))}$$
$$(2\pi k^2(P_r - \mu) - 1) + 3(4\pi k^2(\mu + P_r) + 1)(2\pi k^2(\mu + 4P_\perp + 3P_r)$$
$$-1))^{-1} = 0 \tag{613}$$

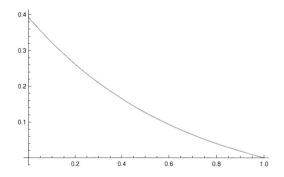

Figure 137: $k^2\mu$ of expression (608) for $n = 1$

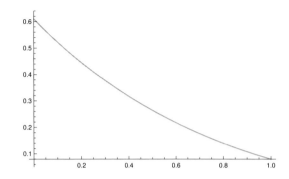

Figure 138: $k^2\mu$ of expression (608) for $n = 2$

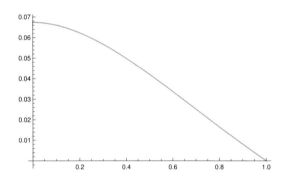

Figure 139: $k^2(\mu + P_r)$ of expression (611) for $n = 1$

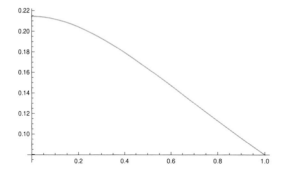

Figure 140: $k^2(\mu + P_r)$ of expression (611) for $n = 2$

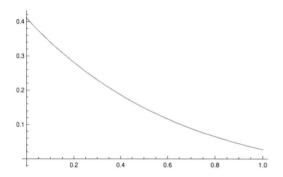

Figure 141: $k^2(\mu + P_\perp)$ of expression (612) for $n = 1$

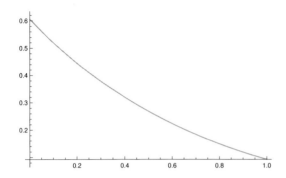

Figure 142: $k^2(\mu + P_\perp)$ of expression (612) for $n = 2$

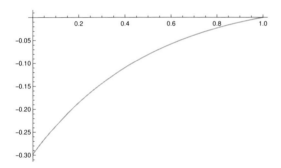

Figure 143: $k^2 P_r$ of expression (609) for $n = 1$

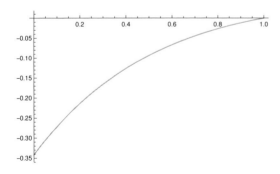

Figure 144: $k^2 P_r$ of expression (609) for $n = 2$

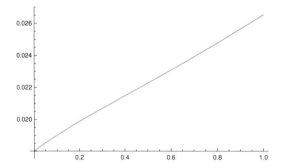

Figure 145: $k^2 P_\perp$ of expression (610) for $n = 1$

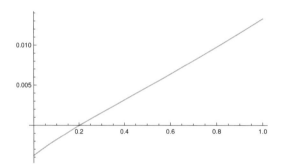

Figure 146: $k^2 P_\perp$ of expression (610) for $n = 2$

Example 2.3.2.2 : Solution with the $f(r)$ and the $h(r)$ of Eq (614)

Consider the solution with

$$f(r) = 2^p p^{-p} k^{2-p} \left(\frac{kp}{2} - k + r \right)^p \quad \text{and} \quad h(r) = b^{-b} k^{1-b} (bk - k + r)^b \quad (614)$$

In order to have shorter expressions of the quantities we shall compute we shall express these quantities in the variables y and n of Eqs (172). Then the non-vanishing components of the Ricci tensor $R_{\mu\nu}$, the Ricci scalar R, the second order curvature invariant R^2 and the eigenvalues B_i, $i = t$, r, θ and ϕ of the Ricci tensor R^ν_μ of this solution, which we obtain from Eqs

163

(5) - (12) and (614), and then we express in the variables y and n are the following:

$$R_{tt} = \frac{1}{2k^2} b^{-2b} n p^p (b + y - 1)^{b-2} (p + 2y - 2)^{-2(p+1)} (b^2((p-4)p -$$
$$4(y-1)^2) + b(p^2(2y-1) + 4p(y-2)(y-1) + 4(y-1)^2) - 4p(y$$
$$-1)^2)(b^b(p+2y-2)^p - np^p(b+y-1)) \tag{615}$$

$$R_{rr} = (np^p(b+y-1)^b(b^2(p(3p-4) + 4(y-1)^2) + b(p^2(6y-7)$$
$$-4p(y^2+y-2) - 4(y-1)^2) + 4(p-1)p(y-1)^2) - 4b^b(p-2)p$$
$$(b+y-1)^2(p+2y-2)^p)(2k^2(b+y-1)^2(p+2y-2)^2(b^b(p+$$
$$2y-2)^p - np^p(b+y-1)^b))^{-1} \tag{616}$$

$$R_{\theta\theta} = \frac{R_{\phi\phi}}{sin^2\theta} = \frac{1}{(b+y-1)(p+2y-2)^2} b^{-b} p^{-p}(b^b(b+y-1)(p^p(p$$
$$+2y-2)^2 - 2(p-1)p(p+2y-2)^p) + np^{p+1}(b+y-1)^b(b(p+2y$$
$$-4) - 2y+2)) \tag{617}$$

$$R = \frac{b^{-b}(p+2y-2)^{-p-2}}{k^2(b+y-1)^2} (4b^{b+1}(y-1)(p^p(p+2y-2)^2 - p(3p$$
$$-4)(p+2y-2)^p) + 2b^{b+2}(p^p(p+2y-2)^2 - p(3p-4)(p+2y-$$
$$2)^p) + 2b^b(y-1)^2(p^p(p+2y-2)^2 - p(3p-4)(p+2y-2)^p) + b^2$$
$$np^p(b+y-1)^b(3p^2 + 4p(y-2) + 4(y-1)^2) + 2n(p-2)p^{p+1}(y$$
$$-1)^2(b+y-1)^b + bnp^p(b+y-1)^b(p^2(4y-5) - 12p(y-1) - 4$$
$$(y-1)^2)) \tag{618}$$

$$R^2 = \frac{4b^{-2b}k^{-2(b+4)}(k(p+2y-2))^{-2(p+2)}}{(b+y-1)^4} A \tag{619}$$

$$B_t = \frac{b^{-b}np^p(b+y-1)^{b-2}(p+2y-2)^{-p-2}}{2k^2} (b^2((4-p)p + 4(y-$$
$$1)^2) + b(-4(p+1)y^2 - 2(p-6)py + (p-8)p + 8y - 4) + 4p(y-$$
$$1)^2) \tag{620}$$

$$B_r = \frac{b^{-b}(p+2y-2)^{-p-2}}{2k^2(b+y-1)^2}(np^p(b+y-1)^b(b^2(p(3p-4)+4(y-1)^2)+b(p^2(6y-7)-4p(y^2+y-2)-4(y-1)^2)+4(p-1)p(y-1)^2)-4b^b(p-2)p(b+y-1)^2(p+2y-2)^p)$$

$$(621)$$

$$B_\theta = B_\phi = -\frac{b^{-b}(p+2y-2)^{-p-2}}{k^2(b+y-1)}(b^b(b+y-1)(2(p-1)p(p+2y-2)^p-p^p(p+2y-2)^2)-np^{p+1}(b+y-1)^b(b(p+2y-4)-2y+2))$$

$$(622)$$

where A of Eq (619) is a very long expression which is regular in the interior region if $p+2y-2 \neq 0$ and $b+y-1 \neq 0$ in this region. If these relations hold, which happens if

$$p > 2 \quad \text{or} \quad p = -1, -2, -3, \ldots \tag{623}$$

and simultaneously

$$b > 1 \quad \text{or} \quad b = -1, -2, -3, \ldots \tag{624}$$

the invariants R and R^2 are regular and real in the interior region. We did not take $p < 0$ and $b < 0$ but we took $p = -1, -2, -3, \ldots$ and $b = -1, -2, -3, \ldots$ in order to avoid imaginary expressions in our calculations. Therefore the solution is regular if its constants p and b satisfy the above relations.

The energy density μ the radial pressure P_r, the tangential pressure $P_\perp$ and the quantities $\mu + P_r$ and $\mu + P_\perp$, which are obtained from Eqs (14) - (18) and (614), are the following in the variables y and n of Eqs (172):

$$\mu = \frac{b^{-b}(p+2y-2)^{-p-2}}{8\pi k^2(b+y-1)}(b^b(b+y-1)(p^p(p+2y-2)^2-p(3p-4)(p+2y-2)^p)+np^{p+1}(b+y-1)^b(2b(p+y-3)+(p-4)(y-1)))$$

$$(625)$$

$$P_r = \frac{b^{-b}(p+2y-2)^{-p-2}}{8\pi k^2(b+y-1)}(p^p(np(y-1)(p-2b)(b+y-1)^b-b^b(b+y-1)(p+2y-2)^2)+b^bp^2(b+y-1)(p+2y-2)^p)$$

$$(626)$$

$$P_\perp = \frac{b^{-b}(p+2y-2)^{-p-2}}{16\pi k^2(b+y-1)^2}(2b^b(p-2)p(b+y-1)^2(p+2y-2)^p$$
$$-np^p(b+y-1)^b(b^2(p^2+4(y-1)^2)+b(-3p^2-4(p+1)y^2+2(p$$
$$(p+2)+4)y-4)+2p^2(y-1)^2)) \tag{627}$$

$$\mu + P_r = -\frac{b^{-b}(p-2)p(p+2y-2)^{-p-2}}{4\pi k^2}(b^b(p+2y-2)^p$$
$$-np^p(b+y-1)^b) \tag{628}$$

$$\mu + P_\perp = \frac{1}{16\pi k^2}(2(b^{-b}np^{p+1}(b+y-1)^{b-1}(p+2y-2)^{-p-2}(b(p+$$
$$2y-4)-2y+2)+p^p(p+2y-2)^{-p}-\frac{2(p-1)p}{(p+2y-2)^2})-b^{-b}np^p(b$$
$$+y-1)^{b-2}(p+2y-2)^{-p-2}(4(b-1)y^2(b-p)-2y(b(4b+(p-6)$$
$$p-4)+4p)+(1-b)(b((p-4)p-4)+4p))) \tag{629}$$

The solution satisfies the WEC for certain values of its constants. We shall consider the case $p = 4$. Cases with other values of p can be examined in a similar fashion. For $p = 4$ we get

$$k^2\mu = \frac{1}{\pi(y+1)^5}(4n\left(\frac{y-1}{b}+1\right)^{b-1}-y^3-3y^2-y+1) \tag{630}$$

The quantity $\frac{y-1}{b}+1$ is positive for b larger than 1 and for b negative and we find with numerical computer calculations that

$$\mu \geq 0 \quad \text{for} \quad n \geq 1 \quad \text{and} \quad b \geq 0 \quad \text{or} \quad b \leq -0.7 \tag{631}$$

For these values of the constants μ is monotonically decreasing.

From Eq (628) we get for $p = 4$

$$k^2(\mu + P_r) = -\frac{1}{2\pi(y+1)^6}((y+1)^4-16b^{-b}n(b+y-1)^b) \tag{632}$$

With numerical computer calculations we find that we have $\mu + P_r \geq 0$ in the interior region

if $n = 1$ and $b \geq 1.084$

if $n = 2$ and $b \geq 1.0355$

if $n = 3$ and $b \geq 1,0235$

if $n = 4$ and $b \geq 1,017$

Also we find that $\mu + P_r$ is non negative and monotonically decreasing in the interior region

if $n = 1$ and $b \geq 1.2465$ or $b = -1, -2, -3, \ldots$

if $n = 2$ and $b \geq 1.2223$ or $b = -1, -2, -3, \ldots$

if $n = 3$ and $b \geq 1.214$ or $b = -1, -2, -3, \ldots$

if $n = 4$ and $b \geq 1.211$ or $b = -1, -2, -3, \ldots$

In addition Eq (629) becomes for $p = 4$

$$k^2(\mu + P_\perp) = \frac{1}{4\pi(y+1)^6}(4b^{-b}n(b + y - 1)^{b-2}(b^2(-((y - 6)y + 1)) + b(y(9y - 14) + 9) - 8(y - 1)^2) - (y + 1)^2(3y(y + 2) - 5)) \tag{633}$$

With numerical computer calculations we find that $\mu + P_\perp$ is positive and monotonically decreasing in the interior region

if $n = 1$ or 2 or 3 or 4 and $b \geq 1$.

Also with numerical computer calculations we find that $\mu + P_\perp$ is positive in the interior region

if $n = 2$ and $b = -11, -12, -13, \ldots$ and

if $n = 3$ and $b = -10, -11, -13, \ldots$

An interesting feature of solutions of this class is that for some values of their constants their radial pressure P_r becomes non negative and monotonically decreasing in the whole interior region and for some other values non positive and monotonically increasing. The solutions in both cases satisfy the WEC.

The line element $d^2 s$ of the solution is obtained from Eqs (1) and (614). We get

$$d^2 s = -(1 - 2^{1-p}b^{-b}k^{-1-b+p}Mp^p \frac{(r - k + bk)^b}{(r - k + pk/2)^p})dt^2 +$$

$$(1 - 2^{1-p}b^{-b}k^{-1-b+p}Mp^p \frac{(r - k + bk)^b}{(r - k + pk/2)^p})^{-1}dr^2 +$$

$$2^p p^{-p}k^{2-p}(r - k + \frac{pk}{2})^p(d^2\theta + \sin^2\theta d^2\phi) \tag{634}$$

We shall consider in the following the solution with $(p, b) = (4, 3)$ and the solution with $(p, b) = (4, 4)$.

Example 2.3.2.2.1 : Solution with the $f(r)$ and the $h(r)$ of Eq (635)

Consider the solution with

$$f(r) = \frac{(k+r)^4}{16k^2} \quad \text{and} \quad h(r) = \frac{(2k+r)^3}{27k^2} \tag{635}$$

These expressions are obtained from the corresponding expressions (614) for $(p, b) = (4, 3)$.

The line element d^2s of this solution, which is obtained from Eq (634) for $(p, b) = (4, 3)$, is

$$d^2s = -(1 - \frac{32M(2k+r)^3}{27(k+r)^4})dt^2 + \frac{dr^2}{1 - \frac{32M(2k+r)^3}{27(k+r)^4}} + \frac{(k+r)^4}{16k^2}$$

$$(d^2\theta + sin^2\theta d^2\phi) \tag{636}$$

Also from Eqs (5) - (12) and (635) we get the following expressions for the non-vanishing components of the Ricci tensor $R_{\mu\nu}$, the Ricci scalar R, the second order curvature invariant R^2 and the eigenvalues B_i, $i = t$, r, θ and ϕ of the Ricci tensor R^ν_μ of this solution:

$$R_{tt} = -\frac{1}{729(k+r)^{10}}32M(2k+r)\left(k^2 + 4kr + r^2\right)(-27k^4 + 4k^3$$

$$(64M - 27r) + 6k^2r(64M - 27r) + 12kr^2(16M - 9r) + r^3(32M$$

$$-27r)) \tag{637}$$

$$R_{rr} = -\frac{12}{(k+r)^2}(9k^4 + k^3(36r - 80M) + 2k^2r(27r - 52M) + 12$$

$$kr^2(3r - 4M) + r^3(9r - 8M))(27k^4 - 4k^3(64M - 27r) - 6k^2r(64$$

$$M - 27r) - 12kr^2(16M - 9r) + r^3(27r - 32M))^{-1} \tag{638}$$

$$R_{\theta\theta} = \frac{R_{\phi\phi}}{sin^2\theta} = \frac{1}{216k^2(k+r)^2}(135k^4 + 4k^3(32M + 27r) + 6k^2r$$

$$(64M - 45r) + 36kr^2(8M - 9r) + r^3(64M - 81r)) \tag{639}$$

$$R = \frac{16}{27(k+r)^6}(27k^4 + 88k^3M + 12k^2r(13M - 9r) + 12kr^2(8M$$

$$-9r) + r^3(20M - 27r)) \tag{640}$$

$$R^2 = \frac{32}{243(k+r)^{12}} (6656k^6 M^2 + 26624k^5 M^2(k+r) + 512k^4 M(9k$$

$$+85M)(k+r)^2 + 512k^3 M(27k + 74M)(k+r)^3 - 16(243k^2 + 216$$

$$kM - 56M^2)(k+r)^6 + 32k^2(243k^2 + 414kM + 604M^2)(k+r)^4$$

$$-1440M(k+r)^7 + 32kM(63k + 184M)(k+r)^5 +$$

$$729(k+r)^8) \tag{641}$$

$$B_t = -\frac{32M(2k+r)\left(k^2 + 4kr + r^2\right)}{27(k+r)^6} \tag{642}$$

$$B_r = \frac{4}{9(k+r)^6}((16k^3 M + 32k^2 M(k+r) + 8M(k+r)^3 + 24kM$$

$$(k+r)^2 - 9(k+r)^4)) \tag{643}$$

$$B_\theta = B_\phi = \frac{2}{27(k+r)^6}(-32k^3 M + 216k^2(k+r)^2 + 64M(k+r)^3$$

$$+96kM(k+r)^2 - 81(k+r)^4) \tag{644}$$

The energy density μ, the radial pressure P_r, the tangential pressure $P_\perp$ and the quantities $\mu + P_r$ and $\mu + P_\perp$, which are obtained in the variables y and n of Eqs (172) from Eqs (625) - (629) for $(p, b) = (4, 3)$, are the following:

$$\mu = \frac{4n(y+2)^2 - 9\left(y^3 + 3y^2 + y - 1\right)}{9\pi k^2(y+1)^5} \tag{645}$$

$$P_r = \frac{(y-1)\left(27(y+1)^2(y+3) - 8n(y+2)^2\right)}{54\pi k^2(y+1)^6} \tag{646}$$

$$P_\perp = \frac{27(y+1)^4 - 8n\left(y^3 + 6y^2 + 15y + 14\right)}{108\pi k^2(y+1)^6} \tag{647}$$

$$\mu + P_r = \frac{16n(y+2)^3 - 27(y+1)^4}{54\pi k^2(y+1)^6} \tag{648}$$

$$\mu + P_\perp = \frac{8n\left(5y^3 + 24y^2 + 33y + 10\right) - 27(y+1)^2\left(3y^2 + 6y - 5\right)}{108\pi k^2(y+1)^6} \tag{649}$$

Since the solution of this example is obtained from the solution of Example 2.3.2.2 for $p = 4$ and $b = 3$ its energy density μ and its quantities

$\mu + P_r$ and $\mu + P_\perp$ for $n = 1$ are positive or non negative and monotonically decreasing in the interior region. Also the same thing happens for $n = 6$. Therefore the solution for these values of n satisfies the WEC. Also with numerical computer calculations we find that in the interior region

P_r for $0 \leq n < \frac{63}{32}$ is non positive and monotonically increasing

P_r for $\frac{63}{32} \leq n < \frac{81}{32}$ is non positive

P_r for $\frac{81}{32} \leq n < 6$ is negative positive or zero

P_r for $6 \leq n$ is non negative and monotonically decreasing

$P_\perp$ for $0 < n < \frac{27}{112}$ is positive

$P_\perp$ for $\frac{27}{112} \leq n < \frac{3}{2}$ is positive zero or negative and

$P_\perp$ for $n \geq \frac{3}{2}$ is non positive and monotonically increasing.

The graphs of $k^2\mu$ of $k^2(\mu + P_r)$ of $k^2(\mu + P_\perp)$ of $k^2 P_r$ and of $k^2 P_\perp$ of Eqs (645) - (649) for $n = 1$ and $n = 6$ are presented in Figures 147 - 156.

An interesting feature of this solution is that in the interior region the radial pressure P_r is for $n = 1$ non positive and monotonically increasing while for $n = 6$ non negative and monotonically decreasing.

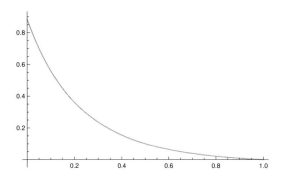

Figure 147: $k^2\mu$ of expression (645) for $n = 1$

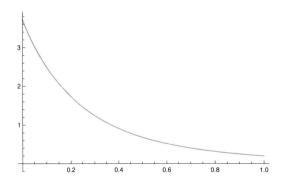

Figure 148: $k^2\mu$ of expression (645) for $n = 6$

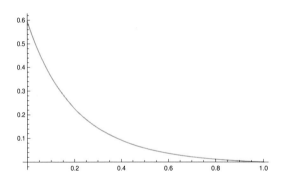

Figure 149: $k^2(\mu + P_r)$ of expression (648) for $n = 1$

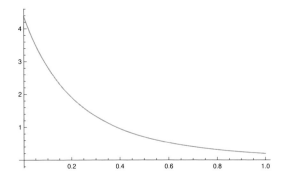

Figure 150: $k^2(\mu + P_r)$ of expression (648) for $n = 6$

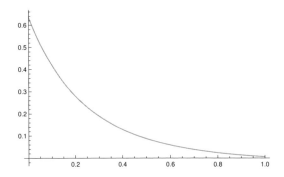

Figure 151: $k^2(\mu + P_\perp)$ of expression (649) for $n = 1$

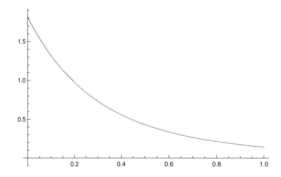

Figure 152: $k^2(\mu + P_\perp)$ of expression (649) for $n = 6$

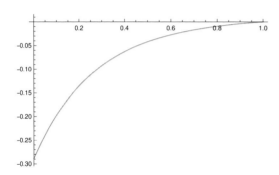

Figure 153: $k^2 P_r$ of expression (646) for $n = 1$

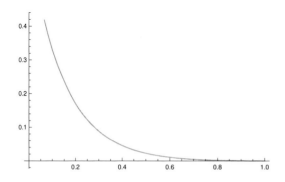

Figure 154: $k^2 P_r$ of expression (646) for $n = 6$

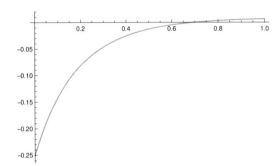

Figure 155: $k^2 P_\perp$ of expression (647) for $n = 1$

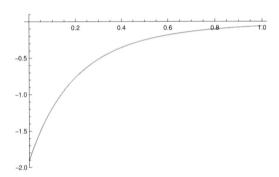

Figure 156: $k^2 P_\perp$ of expression (647) for $n = 6$

Example 2.3.2.2.2 : Solution with the $f(r)$ and the $h(r)$ of Eq (650)

Consider the solution with

$$f(r) = \frac{(k + r)^4}{16k^2} \quad \text{and} \quad h(r) = \frac{(3k + r)^4}{256k^3} \tag{650}$$

These expressions are obtained from the corresponding expressions (614) for $(p, b) = (4, 4)$.

The line element d^2s of this solution, which is obtained from Eq (634) for $(p, b) = (4, 4)$, is

$$d^2s = -(1 - \frac{M(3k + r)^4}{8k(k + r)^4})dt^2 + \frac{dr^2}{1 - \frac{M(3k+r)^4}{8k(k+r)^4}} + \frac{(k + r)^4}{16k^2}$$

$$(d^2\theta + sin^2\theta d^2\phi) \tag{651}$$

Using Eqs (5) - (12) and (650) we can compute the non-vanishing components of the Ricci tensor $R_{\mu\nu}$, the Ricci scalar R, the second order curvature invariant R^2 and the eigenvalues B_i, $i = t$, r, θ and ϕ of the Ricci tensor R_μ^ν of this solution: We get:

$$R_{tt} = \frac{Mr(3k+r)^2}{8k(k+r)^{10}}(k^4(8k-81M) + 4k^3r(8k-27M) + 6k^2r^2(8k$$
$$-9M) + r^4(8k-M) + 4kr^3(8k-3M)) \tag{652}$$

$$R_{rr} = \frac{4}{(k+r)^2}(k^4(81M-8k) + 2k^3r(45M-16k) + 6k^2r^2(7M-$$
$$8k) + r^4(M-8k) + 2kr^3(5M-16k))(k^4(8k-81M) + 4k^3r(8k-$$
$$27M) + 6k^2r^2(8k-9M) + r^4(8k-M) + 4kr^3(8k-3M))^{-1} \tag{653}$$

$$R_{\theta\theta} = \frac{R_{\phi\phi}}{sin^2\theta} = \frac{1}{64k^3(k+r)^2}(k^4(40k+27M) + 4k^3r(8k+27M)$$
$$+10k^2r^2(9M-8k) + 3r^4(M-8k) + 4kr^3(7M-24k)) \tag{654}$$

$$R = \frac{2}{k(k+r)^6}(8k^5 + 27k^4M + 45k^3Mr - 32k^3r^2 + 30k^2Mr^2 -$$
$$32k^2r^3 + 9kMr^3 - 8kr^4 + Mr^4) \tag{655}$$

$$R^2 = \frac{1}{2(k+r)^{12}}(4992k^6M^2 + 13312k^5M^2(k+r) + 64k^4M(32k$$
$$+237M)(k+r)^2 + 64k^3M(64k+153M)(k+r)^3 - 8(128k^2 + 80k$$
$$M - 33M^2)(k+r)^6 + 8k^2(256k^2 + 352kM + 509M^2)(k+r)^4 +$$
$$\frac{3(M-8k)^2(k+r)^8}{k^2} - \frac{40M(8k-M)(k+r)^7}{k} + 16kM(16k+75$$
$$M)(k+r)^5) \tag{656}$$

$$B_t = -\frac{Mr(3k+r)^2}{(k+r)^6} \tag{657}$$

$$B_r = \frac{1}{2k(k+r)^6}(-8k^5 + k^4(81M - 32r) + 6k^3r(15M - 8r) +$$
$$2k^2r^2(21M - 16r) + 2kr^3(5M - 4r) + Mr^4) \tag{658}$$

$$B_\theta = B_\phi = \frac{1}{4k(k+r)^6}(40k^5 + k^4(27M + 32r) + 4k^3r(27M - 20$$
$$r) + 6k^2r^2(15M - 16r) + 4kr^3(7M - 6r) + 3Mr^4) \tag{659}$$

The energy density μ, the radial pressure P_r, the tangential pressure $P_\perp$ and the quantities $\mu + P_r$ and $\mu + P_\perp$, in the variables y and n of Eqs (172), are obtained from Eqs (625) - (629) for $(p, b) = (4, 4)$. We get

$$\mu = \frac{n(y + 3)^3 - 16(y^3 + 3y^2 + y - 1)}{16\pi k^2(y + 1)^5} \tag{660}$$

$$P_r = -\frac{(y - 1)(y + 3)(n(y + 3)^2 - 16(y + 1)^2)}{32\pi k^2(y + 1)^6} \tag{661}$$

$$P_\perp = \frac{16(y + 1)^4 - n(y + 3)^2(y^2 + 2y + 9)}{64\pi k^2(y + 1)^6} \tag{662}$$

$$\mu + P_r = \frac{n(y + 3)^4 - 16(y + 1)^4}{32\pi k^2(y + 1)^6} \tag{663}$$

$$\mu + P_\perp = \frac{n(y + 3)^2(3y^2 + 14y + 3) - 16(y + 1)^2(3y^2 + 6y - 5)}{64\pi k^2(y + 1)^6} \tag{664}$$

Since the solution of this example is obtained from the solution of Example 2.3.2.2 for $p = 4$ and $b = 4$ its energy density μ and its quantities $\mu + P_r$ and $\mu + P_\perp$ for $n = 1$ and $n = 4$ are positive or non negative in the interior region. Therefore these solutions with $n = 1$ and $n = 4$ satisfy the WEC. Also with numerical computer calculations we find for the solution with $p = 4$ and $b = 4$ that in the interior region

P_r for $0 < n \leq \frac{112}{81}$ is non positive and monotonically increasing
P_r for $\frac{112}{81} < n \leq \frac{16}{9}$ is non positive
P_r for $\frac{16}{9} < n < 4$ is negative zero or positive
P_r for $4 \leq n$ is non negative and monotonically decreasing
$P_\perp$ for $0 < n \leq \frac{16}{81}$ is positive
$P_\perp$ for $\frac{16}{81} < n < \frac{4}{3}$ is positive, zero or negative and
$P_\perp$ for $\frac{4}{3} \leq n$ is non positive and monotonically increasing.

In Figures 157 - 166 we present the graphs of $k^2\mu$, of $k^2(\mu + P_r)$, of $k^2(\mu + P_\perp)$, of $k^2 P_r$ and of $k^2 P_\perp$ of Eqs (660) - (664) for $n = 1$ and $n = 4$.

Observe that in the interior region the radial pressure P_r of this solution is for $n = 1$ non positive and monotonically increasing and for $n = 4$ non negative and monotonically decreasing.

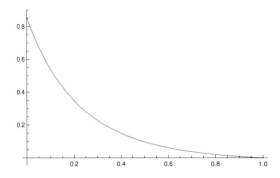

Figure 157: $k^2\mu$ of expression (660) for $n = 1$

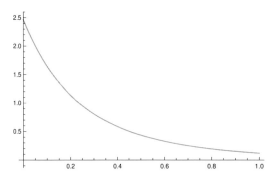

Figure 158: $k^2\mu$ of expression (660) for $n = 4$

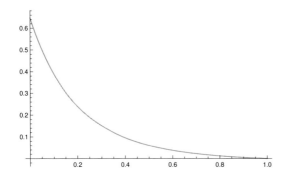

Figure 159: $k^2(\mu + P_r)$ of expression (663) for $n = 1$

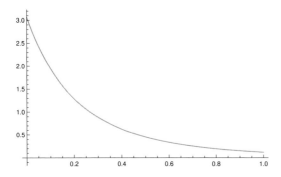

Figure 160: $k^2(\mu + P_r)$ of expression (663) for $n = 4$

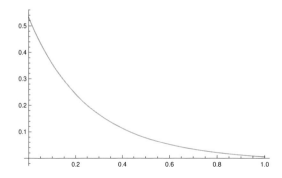

Figure 161: $k^2(\mu + P_\perp)$ of expression (664) for $n = 1$

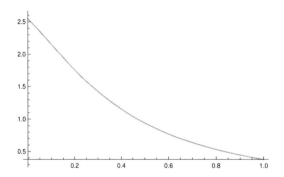

Figure 162: $k^2(\mu + P_\perp)$ of expression (664) for $n = 4$

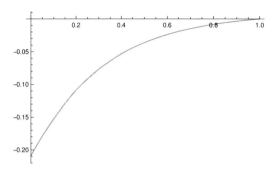

Figure 163: $k^2 P_r$ of expression (661) for $n = 1$

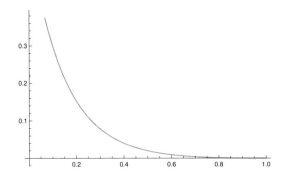

Figure 164: $k^2 P_r$ of expression (661) for $n = 4$

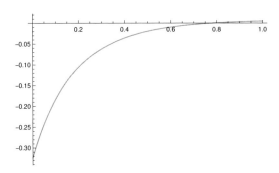

Figure 165: $k^2 P_\perp$ of expression (662) for $n = 1$

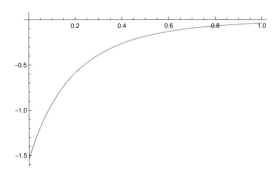

Figure 166: $k^2 P_\perp$ of expression (662) for $n = 4$

Example 2.3.2.3 : Solution with the $f(r)$ and the $h(r)$ of Eq (665)

Consider the solution with

$$f(r) = k^2 e^{\frac{2(r-k)}{k}} \quad \text{and} \quad h(r) = (1-b)ke^{\frac{r-k}{k}} + br \tag{665}$$

The non-vanishing components of the Ricci tensor $R_{\mu\nu}$, the Ricci scalar R, the second order curvature invariant R^2 and the eigenvalues B_i, $i = t$, r, θ, and ϕ of the Ricci tensor R_μ^ν of this solution are obtained from Eqs (5) - (12) and (665). We get

$$R_{tt} = -\frac{1}{k^5} M e^{\frac{4(k-r)}{k}}((b-1)e^{\frac{r-k}{k}} - 2b)(2(b-1)kMe^{\frac{r-k}{k}} -$$
$$2bMr + k^2 e^{\frac{2(r-k)}{k}}) \tag{666}$$

$$R_{rr} = -\frac{3(b-1)kMe^{\frac{r-k}{k}} + 2bM(k-2r) + 2k^2 e^{\frac{2(r-k)}{k}}}{k^2 \left(2(b-1)kMe^{\frac{r-k}{k}} - 2bMr + k^2 e^{\frac{2(r-k)}{k}}\right)} \tag{667}$$

$$R_{\theta\theta} = \frac{R_{\phi\phi}}{sin^2\theta} = -\frac{1}{k}(2(b-1)Me^{\frac{r-k}{k}} - 2bM + 2ke^{\frac{2(r-k)}{k}} - k) \tag{668}$$

$$R = \frac{2}{k^4}(e^{\frac{2(k-r)}{k}} \left(2bMr + k^2\right) - 3(b-1)kMe^{\frac{k-r}{k}} - 3k^2) \tag{669}$$

$$R^2 = 4e^{\frac{4(k-r)}{k}}((-40b^2kM^2r + 28b^2M^2r^2 + 4bk^2M(5bM+r) + k^4) + 8(b-1)k^3Me^{\frac{3(r-k)}{k}} - k^2 e^{\frac{2(r-k)}{k}}(4bkM + M(4br - 9(b-1)^2 M) + 2k^2) - 4(b-1)kMe^{\frac{r-k}{k}}(-2bkM + 6bMr + k^2) + 3k^4 e^{\frac{4(r-k)}{k}}) \tag{670}$$

$$B_t = \frac{M}{k^3}e^{\frac{2(k-r)}{k}}\left(b\left(e^{\frac{r-k}{k}} - 2\right) - e^{\frac{r-k}{k}}\right) \tag{671}$$

$$B_r = \frac{1}{k^4}e^{\frac{2(k-r)}{k}}\left(-3(b-1)kMe^{\frac{r-k}{k}} - 2bM(k-2r) - 2k^2 e^{\frac{2(r-k)}{k}}\right) \tag{672}$$

$$B_\theta = B_\phi = \frac{1}{k^3}e^{\frac{2(k-r)}{k}}\left(-2(b-1)Me^{\frac{r-k}{k}} + 2bM - 2ke^{\frac{2(r-k)}{k}} + k\right) \tag{673}$$

It is obvious from Eqs (669) and (670) that the solution is regular.

The energy density μ, the radial pressure P_r, the tangential pressure $P_\perp$ and the quantities $\mu + P_r$ and $\mu + P_\perp$, which are obtained from Eqs (14) - (18) and (665), are the following in the variables y and n of Eqs (172):

$$\mu = \frac{1}{8\pi k^2}e^{2(1-y)}\left(-2(b-1)ne^{y-1} + bn(y+1) - 3e^{2(y-1)} + 1\right) \quad (674)$$

$$P_r = \frac{1}{8\pi k^2}e^{2(1-y)}\left(bn(y-1) + e^{2(y-1)} - 1\right) \quad (675)$$

$$P_\perp = \frac{1}{16\pi k^2}e^{2(1-y)}\left((b-1)ne^{y-1} - 2bn(y-1) + 2e^{2(y-1)}\right) \quad (676)$$

$$\mu + P_r = \frac{1}{4\pi k^2}e^{2(1-y)}\left(-(b-1)ne^{y-1} + bny - e^{2(y-1)}\right) \quad (677)$$

$$\mu + P_\perp = \frac{1}{16\pi k^2}e^{2(1-y)}\left(-3(b-1)ne^{y-1} + 4bn - 4e^{2(y-1)} + 2\right) \quad (678)$$

The line element d^2s of the solution which is obtained from Eqs (1) and (665) is the following:

$$d^2s = -\left(1 - \frac{2M((1-b)ke^{(r-k)/k} + br)}{e^{2(-k+r)/k}k^2}\right)dt^2 +$$

$$\frac{dr^2}{1 - \frac{2M((1-b)ke^{(r-k)/k}+br)}{e^{2(-k+r)/k}k^2}} + e^{2\frac{-k+r}{k}}k^2(d\theta^2 + \sin^2\theta d\phi^2) \quad (679)$$

To find the equation of state of the solution we proceed as follows. From the first of Eqs (665) we get $f'(r) = \frac{2f(r)}{k}$ and $f''(r) = \frac{4f(r)}{k^2}$. Substituting these expressions in Eqs (21) and (22) we get

$$h'(r) = \frac{f(r)\left(4\pi k^2(\mu - P_r) + 2\right) - k^2}{2kM} \quad (680)$$

$$h''(r) = \frac{f(r)\left(2 - 8\pi k^2(P_\perp + P_r)\right) - k^2}{k^2 M} \quad (681)$$

If using Eq (665) for $h(r)$ and $f(r)$ we express Eq (681) in the variable $z = e^{\frac{r-k}{k}} = e^{y-1}$ solve the resulting relation for z and introduce the variable n from the relation $M = \frac{kn}{2}$ we get

$$z = \frac{\sqrt{-k^2\left(32\left(4\pi k^2(P_\perp + P_r) - 1\right) - (b-1)^2 n^2\right)} + (b-1)kn}{8k\left(4\pi k^2(P_\perp + P_r) - 1\right)} \quad (682)$$

Also if we express Eq (680) in the variables z and n, replace its z by expression (682) and solve the resulting relation for μ we get

$$\mu = -\frac{1}{32\pi k^2}(32\pi k^2(2P_\perp(bn+1) + P_r(2bn+1)) - (bn+1)$$
$$((b-1)^2n^2 + 16) + 2(b-1)^2n + 16) - \frac{1}{32\pi k^2}((b-1)(bn^2 +$$
$$n-2))\sqrt{(b-1)^2n^2 - 32(4\pi k^2(P_r + P_\perp) - 1))} \tag{683}$$

The above equation is satisfied if we replace μ, P_r and $P_\perp$ by their expressions of Eqs (674), (675) and (676) respectively. Eq (683) is the equation of state of the solution.

For $n = 1$, $n = 2$, $n = 10$ and $n = 13$ with numerical computer calculations we find the following for the quantities μ, P_r, $P_\perp$ $\mu + P_r$ and $\mu + P_\perp$ in the interior region

(A) $n = 1$

μ is non positive for $b \leq \frac{3-2e-e^2}{e(e-2)} = -5.03235$ and non positive and monotonically increasing for $b \leq -\frac{2(e+1)}{e-2} = -10.3533$. It takes positive, zero and negative values for $-5.05235 < b \leq -3.821$, while it is non negative for $b > -3.821$.

P_r is positive or zero for $b \leq -2$, positive zero or negative for $-2 < b \leq \frac{1-e^2}{e^2} = -0.864665$ and negative or zero for $b > -0.864665$. For $b \geq -\frac{2}{3}$ it is negative and monotonically increasing or zero.

$P_\perp$ is negative for $b < -1$, negative, zero or positive for $-1 \leq b \leq \frac{-2+e}{e(1+2e)} = 0.0410531$ and positive for $b \geq 0.0410531$.

$\mu + P_r$ is non negative for $b \leq \frac{e-1}{e} = 0.632121$ and non negative and monotonically decreasing for $b \leq \frac{1}{e+1} = 0.268941$. It takes positive, zero and negative values for $b > 0.632121$.

$\mu + P_\perp$ is negative for $b < -1.15$ and takes positive, zero and negative values for $-1.15 \leq b \leq \frac{4-3e-2e^2}{e(-3+4e)} = -0.884661$. It is positive for $b > -0.884661$ and positive and monotonically decreasing for $b \geq \frac{-3-4e}{-3+8e}$.

(B) $n = 2$

μ takes positive, zero and negative values for $b \leq -3.638$, while it is positive for $b > -3.638$. It is positive and monotonically decreasing if $b \geq -2.7$

P_r is positive or zero for $b \leq -1$, positive zero or negative for $-1 < b \leq \frac{1-e^2}{2e^2} = -0.432332$ and negative or zero for $b > -0.432332$. For $b \geq -\frac{1}{3}$ it is negative and monotonically increasing or zero.

$P_\perp$ is negative for $b < 0$, negative, zero or positive for $0 \leq b \leq 0.1506$ and positive for $b \geq 0.1506$.

$\mu + P_r$ is positive for $b \leq \frac{2e-1}{2e} = 0.81606$ and positive and monotonically decreasing for $b \leq \frac{1}{e+1} = 0.268941$. It takes positive, zero and negative values for $b > 0.81606$.

$\mu + P_\perp$ is negative for $b < -2$ and takes positive, zero and negative values for $-2 \leq b \leq \frac{2-3e-e^2}{e(-3+4e)} = -0.632852$. It is positive for $b > -0.632852$ and positive and monotonically decreasing for $b \geq \frac{-3-2e}{-3+8e} = -0.45004$.

(C) $n = 10$

μ takes positive, zero and negative values for $b \leq -2.995$, while it is positive for $b > -2.995$. It is positive and monotonically decreasing if $b \geq -1.788$

P_r is positive or zero for $b \leq -0.2$, positive zero or negative for $-0.2 < b \leq \frac{1-e^2}{10e^2} = -0.0864665$ and negative or zero for $b > -0.0864665$. For $b \geq -\frac{1}{15}$ it is negative and monotonically increasing or zero.

$P_\perp$ is negative for $b < \frac{-1+5e}{5e(1+2e)} = 0.143931$, negative, zero or positive for $0.143931 \leq b \leq 0.8$ and positive for $b \geq 0.8$.

$\mu + P_r$ is positive for $b \leq \frac{10e-1}{10e} = 0.963212$ and positive and monotonically decreasing for $b \leq \frac{1}{e+1} = 0.268941$. It takes positive, zero and negative values for $b > 0.963212$.

$\mu + P_\perp$ is negative for $b < -2.8$ and takes positive, zero and negative values for $-2.8 \leq b \leq \frac{2-15e-e^2}{5e(-3+4e)} = -0.431405$. It is positive for $b > -0.431405$ and positive and monotonically decreasing for $b \geq \frac{-15-2e}{5(-3+8e)} = -0.218034$.

(D) $n = 13$

μ takes positive, zero and negative values for $b \leq -2.949$, while it is positive for $b > -2.949$. It is positive and monotonically decreasing if $b \geq -1.73$

P_r is positive or zero for $b \leq -0.153846$, positive zero or negative for $-0.153846 < b \leq \frac{1-e^2}{13e^2} = -0.0665127$ and negative or zero for $b > -0.0665127$. For $b \geq -\frac{2}{39}$ it is negative and monotonically increasing or zero.

$P_\perp$ is negative for $b < \frac{-2+13e}{13e(1+2e)} = 0.146569$, negative, zero or positive for $0.146569 \leq b \leq 0.845$ and positive for $b > 0.845$.

$\mu + P_r$ is positive for $b \leq \frac{13e-1}{13e} = 0.971702$ and positive and monotonically decreasing for $b \leq \frac{1}{e+1} = 0.268941$. It takes positive, zero and negative values for $b > 0.971702$.

$\mu + P_\perp$ is negative for $b < -2.84515$ and takes positive, zero and negative values for $-2.84615 \leq b \leq \frac{4-39e-2e^2}{43e(-3+4e)} = -0.419783$. It is positive for $b >$

-0.419783 and positive and monotonically decreasing for $b \geq \frac{-39-4e}{13(-3+8e)} = -0.204649$.

From the above relations we can find solutions with P_r non negative in the whole interior region which satisfy the WEC. Such solutions are those with $(n,b) = (10, -0.2)$ and $(n,b) = (13, -0.2)$. Also we can find solutions with P_r non positive in the whole interior region which again satisfy the WEC for example the solutions with $(n,b) = (1, 0.2)$ and $(n,b) = (2, 0.2)$. We shall consider in the following these solutions.

Example 2.3.2.3.1 : Solution with the $f(r)$ and the $h(r)$ of Eq (684)

Consider the solution with

$$f(r) = k^2 e^{\frac{2(r-k)}{k}} \quad \text{and} \quad h(r) = 1.2ke^{\frac{r-k}{k}} - 0.2r \tag{684}$$

This solution is obtained from the solution of Example 2.3.2.3 for $b = -0.2$. Its line element d^2s, which is obtained from the expression (679), for $b = -0.2$ is the following:

$$d^2s = -(1 - \frac{2M(1.2ke^{(r-k)/k} - 0.2r)}{e^{2(-k+r)/k}k^2})dt^2 +$$

$$\frac{dr^2}{1 - \frac{2M(1.2ke^{(r-k)/k} - 0.2r)}{e^{2(-k+r)/k}k^2}} + e^{\frac{2(-k+r)}{k}}k^2(d\theta^2 + \sin^2\theta d\phi^2) \tag{685}$$

The non-vanishing components of the Ricci tensor $R_{\mu\nu}$, the Ricci scalar R, the second order curvature invariant R^2 and the eigenvalues B_i, $i = t, r, \theta$ and ϕ of the Ricci tensor R^ν_μ are obtained from Eqs (666) - (673) for $b = -0.2$. We get

$$R_{tt} = -\frac{1}{k^5}Me^{\frac{4(k-r)}{k}}(0.4 - 1.2e^{\frac{r-k}{k}})(k^2e^{\frac{2(r-k)}{k}} - 2.4kMe^{\frac{r-k}{k}} + 0.4Mr) \tag{686}$$

$$R_{rr} = -\frac{2k^2e^{\frac{2(r-k)}{k}} - 3.6kMe^{\frac{r-k}{k}} - 0.4M(k-2r)}{k^2\left(k^2e^{\frac{2(r-k)}{k}} - 2.4kMe^{\frac{r-k}{k}} + 0.4Mr\right)} \tag{687}$$

$$R_{\theta\theta} = \frac{R_{\phi\phi}}{\sin^2\theta} = -\frac{1}{k}(-2.4Me^{\frac{r-k}{k}} + 2ke^{\frac{2(r-k)}{k}} - k + 0.4M) \tag{688}$$

$$R = \frac{2}{k^4}(e^{\frac{2(k-r)}{k}}\left(-0.4Mr + k^2\right) + 3.6kMe^{\frac{k-r}{k}} - 3k^2) \tag{689}$$

$$R^2 = \frac{4e^{-\frac{4(r-k)}{k}}}{k^8}(3k^4e^{\frac{4(r-k)}{k}} + k^4 - 9.6k^3Me^{\frac{3(r-k)}{k}} - k^2e^{\frac{2(r-k)}{k}}(2k^2$$
$$-0.8kM + M(-12.96M - 0.8r)) - 0.8k^2M(r - M) + 4.8kM$$
$$e^{\frac{r-k}{k}}(k^2 + 0.4kM - 1.2Mr) - 1.6kM^2r + 1.12M^2r^2) \tag{690}$$

$$B_t = \frac{M}{k^3}e^{\frac{2(k-r)}{k}}\left(-0.2\left(e^{\frac{r-k}{k}} - 2\right) - e^{\frac{r-k}{k}}\right) \tag{691}$$

$$B_r = \frac{1}{k^4}e^{\frac{2(k-r)}{k}}\left(3.6kMe^{\frac{r-k}{k}} + 0.4M(k - 2r) - 2k^2e^{\frac{2(r-k)}{k}}\right) \tag{692}$$

$$B_\theta = B_\phi = \frac{1}{k^3}e^{\frac{2(k-r)}{k}}\left(3.6Me^{\frac{r-k}{k}} - 0.4M - 2ke^{\frac{2(r-k)}{k}} + k\right) \tag{693}$$

The energy density μ, the radial pressure P_r, the tangential pressure $P_\perp$ and the quantities $\mu + P_r$ and $\mu + P_\perp$, which are obtained from Eqs (674) - (678) and (665), are the following in the variables y and n of Eqs (172):

$$\mu = \frac{1}{8\pi k^2}e^{2(1-y)}\left(2.4ne^{y-1} - 0.2n(y+1) - 3e^{2(y-1)} + 1\right) \tag{694}$$

$$P_r = \frac{1}{8\pi k^2}e^{2(1-y)}\left(-0.2n(y-1) + e^{2(y-1)} - 1\right) \tag{695}$$

$$P_\perp = \frac{1}{16\pi k^2}e^{2(1-y)}\left(-1.2ne^{y-1} + 0.4n(y-1) + 2e^{2(y-1)}\right) \tag{696}$$

$$\mu + P_r = \frac{1}{4\pi k^2}e^{2(1-y)}\left(1.2ne^{y-1} - 0.2ny - e^{2(y-1)}\right) \tag{697}$$

$$\mu + P_\perp = \frac{1}{16\pi k^2}e^{2(1-y)}\left(3.6ne^{y-1} - 0.8n - 4e^{2(y-1)} + 2\right) \tag{698}$$

The graphs of the above quantities after multiplication by k^2 for $n = 10$ and 13 are given by Figures 167 - 176. From these Figures we find that the solutions we get for both values of n satisfy the WEC and that their radial pressure P_r is non negative and monotonically decreasing in the whole interior region. These solutions show that we can get solutions which satisfy the WEC and have non negative radial pressure in the whole interior region by choosing properly their constants.

The equation of state of the solution is obtained from Eq (683) for $b = -0.2$. We get

$$\mu = -\frac{1}{32\pi k^2}(32\pi k^2(2P_\perp(-0.2n + 1) + P_r(-0.4n + 1)) - (-0.2n$$

$$+1)(1.44n^2 + 16) + 2.88n + 16) - \frac{1}{32\pi k^2}((-1.2(-0.2n^2 +$$

$$n - 2))\sqrt{1.44n^2 - 32(4\pi k^2(P_r + P_\perp) - 1)}) \tag{699}$$

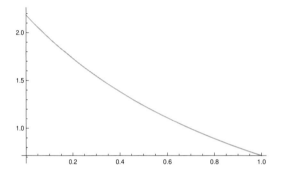

Figure 167: $k^2\mu$ of expression (694) for $n = 10$

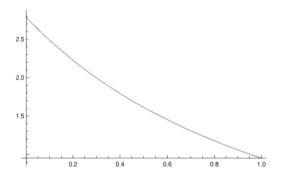

Figure 168: $k^2\mu$ of expression (694) for $n = 13$

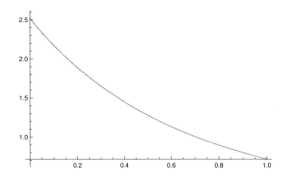

Figure 169: $k^2(\mu + P_r)$ of expression (697) for $n = 10$

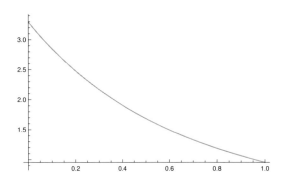

Figure 170: $k^2(\mu + P_r)$ of expression (697) for $n = 13$

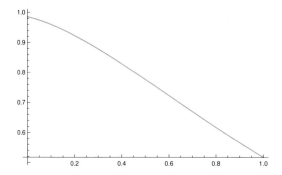

Figure 171: $k^2(\mu + P_\perp)$ of expression (698) for $n = 10$

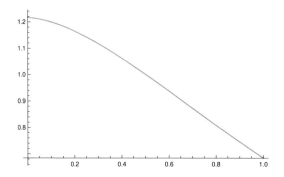

Figure 172: $k^2(\mu + P_\perp)$ of expression (698) for $n = 13$

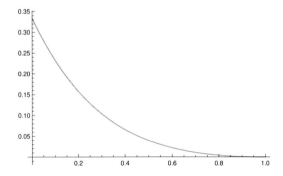

Figure 173: $k^2 P_r$ of expression (695) for $n = 10$

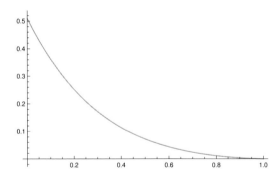

Figure 174: $k^2 P_r$ of expression (695) for $n = 13$

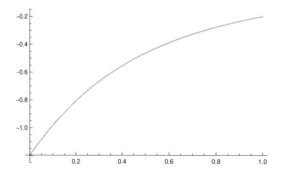

Figure 175: $k^2 P_\perp$ of expression (696) for $n = 10$

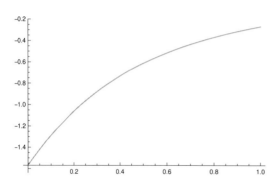

Figure 176: $k^2 P_\perp$ of expression (696) for $n = 13$

Example 2.3.2.3.2 : Solution with the $f(r)$ and the $h(r)$ of Eq (700)

Consider the solution with

$$f(r) = k^2 e^{\frac{2(r-k)}{k}} \quad \text{and} \quad h(r) = 0.8k e^{\frac{r-k}{k}} + 0.2r \tag{700}$$

This solution is obtained from the solution of Example 2.3.2.3 for $b = 0.2$. Its line element $d^2 s$, which is obtained from the expression (679) for $b = 0.2$, is

$$d^2 s = -(1 - \frac{2M(0.8k e^{(r-k)/k} + 0.2r)}{e^{2(-k+r)/k} k^2}) dt^2 +$$

$$\frac{dr^2}{1 - \frac{2M(0.8ke^{(r-k)/k}+0.2r)}{e^{2(-k+r)/k}k^2}} + e^{\frac{2(-k+r)}{k}}k^2(d\theta^2 + \sin^2\theta d\phi^2) \qquad (701)$$

The non-vanishing components of the Ricci tensor $R_{\mu\nu}$, the Ricci scalar R, the second order curvature invariant R^2 and the eigenvalues B_i, $i = t$, r, θ and ϕ of the Ricci tensor R^ν_μ are obtained from Eqs (666) - (673) for $b = 0.2$. We get

$$R_{tt} = -\frac{1}{k^5}Me^{\frac{4(k-r)}{k}}(-0.8e^{\frac{r-k}{k}} - 0.4)(-1.6kMe^{\frac{r-k}{k}} -$$
$$0.4Mr + k^2e^{\frac{2(r-k)}{k}}) \qquad (702)$$

$$R_{rr} = -\frac{-0.24kMe^{\frac{r-k}{k}} + 0.4M(k-2r) + 2k^2e^{\frac{2(r-k)}{k}}}{k^2\left(-1.6kMe^{\frac{r-k}{k}} - 0.4Mr + k^2e^{\frac{2(r-k)}{k}}\right)} \qquad (703)$$

$$R_{\theta\theta} = \frac{R_{\phi\phi}}{sin^2\theta} = -\frac{1}{k}(-1.6Me^{\frac{r-k}{k}} - 0.4M + 2ke^{\frac{2(r-k)}{k}} - k) \qquad (704)$$

$$R = \frac{2}{k^4}(e^{\frac{2(k-r)}{k}}\left(0.4Mr + k^2\right) + 2.4kMe^{\frac{k-r}{k}} - 3k^2) \qquad (705)$$

$$R^2 = \frac{4e^{-\frac{4(r-k)}{k}}}{k^8}(3k^4e^{\frac{4(r-k)}{k}} + k^4 - 6.4k^3Me^{\frac{3(r-k)}{k}} - k^2e^{\frac{2(r-k)}{k}}(2k^2$$
$$+0.8kM + M(0.8r - 5.76M)) + 0.8k^2M(M + r) + 3.2kM$$
$$e^{\frac{r-k}{k}}(k^2 - 0.4kM + 1.2Mr) - 1.6kM^2r + 1.12M^2r^2) \qquad (706)$$

$$B_t = \frac{M}{k^3}e^{\frac{2(k-r)}{k}}\left(0.2\left(e^{\frac{r-k}{k}} - 2\right) - e^{\frac{r-k}{k}}\right) \qquad (707)$$

$$B_r = \frac{1}{k^4}e^{\frac{2(k-r)}{k}}\left(2.4kMe^{\frac{r-k}{k}} - 0.4M(k - 2r) - 2k^2e^{\frac{2(r-k)}{k}}\right) \qquad (708)$$

$$B_\theta = B_\phi = \frac{1}{k^3}e^{\frac{2(k-r)}{k}}\left(1.6Me^{\frac{r-k}{k}} + 0.4M - 2ke^{\frac{2(r-k)}{k}} + k\right) \qquad (709)$$

The energy density μ, the radial pressure P_r, the tangential pressure $P_\perp$ and the quantities $\mu + P_r$ and $\mu + P_\perp$, which are obtained from Eqs (674) - (678) and (665) for $b = 0.2$, are the following in the variables y and n of Eqs (172) :

$$\mu = \frac{1}{8\pi k^2}e^{2(1-y)}\left(1.6ne^{y-1} + 0.2n(y + 1) - 3e^{2(y-1)} + 1\right) \qquad (710)$$

$$P_r = \frac{1}{8\pi k^2}e^{2(1-y)}\left(0.2n(y-1) + e^{2(y-1)} - 1\right) \tag{711}$$

$$P_\perp = \frac{1}{16\pi k^2}e^{2(1-y)}\left(-0.8ne^{y-1} - 0.4n(y-1) + 2e^{2(y-1)}\right) \tag{712}$$

$$\mu + P_r = \frac{1}{4\pi k^2}e^{2(1-y)}\left(0.8ne^{y-1} + 0.2ny - e^{2(y-1)}\right) \tag{713}$$

$$\mu + P_\perp = \frac{1}{16\pi k^2}e^{2(1-y)}\left(2.4ne^{y-1} + 0.8n - 4e^{2(y-1)} + 2\right) \tag{714}$$

The graphs of $k^2\mu$, k^2P_r, $k^2P_\perp$, $k^2(\mu + P_r)$ and $k^2(\mu + P_\perp)$ of Eqs (710) - (714) for $n = 1$ and 2 are given by Figures 177 - 186. From these graphs we find that in both cases the solution satisfies the WEC and has radial pressure P_r non positive and monotonically increasing in the interior region.

The equation of state of the solution is obtained from Eq (683) for $b = 0.2$. We get

$$\mu = -\frac{1}{32\pi k^2}(32\pi k^2(2P_\perp(0.2n + 1) + P_r(0.4n + 1)) - (0.2n + 1)$$

$$(0.64n^2 + 16) + 1.28n + 16) - \frac{1}{32\pi k^2}(-0.8(0.2n^2 +$$

$$n - 2))\sqrt{0.64n^2 - 32(4\pi k^2(P_r + P_\perp) - 1))} \tag{715}$$

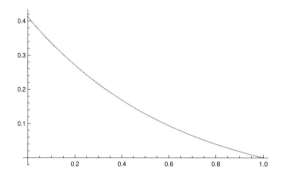

Figure 177: $k^2\mu$ of expression (710) for $n = 1$

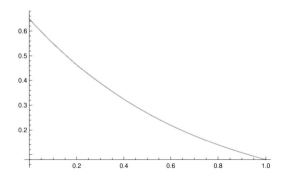

Figure 178: $k^2\mu$ of expression (710) for $n = 2$

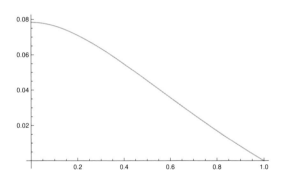

Figure 179: $k^2(\mu + P_r)$ of expression (713) for $n = 1$

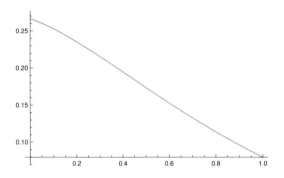

Figure 180: $k^2(\mu + P_r)$ of expression (713) for $n = 2$

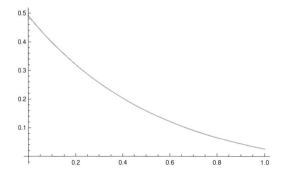

Figure 181: $k^2(\mu + P_\perp)$ of expression (714) for $n = 1$

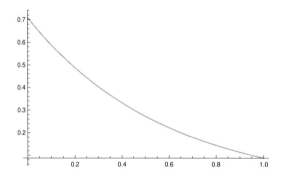

Figure 182: $k^2(\mu + P_\perp)$ of expression (714) for $n = 2$

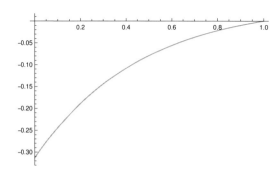

Figure 183: $k^2 P_r$ of expression (711) for $n = 1$

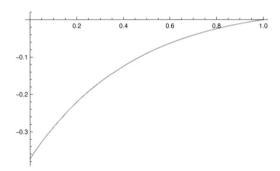

Figure 184: $k^2 P_r$ of expression (711) for $n = 2$

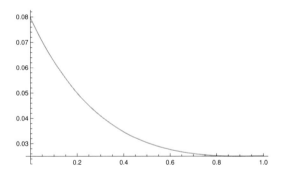

Figure 185: $k^2 P_\perp$ of expression (712) for $n = 1$

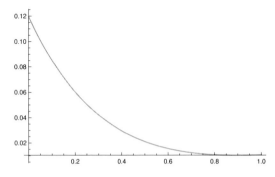

Figure 186: $k^2 P_\perp$ of expression (712) for $n = 2$

Example 2.3.2.4 : Solution with the $f(r)$ and the $h(r)$ of Eq (716)

Consider the solution with

$$f(r) = k^2 \left(\frac{2r}{bk} - \frac{2}{b} + 1\right)^b \quad \text{and} \quad h(r) = ke^{\frac{r-k}{k}} \tag{716}$$

The non vanishing components of the Ricci tensor $R_{\mu\nu}$, the Ricci scalar R, the second order curvature invariant R^2 and the eigenvalues B_i, $i = t, r, \theta$ and ϕ of the Ricci tensor R_μ^ν of this solution are obtained from Eqs (5) - (12) and (716). We get

$$R_{tt} = \frac{Mk^{b-4}e^{\frac{r-k}{k}}}{((b-2)k+2r)^{2(1+b)}}\left(\frac{1}{b}\right)^{-2b}(((b-4)b-4)k^2 + 8kr - 4r^2)$$

$$\left(\left(\frac{1}{b}\right)^b k((b-2)k+2r)^b - 2Mk^b e^{\frac{r-k}{k}}\right) \tag{717}$$

$$R_{rr} = \frac{1}{((b-2)k+2r)^2}\left(\frac{Mk^{b-2}e^{\frac{r-k}{k}}(((b-4)b-4)k^2 + 8kr - 4r^2)}{2Mk^b e^{\frac{r-k}{k}} - \left(\frac{1}{b}\right)^b k((b-2)k+2r)^b}\right)$$

$$-2(b-2)b) \tag{718}$$

$$R_{\theta\theta} = \frac{R_{\phi\phi}}{sin^2\theta} = -\frac{k^{-b}}{((b-2)k+2r)^2}(2(b-1)\left(\frac{1}{b}\right)^{b-1}k^2((b-2)k +$$

$$2r)^b - k^b(2bMe^{\frac{r-k}{k}}((b-4)k+2r) + ((b-2)k+2r)^2)) \tag{719}$$

$$R = \frac{1}{k^3((b-2)k+2r)^{2+b}}\left(\frac{1}{b}\right)^{-b} 2k^b(Me^{\frac{r-k}{k}}((b-2)(3b-2)k^2 +$$

$$4(b-2)kr + 4r^2) + k((b-2)k+2r)^2) - 2\left(\frac{1}{b}\right)^{b-1}(3b-4)k^3$$

$$((b-2)k+2r)^b \tag{720}$$

$$R^2 = \frac{4}{k^6((b-2)k+2r)^{2(b+2)}}\left(\frac{1}{b}\right)^{-2b}(M^2k^{2b}e^{\frac{2(r-k)}{k}}((b(9b^3 + 152b$$

$$+64) + 16)k^4 - 8(b(b(b+18) + 20) + 8)k^3r + 8(b+2)(5b+6)k^2$$

$$r^2 - 32(b+2)kr^3 + 16r^4) + 4b^2Mk^{b+3}e^{\frac{r-k}{k}}(k^b((b-2)k+2r)^2 -$$

$$2(\frac{1}{b})^b k((b-2)k+2r)^b(((b-4)b+6)k+(b-2)r))+k^2(-2$$

$$(\frac{1}{b})^{b-2}k^{b+2}((b-2)k+2r)^{b+2}+k^{2b}((b-2)k+2r)^4+(b(3b-8)+$$

$$8)(\frac{1}{b})^{2b-2}k^4((b-2)k+2r)^{2b})) \tag{721}$$

$$B_t = \frac{Mk^{b-3}e^{\frac{r-k}{k}}}{((b-2)k+2r)^{2+b}}\left(\frac{1}{b}\right)^{-b}((4-(b-4)b)k^2-8kr+4r^2) \tag{722}$$

$$B_r = \frac{1}{k^3((b-2)k+2r)^{2+b}}\left(\frac{1}{b}\right)^{-b}(Mk^b e^{\frac{r-k}{k}}((b(3b-4)+4)k^2-$$

$$8kr+4r^2)-2(b-2)(\frac{1}{b})^{b-1}k^3((b-2)k+2r)^b) \tag{723}$$

$$B_\theta = B_\phi = \frac{1}{k^2((b-2)k+2r)^{2+b}}\left(\frac{1}{b}\right)^{-b}(k^b(2bMe^{\frac{r-k}{k}}((b-4)k+$$

$$2r)+((b-2)k+2r)^2)-2(b-1)(\frac{1}{b})^{b-1}k^2((b-2)k+2r)^b) \tag{724}$$

From Eqs (720) and (721) we find that the solution is regular and real if

$$b>2 \quad \text{or} \quad b=-1,-2,-3,... \tag{725}$$

We took $b = -1,-2,-3,...$ and not $b < 0$ in order to avoid imaginary expressions in our calculations.

The energy density μ, the radial pressure P_r, the tangential pressure $P_\perp$ and the quantities $\mu + P_r$ and $\mu + P_\perp$, which are obtained from Eqs (14) - (18) and (716), are the following in the variables y and n of Eqs (172):

$$\mu = \frac{1}{8\pi k^2(b+2y-2)^{2+b}}\left(\frac{1}{b}\right)^{-b}(2bne^{y-1}(b+y-3)+(4-3b)$$

$$(\frac{1}{b})^{b-1}(b+2y-2)^b+(b+2y-2)^2) \tag{726}$$

$$P_r = \frac{1}{8\pi k^2(b+2y-2)^{2+b}}(\frac{1}{b})^{-b}(-2bne^{y-1}(y-1)+(\frac{1}{b})^{b-2}(b+2y$$

$$-2)^b-(b+2y-2)^2) \tag{727}$$

$$P_\perp = \frac{1}{16\pi k^2(b+2y-2)^{2+b}} \left(\frac{1}{b}\right)^{-b} (2(b-2)(\frac{1}{b})^{b-1}(b+2y-2)^b -$$
$$ne^{y-1}(b^2+4(y-1)^2)) \tag{728}$$

$$\mu + P_r = -\frac{b-2}{4\pi k^2(b+2y-2)^{2+b}} \left(\frac{1}{b}\right)^{-b-1} \left(\left(\frac{1}{b}\right)^b (b+2y-2)^b - ne^{y-1}\right) \tag{729}$$

$$\mu + P_\perp = \frac{1}{16\pi k^2(b+2y-2)^{2+b}} \left(\frac{1}{b}\right)^{-b} (2(b^2 - 2(\frac{1}{b})^{b-2}(b+2y-$$
$$2)^b + 2(\frac{1}{b})^{b-1}(b+2y-2)^b + 4b(y-1) + 4y^2 - 8y + 4) - ne^{y-1}$$
$$(-3b^2 - 4b(y-3) + 4(y-1)^2)) \tag{730}$$

We shall take the values of b of relations (725). Then with numerical computer calculations for $n = 1$, $n = 2$ and $n = 3$ we find the following for the quantities μ, P_r, $P_\perp$, $\mu + P_r$ and $\mu + P_\perp$ in the interior region:

(A) $n = 1$

μ is non positive if $2 < b < 2.5$ and positive, zero or negative for $2.5 \le b < 2.852$. For $b \ge 2.852$ it is non negative and for $b \ge 2.94$ it is non negative and monotonically decreasing. For $b = -1$, -2, $-3, ...$ μ is non negative and monotonically decreasing.

P_r is non negative for $b \le 3$ and positive zero or negative for $3 < b < 3.976$. For $b \ge 3.976$ it is non positive and for $b \ge 4.25$ it is non positive and monotonically increasing. For $b = -1$, -2, $-3, ...$ P_r is non positive and monotonically increasing.

$P_\perp$ is negative for $2 < b < 4$, negative or zero for $b = 4$ and negative zero or positive for $b > 4$. Also $P_\perp$ is positive zero or negative for $b = -11$, -12, $-13, ...$ and positive for $b = -1$, -2, $-3, ... - 10$.

$\mu + P_r$ is non negative for $b > 2$ and for $b = -1$, -2, $-3, ...$

$\mu + P_\perp$ is negative for $2 < b \le 3,217$, negative zero or positive for $3.217 < b \le 4$ and positive for $b \ge 4$. Also $\mu + P_\perp$ is positive and monotonically decreasing for $b = -1$, -2, $-3, ...$

(B) $n = 2$

μ is positive , zero or negative for $2 < b < 2.915$ and positive for $b \ge 2.915$. For $b \ge 3.01$ it is positive and monotonically decreasing. For $b = -1$, -2, $-3, ...$ μ is positive and for $b = -2$, -3, $-4, ...$ positive and monotonically decreasing.

P_r is non negative for $b \leq 4$ and positive zero or negative for $4 < b < 5.084$. For $b \geq 5.084$ it is non positive and for $b \geq 5.45$ it is non positive and monotonically increasing. For $b = -1, \ -2, \ -3, \ldots$ P_r is non positive and monotonically increasing.

$P_\perp$ is negative for $b > 2$. Also $P_\perp$ is positive zero or negative for $b = -1, \ -2, \ -3, \ldots$.

$\mu + P_r$ is positive for $b > 2$ and for $b = -1, \ -2, \ -3, \ldots$.

$\mu + P_\perp$ is negative for $2 < b \leq 3$, negative zero or positive for $3 < b \leq 3.848$ and positive for $b > 3.848$. It is positive and monotonically decreasing for $b \geq 4.08$, Also $\mu + P_\perp$ is positive for $b = -1, \ -2, \ -3, \ldots$.

(C) $n = 3$

μ is positive , zero or negative for $2 < b < 2.94$ and positive for $b \geq 2.94$. For $b \geq 3.04$ it is positive and monotonically decreasing. For $b = -1, \ -2, \ -3, \ldots$ μ is positive and for $b = -3, \ -4, \ -5, \ldots$ positive and monotonically decreasing.

P_r is non negative for $b \leq 5$ and positive zero or negative for $5 < b < 6.09$. For $b \geq 6.09$ it is non positive and for $b \geq 6.42$ it is non positive and monotonically increasing. For $b = -1, \ -2, \ -3, \ldots$ P_r is non positive and monotonically increasing.

$P_\perp$ is negative for $b > 2$. Also $P_\perp$ is negative for $b = -5, \ -6, \ -7, \ldots$, negative or zero for $b = -4$ and negative zero or positive for $b = -1, -2, -3$.

$\mu + P_r$ is positive for $b > 2$ and for $b = -1, \ -2, \ -3, \ldots$.

$\mu + P_\perp$ is negative for $2 < b \leq 3.855$, negative zero or positive for $3.855 < b \leq 3.968$ and positive for $b > 3.968$. It is positive and monotonically decreasing for $b \geq 4.25$ Also $\mu + P_\perp$ is positive for $b = -1, \ -2, \ -3, \ldots$.

With the help of the above results we can find solutions with non negative radial pressure Pr which satisfy the WEC. The solutions with $(b, n) = (4, 2)$ and with $(b, n) = (4, 3)$ are of this type. Also we can find solutions with non positive Pr which satisfy the WEC. Of this type is the solution with $(b, n) = (6, 1)$ and also the solution with $(b, n) = (6, 2)$. We shall consider in the following these solutions.

The line element d^2s of the solution is obtained from Eqs (1) and (716). We get

$$d^2 s - (1 - \frac{2M}{k} e^{\frac{r-k}{k}} (1 - \frac{2}{b} + \frac{2r}{bk})^{-b}) dt^2 +$$
$$\frac{dr^2}{1 - \frac{2M}{k} e^{\frac{r-k}{k}} (1 - \frac{2}{b} + \frac{2r}{bk})^{-b}} + k^2 (1 - \frac{2}{b} + \frac{2r}{bk})^{b} (d\theta^2 +$$

$$\sin^2 \theta d\phi^2) \tag{731}$$

Example 2.3.2.4.1 : Solution with the $f(r)$ and the $h(r)$ of Eq (732)

Consider the solution with

$$f(r) = \frac{(k+r)^4}{16k^2} \quad \text{and} \quad h(r) = ke^{\frac{r-k}{k}} \tag{732}$$

This solution is obtained from the solution of Example 2,3,2.4 for $b = 4$. Its line element d^2s, which is obtained from the expression (731), for $b = 4$ is

$$d^2s = -(1 - \frac{32Mk^3e^{(r-k)/k}}{(r+k)^4})dt^2 + \frac{dr^2}{1 - \frac{32Mk^3e^{(r-k)/k}}{(r+k)^4}} +$$

$$\frac{(k+r)^4}{16k^2}(d\theta^2 + \sin^2\theta d\phi^2) \tag{733}$$

The non-vanishing components of the Ricci tensor $R_{\mu\nu}$, the Ricci scalar R, the second order curvature invariant R^2 and the eigenvalues B_i, $i = t, r, \theta$ and ϕ of the Ricci tensor R^ν_μ are obtained from Eqs (717) - (724) for $b = 4$. We get

$$R_{tt} = -\frac{16kMe^{\frac{r-k}{k}}(k-r)^2\left((k+r)^4 - 32k^3Me^{\frac{r-k}{k}}\right)}{(k+r)^{10}} \tag{734}$$

$$R_{rr} = \frac{16kMe^{\frac{r-k}{k}}(9k^2 - 2kr + r^2) - 4(k+r)^4}{(k+r)^2\left((k+r)^4 - 32k^3Me^{\frac{r-k}{k}}\right)} \tag{735}$$

$$R_{\theta\theta} = \frac{R_{\phi\phi}}{sin^2\theta} = \frac{1}{8}\left(-\frac{3r(2k+r)}{k^2} + \frac{32Mre^{\frac{r-k}{k}}}{(k+r)^2} + 5\right) \tag{736}$$

$$R = \frac{16\left(2kMe^{\frac{r-k}{k}}(5k^2 + 2kr + r^2) + (k^2 - 2kr - r^2)(k+r)^2\right)}{(k+r)^6} \tag{737}$$

$$R^2 = \frac{32}{(k+r)^{12}}(32k^2Me^{\frac{r-k}{k}}(k-r)(13k^2 + 6kr + r^2)(k+r)^2 +$$

$$32k^2M^2e^{\frac{2(r-k)}{k}}(313k^4 - 220k^3r + 78k^2r^2 - 12kr^3 + r^4) + (19k^4 -$$

$$20k^3r + 2k^2r^2 + 12kr^3 + 3r^4)(k+r)^4) \tag{738}$$

$$B_t = \frac{16kMe^{\frac{r-k}{k}}(k-r)^2}{(k+r)^6} \tag{739}$$

$$B_r = -\frac{4\left((k+r)^4 - 4kMe^{\frac{r-k}{k}}\left(9k^2 - 2kr + r^2\right)\right)}{(k+r)^6} \tag{740}$$

$$B_\theta = B_\phi = \frac{2\left(32k^2Mre^{\frac{r-k}{k}} + 8k^2(k+r)^2 - 3(k+r)^4\right)}{(k+r)^6} \tag{741}$$

The energy density μ, the radial pressure P_r, the tangential pressure $P_\perp$ and the quantities $\mu + P_r$ and $\mu + P_\perp$, which are obtained from Eqs (726) - (730) for $b = 4$ are the following in the variables y and n of Eqs (172):

$$\mu = \frac{4ne^{y-1} - y^3 - 3y^2 - y + 1}{\pi k^2(y+1)^5} \tag{742}$$

$$P_r = \frac{(y-1)\left((y+1)^2(y+3) - 8ne^{y-1}\right)}{2\pi k^2(y+1)^6} \tag{743}$$

$$P\perp = \frac{(y+1)^4 - 4ne^{y-1}\left(y^2 - 2y + 5\right)}{4\pi k^2(y+1)^6} \tag{744}$$

$$\mu + P_r = \frac{16ne^{y-1} - (y+1)^4}{2\pi k^2(y+1)^6} \tag{745}$$

$$\mu + P_\perp = -\frac{4ne^{y-1}\left(y^2 - 6y + 1\right) + \left(3y^2 + 6y - 5\right)(y+1)^2}{4\pi k^2(y+1)^6} \tag{746}$$

The graphs of $k^2\mu$, $k^2 P_r$, $k^2 P_\perp$, $k^2(\mu + P_r)$ and $k^2(\mu + P_\perp)$ of Eqs (742 - 746) for $n = 2$ and 3 are given by Figures 187 - 196. From these graphs we find that in both cases the solution satisfies the WEC and has radial pressure P_r non negative and monotonically decreasing in the interior region.

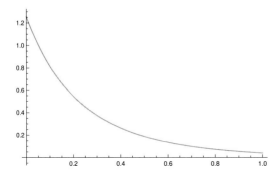

Figure 187: $k^2\mu$ of expression (742) for $n = 2$

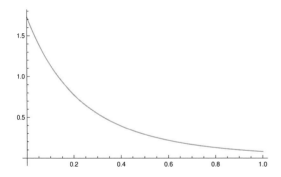

Figure 188: $k^2\mu$ of expression (742) for $n = 3$

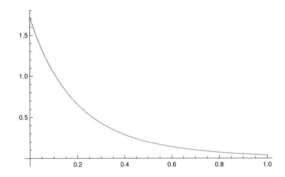

Figure 189: $k^2(\mu + P_r)$ of expression (745) for $n = 2$

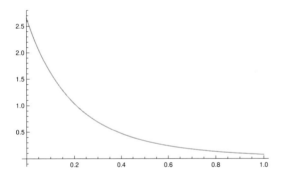

Figure 190: $k^2(\mu + P_r)$ of expression (745) for $n = 3$

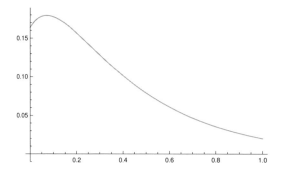

Figure 191: $k^2(\mu + P_\perp)$ of expression (746) for $n = 2$

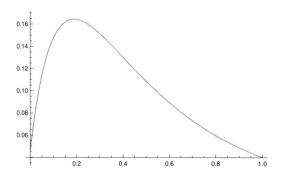

Figure 192: $k^2(\mu + P_\perp)$ of expression (746) for $n = 3$

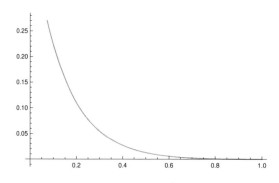

Figure 193: $k^2 P_r$ of expression (743) for $n = 2$

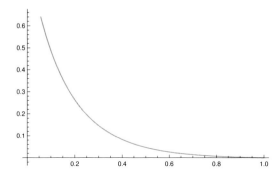

Figure 194: $k^2 P_r$ of expression (743) for $n = 3$

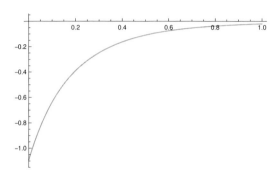

Figure 195: $k^2 P_\perp$ of expression (744) for $n = 2$

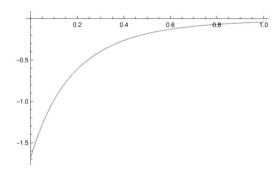

Figure 196: $k^2 P_\perp$ of expression (744) for $n = 3$

Example 2.3.2.4.2 : Solution with the $f(r)$ and the $h(r)$ of Eq (747)

Consider the solution with

$$f(r) = \frac{(2k + r)^6}{729k^4} \quad \text{and} \quad h(r) = ke^{\frac{r-k}{k}} \tag{747}$$

This solution is obtained from the solution of Example 2.3.2.4 for $b = 6$. Its line element d^2s, which is obtained from the expression (731), for $b = 6$ is

$$d^2s = -(1 - \frac{1458k^5 Me^{\frac{r-k}{k}}}{(2k + r)^6})dt^2 + \frac{dr^2}{1 - \frac{1458k^5 M \; e^{\frac{r-k}{k}}}{(2k+r)^6}} +$$

$$\frac{(2k + r)^6}{729k^4}(d\theta^2 + \sin^2\theta d\phi^2) \tag{748}$$

The non-vanishing components of the Ricci tensor $R_{\mu\nu}$, the Ricci scalar R, the second order curvature invariant R^2 and the eigenvalues B_i, $i = t, r, \theta$ and ϕ of the Ricci tensor R^ν_μ, which are obtained from Eqs (717) - (724) for $b = 6$ are the following:

$$R_{tt} = \frac{729k^3 Me^{\frac{r-k}{k}}(2k^2 + 2kr - r^2)\left((2k + r)^6 - 1458k^5 Me^{\frac{r-k}{k}}\right)}{(2k + r)^{14}} \tag{749}$$

$$R_{rr} = -\frac{3\left(4(2k + r)^6 - 243k^3 Me^{\frac{r-k}{k}}(22k^2 - 2kr + r^2)\right)}{(2k + r)^2\left((2k + r)^6 - 1458k^5 Me^{\frac{r-k}{k}}\right)} \tag{750}$$

$$R_{\theta\theta} = \frac{R_{\phi\phi}}{sin^2\theta} = \frac{1}{243k^4(2k + r)^2}(1458k^4 Me^{\frac{r-k}{k}}(k + r) + (2k + r)^2$$
$$(163k^4 - 160k^3 r - 120k^2 r^2 - 40kr^3 - 5r^4)) \tag{751}$$

$$R = \frac{6}{(2k + r)^8}(243k^3 Me^{\frac{r-k}{k}}(16k^2 + 4kr + r^2) + (2k + r)^2(131k^4$$
$$-224k^3 r - 168k^2 r^2 - 56kr^3 - 7r^4)) \tag{752}$$

$$R^2 = \frac{36}{(2k + r)^{16}}(59049k^6 M^2 e^{\frac{2(r-k)}{k}}(1096k^4 - 496k^3 r + 144k^2 r^2 -$$
$$16kr^3 + r^4) + 2916k^4 Me^{\frac{r-k}{k}}(2k + r)^2(585k^5 - 320k^4 r - 280k^3 r^2$$
$$-120k^2 r^3 - 25kr^4 - 2r^5) + (2k + r)^4(40073k^8 - 29248k^7 r - 4528$$
$$k^6 r^2 + 18800k^5 r^3 + 17582k^4 r^4 + 7616k^3 r^5 + 1904k^2 r^6 + 272kr^7 +$$
$$17r^8)) \tag{753}$$

$$B_t = -\frac{729k^3 M e^{\frac{r-k}{k}}(2k^2 + 2kr - r^2)}{(2k+r)^8} \qquad (754)$$

$$B_r = -\frac{3\left(4(2k+r)^6 - 243k^3 M e^{\frac{r-k}{k}}(22k^2 - 2kr + r^2)\right)}{(2k+r)^8} \qquad (755)$$

$$B_\theta = B_\phi = \frac{3\left(1458k^4 M e^{\frac{r-k}{k}}(k+r) + 243k^4(2k+r)^2 - 5(2k+r)^6\right)}{(2k+r)^8} \qquad (756)$$

The energy density μ, the radial pressure P_r, the tangential pressure $P_\perp$ and the quantities $\mu + P_r$ and $\mu + P_\perp$ are obtained from Eqs (726) - (730) for $b = 6$. We get in the variables y and n of Eqs (172):

$$\mu = -\frac{3}{8\pi k^2 (y+2)^8}((y+2)^2(7y^4 + 56y^3 + 168y^2 + 224y - 131) -$$
$$729ne^{y-1}(y+3)) \qquad (757)$$

$$P_r = \frac{9(y-1)\left((y+2)^2(y^3 + 9y^2 + 33y + 65) - 243ne^{y-1}\right)}{8\pi k^2 (y+2)^8} \qquad (758)$$

$$P_\perp = \frac{3\left(4(y+2)^6 - 243ne^{y-1}(y^2 - 2y + 10)\right)}{16\pi k^2 (y+2)^8} \qquad (759)$$

$$\mu + P_r = -\frac{3\left((y+2)^6 - 729ne^{y-1}\right)}{2\pi k^2 (y+2)^8} \qquad (760)$$

$$\mu + P_\perp = -\frac{3}{16\pi k^2 (y+2)^8}(243ne^{y-1}(y^2 - 8y - 8) + 2(5y^4 + 40y^3$$
$$+120y^2 + 160y - 163)(y+2)^2) \qquad (761)$$

The graphs of $k^2\mu$, $k^2 P_r$, $k^2 P_\perp$, $k^2(\mu + P_r)$ and $k^2(\mu + P_\perp)$ of Eqs (757) - (761) for $n = 1$ and 2 are given by Figures 197 - 206. From these graphs we find that in both cases the solution satisfies the WEC and the radial pressure P_r is non positive and monotonically increasing in the interior region.

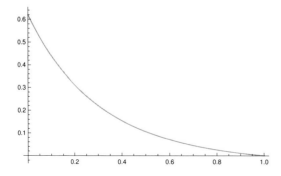

Figure 197: $k^2\mu$ of expression (757) for $n = 1$

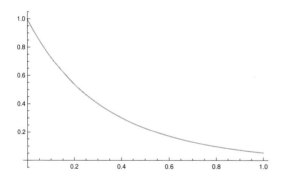

Figure 198: $k^2\mu$ of expression (757) for $n = 2$

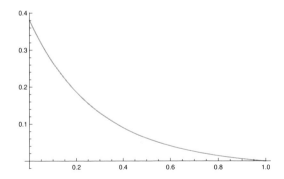

Figure 199: $k^2(\mu + P_r)$ of expression (760) for $n = 1$

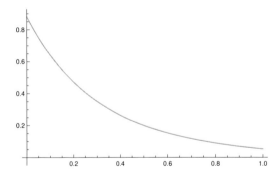

Figure 200: $k^2(\mu + P_r)$ of expression (760) for $n = 2$

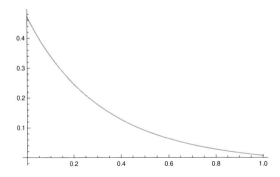

Figure 201: $k^2(\mu + P_\perp)$ of expression (761) for $n = 1$

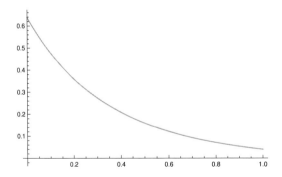

Figure 202: $k^2(\mu + P_\perp)$ of expression (761) for $n = 2$

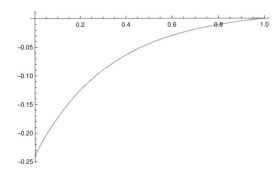

Figure 203: $k^2 P_r$ of expression (758) for $n = 1$

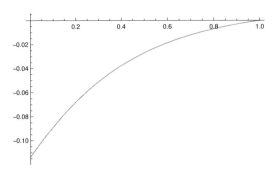

Figure 204: $k^2 P_r$ of expression (758) for $n = 2$

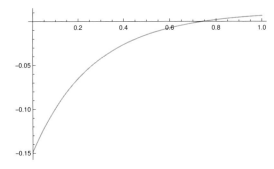

Figure 205: $k^2 P_\perp$ of expression (759) for $n = 1$

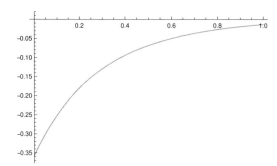

Figure 206: $k^2 P_\perp$ of expression (759) for $n = 2$

Example 2.3.2.5 : Solution with the $f(r)$ and the $h(r)$ of Eq (762)

Consider the solution with

$$f(r) = \frac{(k^2 + r^2)^2}{4k^2} \quad \text{and} \quad h(r) = b^{-1}k^{1-b}((b-1)k^b + r^b) \qquad (762)$$

The non-vanishing components of the Ricci tensor $R_{\mu\nu}$ the Ricci scalar R the second order curvature invariant R^2 and the eigenvalues B_i, $i = t$, r, θ and ϕ of the Ricci tensor R^ν_μ of this solution are obtained from Eqs (5) - (12) and (762). We get

$$R_{tt} = \frac{4Mk^{3-2b}}{b^2 r^2(k^2 + r^2)^6}(4(b-1)r^2 k^b(k-r)(k+r) + r^b((1-b)bk^4$$
$$-2((b-3)b-2)k^2 r^2 - (b-4)(b-1)r^4))(8k^3 M(k^b - r^b) + bk^b$$
$$(k^4 - 8k^3 M + 2k^2 r^2 + r^4)) \qquad (763)$$

$$R_{rr} = \frac{r^{-2}}{(k^2 + r^2)^2(8k^3 M(k^b - r^b) + bk^b(k^4 - 8k^3 M + 2k^2 r^2 + r^4))}$$
$$(4k^3 Mr^b((b-1)bk^4 + 2(b-2)(b-1)k^2 r^2 + ((b-5)b+12)r^4) -$$
$$4r^2 k^b(k^5(b(k-4M) + 4M) + 3k^3 r^2(b(k-4M) + 4M) +$$
$$3bk^2 r^4 + br^6)) \qquad (764)$$

$$R_{\theta\theta} = \frac{R_{\phi\phi}}{sin^2\theta} = -\frac{k^{-b-2}}{2b(k^2 + r^2)^2}(k^b(-k^5(bk + 8(b-1)M) + k^3 r^2(bk$$

213

$$+8(b-1)M) + 5bk^2r^4 + 3br^6) - 8k^3Mr^b((b+1)k^2 + (b-1)$$
$$r^2)) \tag{765}$$

$$R = \frac{k^{-b}}{b\left(k^2+r^2\right)^3}(8k^3Mr^{b-2}\left((b-1)b\left(k^2+r^2\right)+4r^2\right) -$$
$$16k^b\left(-2(b-1)k^3M + bk^2r^2 + br^4\right)) \tag{766}$$

$$R^2 = \frac{32k^{-2b}}{b^2r^4(k^2+r^2)^8}(2b^4k^6M^2r^{2b}(k^2+r^2)^4 - 4b^3k^6\,M^2r^b(k^2+$$
$$r^2)^2(r^b(k^2+r^2)(k^2+9r^2) + 4r^2k^b(k^2-5r^2)) + b^2(2k^6M^2r^{2b}(k^2$$
$$+r^2)^2(k^4 + 10k^2r^2 + 137r^4) + 8Mk^{b+3}r^{b+2}(k^2+r^2)(4k^7M - k^5r^2$$
$$(k-8M) - k^3r^4(3k+124M) - 3k^2r^6 - r^8) + r^4k^{2b}(12k^6r^6 + k^3$$
$$r^8(13k-16M) + 10k^2r^{10} + k^{10}(3k^2 - 16kM + 96M^2) + 2k^8r^2(5$$
$$k^2 - 224M^2) + k^6r^4(13k^2 + 32kM + 1248M^2) + 3r^{12})) + 32k^6M^2$$
$$r^4(3k^4 - 14k^2r^2 + 39r^4)(k^b - r^b)^2 + 16bk^3Mr^2(k^b - r^b)(r^2k^b(k^7$$
$$(k-12M) + 56k^5Mr^2 - 2k^3r^4(k+78M) + r^8) - k^3Mr^b(k^2+r^2)$$
$$(k^4 + 8k^2r^2 - 57r^4))) \tag{767}$$

$$B_t = \frac{4Mk^{3-b}}{br^2(k^2+r^2)^4}(4(b-1)r^2k^b(r-k)(k+r) + r^b((b-1)bk^4 +$$
$$2((b-3)b-2)k^2r^2 + (b-4)(b-1)r^4)) \tag{768}$$

$$B_r = -\frac{4k^{-b}}{br^2\left(k^2+r^2\right)^4}(-b^2k^3Mr^b(k^2+r^2)^2 + 4k^3Mr^2(k^2+3r^2)$$
$$(k^b - r^b) + b(-12Mr^4k^{b+3} - 4Mr^2k^{b+5} + 3r^6k^{b+2} + 3r^4k^{b+4} +$$
$$r^2k^{b+6} + r^8k^b + k^7Mr^b + 6k^5Mr^{b+2} + 5k^3Mr^{b+4})) \tag{769}$$

$$B_{\theta\theta} = B_{\phi\phi} = -\frac{2k^{-b}}{b\left(k^2+r^2\right)^4}(k^b(-k^5(bk + 8(b-1)M) + k^3r^2(bk +$$
$$8(b-1)M) + 5bk^2r^4 + 3br^6) - 8k^3Mr^b((b+1)k^2 +$$
$$(b-1)r^2)) \tag{770}$$

From Eqs (766) and (767) we find that R and R^2 are regular and therefore the solution is regular if

$$b \geq 2 \tag{771}$$

The energy density μ, the radial pressure P_r, the tangential pressure $P_\perp$ and the quantities $\mu + P_r$ and $\mu + P_\perp$, which are obtained from Eqs (14) - (18) and (762), are the following in the variables y and n of Eqs (172):

$$\mu = \frac{n\left(2\left(y^b - 1\right) + b\left(y^{b+2} + y^b + 2\right)\right) - b\left(y^3 + y\right)^2}{\pi b k^2 \left(y^2 + 1\right)^4} \tag{772}$$

$$P_r = \frac{4ny^2\left(y^b - 1\right) + b\left(-2ny^{b+2} - 2ny^b + (4n-1)y^2 + y^6 + y^4 - 1\right)}{2\pi b k^2 \left(y^2 + 1\right)^4} \tag{773}$$

$$P_\perp = \frac{1}{4\pi b k^2 \left(y^2 + 1\right)^4}(-b^2 n(y^2 + 1)^2 y^{b-2} - 8ny^2(y^b - 1) + b(n$$
$$y^{b-2} + 5ny^{b+2} + 6ny^b + (3 - 8n)y^2 + y^6 + 3y^4 + 1)) \tag{774}$$

$$\mu + P_r = \frac{4n\left(y^b - 1\right) + b\left(4n - (y^2 + 1)^2\right)}{2\pi b k^2 \left(y^2 + 1\right)^3} \tag{775}$$

$$\mu + P_\perp = \frac{1}{4\pi b k^2 \left(y^2 + 1\right)^4}(-y^2(8(b-1)n + b) - n((b-8)(b-1)$$
$$y^4 + 2((b-5)b - 4)y^2 + (b-1)b)y^{b-2} + 8bn - 3by^6 - 5by^4 + b -$$
$$8n) \tag{776}$$

The line element d^2s of the solution is obtained from Eqs (1) and (762). We get

$$d^2s = -(1 - \frac{8Mk^{3-b}((b-1)k^b + r^b)}{b(k^2 + r^2)^2})dt^2 + \frac{dr^2}{1 - \frac{8Mk^{3-b}((b-1)k^b + r^b)}{b(k^2 + r^2)^2}}$$
$$+\frac{(r^2 + k^2)^2}{4k^2}(d\theta^2 + \sin^2\theta d\phi^2) \tag{777}$$

With numerical computer calculations we find that in the interior region the quantities μ, P_r, $P_\perp$, $\mu + P_r$ and $\mu + P_\perp$ for $n = 1$ and $n = 2$ take the following values :

(A) $n = 1$

μ for $6 \geq b \geq 2$ is non negative and monotonically decreasing and for $b > 6$ positive zero or negative

P_r for $4 \geq b \geq 2$ is non positive and monotonically increasing and for $b > 4$ positive zero or negative

$P_\perp$ for $2.296 \geq b$ is non negative and for $b > 2.296$ positive zero or negative

$\mu + P_r$ for $b \geq 2$ is non negative and monotonically decreasing

$\mu + P_\perp$ for $3 \geq b \geq 2$ is non negative and monotonically decreasing and for $b > 3$ positive zero or negative

(B) $n = 2$

μ for $b \geq 2$ is positive and for $6 \geq b \geq 2$ positive and monotonically decreasing

P_r for $3 \geq b \geq 2$ is non positive and monotonically increasing and for $b > 3$ positive zero or negative

$P_\perp$ for $b = 2$ is non positive and monotonically increasing and for $b > 2$ positive zero or negative

$\mu + P_r$ for $b \geq 2$ is positive and monotonically decreasing

$\mu + P_\perp$ for $4 \geq b \geq 2$ is non negative and monotonically decreasing and for $b > 4$ positive zero or negative

(C) $n = 3$

μ for $b \geq 2$ is positive and for $6 \geq b \geq 2$ positive and monotonically decreasing

P_r for $2.66 \geq b \geq 2$ is non positive and monotonically increasing and for $b > 2.66$ positive zero or negative

$P_\perp$ for $b = 2$ is negative and monotonically increasing and for $b > 2$ positive zero or negative

$\mu + P_r$ for $b \geq 2$ is positive and monotonically decreasing

$\mu + P_\perp$ for $4.333 \geq b \geq 2$ is non negative and monotonically decreasing and for $b > 4.333$ positive zero or negative

Therefore the solution satisfies the WEC for $n = 1$ if $2 \leq b \leq 3$ for $n = 2$ if $2 \leq b \leq 4$ and for $n = 3$ if $2 \leq b \leq 4.333$. Below we shall study further the solutions we get for $b = 3$ and $n = 1$ or 2 and for $b = 4$ and $n = 2$ or 3 .

Example 2.3.2.5.1 : Solution with the $f(r)$ and the $h(r)$ of Eq (778)

Consider the solution with

$$f(r) = \frac{(k^2 + r^2)^2}{4k^2} \quad \text{and} \quad h(r) = \frac{2k^3 + r^3}{3k^2} \tag{778}$$

which is obtained from the solution of Example 2.3.2.5 for $b = 3$. This solution has the line element

$$d^2s = -(1 - \frac{8M(2k^3 + r^3)}{3(k^2 + r^2)^2})dt^2 + \frac{dr^2}{1 - \frac{8M(2k^3+r^3)}{3(k^2+r^2)^2}} +$$

$$\frac{(r^2 + k^2)^2}{4k^2}(d\theta^2 + \sin^2\theta d\phi^2) \tag{779}$$

which is obtained from the line element of Eq (777) for $b = 3$.

The non-vanishing components of the Ricci tensor $R_{\mu\nu}$ the Ricci scalar R the second order curvature invariant R^2 and the eigenvalues B_i, $i = t, r, \theta$ and ϕ of the Ricci tensor R^ν_μ of this solution are obtained from Eqs (763) - (770) for $b = 3$. We get

$$R_{tt} = -\frac{8M}{9(k^2 + r^2)^6}(k - r)^2(k + r)(4k^2 + kr + r^2)(-3k^4 + 16k^3M$$

$$-6k^2r^2 + r^3(8M - 3r)) \tag{780}$$

$$R_{rr} = -\frac{4}{(k^2 + r^2)^2 (3k^4 - 16k^3M + 6k^2r^2 + r^3(3r - 8M))}(3k^6 -$$

$$8k^5M + 3k^4r(3r - 2M) - 24k^3Mr^2 + k^2r^3(9r - 4M) + 3r^5(r - 2M)) \tag{781}$$

$$R_{\theta\theta} = \frac{R_{\phi\phi}}{\sin^2\theta} = \frac{1}{6k^2 (k^2 + r^2)^2}(3k^6 + 16k^5M - 3k^4r^2 - 16k^3Mr^2$$

$$+k^2r^3(32M - 15r) + r^5(16M - 9r)) \tag{782}$$

$$R = \frac{16(4k^3M + 3k^2r(M - r) + r^3(5M - 3r))}{3(k^2 + r^2)^3} \tag{783}$$

$$R^2 = \frac{32}{9(k^2 + r^2)^8}(27k^{12} - 96k^{11}M + 6k^{10}(64M^2 + 15r^2) - 192k^9$$

$$M^2r + k^8r^2(-1720M^2 - 120Mr + 117r^2) + 192k^7Mr^3(11M + r)$$

$$+36k^6r^4(128M^2 - 8Mr + 3r^2) - 3904k^5M^2r^5 + 3k^4r^6(368M^2 -$$

$$112Mr + 39r^2) + 96k^3Mr^7(10M - r) + 2k^2r^8(-32M^2 - 144Mr$$

$$+45r^2) + 3r^{10}(56M^2 - 40Mr + 9r^2)) \tag{784}$$

217

$$B_t = -\frac{8M(k-r)^2(k+r)\left(4k^2 + kr + r^2\right)}{3\left(k^2 + r^2\right)^4} \tag{785}$$

$$B_r = -\frac{4}{3\left(k^2 + r^2\right)^4}(3k^6 - 8k^5 M + 3k^4 r(3r - 2M) - 24k^3 Mr^2 +$$
$$k^2 r^3(9r - 4M) + 3r^5(r - 2M)) \tag{786}$$

$$B_\theta = B_\phi = \frac{2}{3\left(k^2 + r^2\right)^4}(3k^6 + 16k^5 M - 3k^4 r^2 - 16k^3 Mr^2 + k^2 r^3$$
$$(32M - 15r) + r^5(16M - 9r)) \tag{787}$$

The energy density μ, the radial pressure P_r, the tangential pressure $P_\perp$ and the quantities $\mu + P_r$ and $\mu + P_\perp$ are obtained from Eqs (772) - (776) for $b = 3$. We get in the variables y and n of Eqs (172):

$$\mu = \frac{n\left(3y^5 + 5y^3 + 4\right) - 3\left(y^3 + y\right)^2}{3\pi k^2 \left(y^2 + 1\right)^4} \tag{788}$$

$$P_r = \frac{-2ny^5 - 6ny^3 + (8n - 3)y^2 + 3y^6 + 3y^4 - 3}{6\pi k^2 \left(y^2 + 1\right)^4} \tag{789}$$

$$P_\perp = \frac{3\left(y^2 + 1\right)^3 - 2ny\left(y^4 + 8y + 3\right)}{12\pi k^2 \left(y^2 + 1\right)^4} \tag{790}$$

$$\mu + P_r = \frac{4n\left(y^3 + 2\right) - 3\left(y^2 + 1\right)^2}{6\pi k^2 \left(y^2 + 1\right)^3} \tag{791}$$

$$\mu + P_\perp = \frac{2n\left(5y^5 + 10y^3 - 8y^2 - 3y + 8\right) - 3\left(y^2 + 1\right)^2\left(3y^2 - 1\right)}{12\pi k^2 \left(y^2 + 1\right)^4} \tag{792}$$

The graphs of $k^2\mu$, $k^2 P_r$, $k^2 P_\perp$, $k^2(\mu + P_r)$ and $k^2(\mu + P_\perp)$ of Eqs (788) - (792) for $n = 1$ and 2 are given by Figures 207 - 216. From these graphs we find that in both cases the solution satisfies the WEC and has radial pressure P_r non positive and monotonically increasing in the interior region.

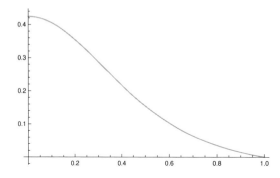

Figure 207: $k^2\mu$ of expression (788) for $n = 1$

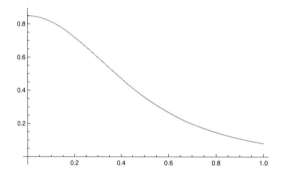

Figure 208: $k^2\mu$ of expression (788) for $n = 2$

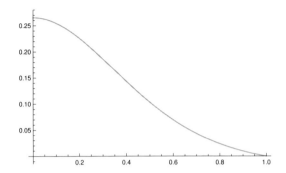

Figure 209: $k^2(\mu + P_r)$ of expression (791) for $n = 1$

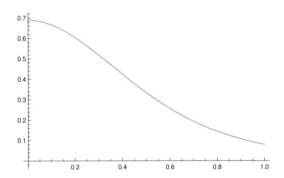

Figure 210: $k^2(\mu + P_r)$ of expression (791) for $n = 2$

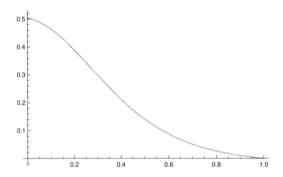

Figure 211: $k^2(\mu + P_\perp)$ of expression (792) for $n = 1$

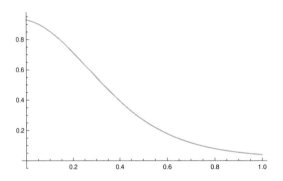

Figure 212: $k^2(\mu + P_\perp)$ of expression (792) for $n = 2$

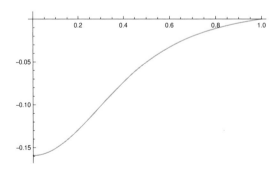

Figure 213: $k^2 P_r$ of expression (789) for $n = 1$

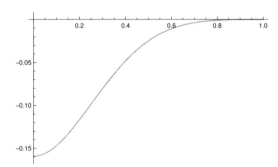

Figure 214: $k^2 P_r$ of expression (789) for $n = 2$

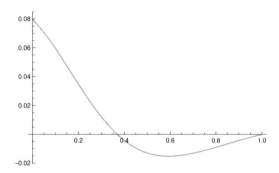

Figure 215: $k^2 P_\perp$ of expression (790) for $n = 1$

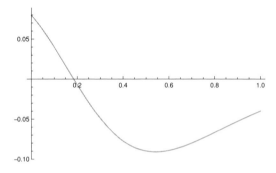

Figure 216: $k^2 P_\perp$ of expression (790) for $n = 2$

Example 2.3.2.5.2 : Solution with the $f(r)$ and the $h(r)$ of Eq (793)

Consider the solution with

$$f(r) = \frac{(k^2 + r^2)^2}{4k^2} \quad \text{and} \quad h(r) = \frac{3k^4 + r^4}{4k^3} \qquad (793)$$

which is obtained from the solution of Example 2.3.2.5 for $b = 4$. The line element d^2s of this solution is obtained from the expression (777) for $b = 4$. We get

$$d^2s = -(1 - \frac{2M(3k^4 + r^4)}{k(k^2 + r^2)^2})dt^2 + \frac{dr^2}{1 - \frac{2M(3k^4+r^4)}{k(k^2+r^2)^2}} +$$

$$\frac{(r^2 + k^2)^2}{4k^2}(d\theta^2 + \sin^2\theta d\phi^2) \qquad (794)$$

If we put $b = 4$ in Eqs (763) - (770) of Example 2.3.2.5 we get the non-vanishing components of the Ricci tensor $R_{\mu\nu}$, the Ricci scalar R, the second order curvature invariant R^2 and the eigenvalues B_i, $i = t, r, \theta$ and ϕ of the Ricci tensor R_μ^ν of this solution. We have

$$R_{tt} = \frac{4M\left(3k^4 - 6k^2r^2 - r^4\right)\left(k^4(k - 6M) + 2k^3r^2 + r^4(k - 2M)\right)}{(k^2 + r^2)^6} \qquad (795)$$

$$R_{rr} = -\frac{4k^2(k - 3M)}{k^4(k - 6M) + 2k^3r^2 + r^4(k - 2M)} + \frac{4k^2}{(k^2 + r^2)^2} -$$

$$\frac{4}{k^2 + r^2} \qquad (796)$$

$$R_{\theta\theta} = \frac{R_{\phi\phi}}{\sin^2\theta} = \frac{1}{2k^3(k^2 + r^2)^2}(k^7 + 6k^6M - k^5r^2 - 6k^4Mr^2 -$$

$$5k^3r^4 + 10k^2Mr^4 - 3kr^6 + 6Mr^6) \qquad (797)$$

$$R = \frac{8\left(3k^4M + k^2r^2(3M - 2k) - 2r^4(k - 2M)\right)}{k\left(k^2 + r^2\right)^3} \qquad (798)$$

$$R^2 = \frac{32}{k^2\left(k^2 + r^2\right)^8}(2k^2r^{10}(5k - 6M)(k - 2M) + 3k^{12}(k^2 - 4kM$$

$$+18M^2) + 2k^{10}r^2(5k^2 - 144M^2) + k^8r^4(13k^2 + 12kM + 1008$$

$$M^2) + 4k^6r^6(3k^2 - 8kM - 90M^2) + k^4r^8(13k^2 - 52kM + 94M^2)$$

$$+3r^{12}(k - 2M)^2) \qquad (799)$$

$$B_t = \frac{4kM\left(-3k^4 + 6k^2r^2 + r^4\right)}{\left(k^2 + r^2\right)^4} \tag{800}$$

$$B_r = \frac{1}{k(k^2 + r^2)^4}\left(-4k^6(k - 3M) - 12k^4r^2(k - 4M) + 12k^2r^4(M\right.$$
$$\left. -k) - 4r^6(k - 2M)\right) \tag{801}$$

$$B_\theta = B_\phi = \frac{2}{k\left(k^2 + r^2\right)^4}\left(k^6(k + 6M) - k^4r^2(k + 6M) - 5k^2r^4(k\right.$$
$$\left. -2M) - 3r^6(k - 2M)\right) \tag{802}$$

The energy density μ, the radial pressure P_r, the tangential pressure $P_\perp$ and the quantities $\mu + P_r$ and $\mu + P_\perp$ are obtained from Eqs (772) - (776) for $b = 4$. We get in the variables y and n of Eqs (172):

$$\mu = \frac{n\left(2y^6 + 3y^4 + 3\right) - 2\left(y^3 + y\right)^2}{2\pi k^2\left(y^2 + 1\right)^4} \tag{803}$$

$$P_r = -\frac{\left(y^2 - 1\right)\left((n - 1)y^4 + (3n - 2)y^2 - 1\right)}{2\pi k^2\left(y^2 + 1\right)^4} \tag{804}$$

$$P_\perp = \frac{-(n - 1)y^6 + (3 - 2n)y^4 + (3 - 9n)y^2 + 1}{4\pi k^2\left(y^2 + 1\right)^4} \tag{805}$$

$$\mu + P_r = \frac{n\left(y^4 + 3\right) - \left(y^2 + 1\right)^2}{2\pi k^2\left(y^2 + 1\right)^3} \tag{806}$$

$$\mu + P_\perp = \frac{n\left(3y^6 + 4y^4 - 9y^2 + 6\right) - \left(y^2 + 1\right)^2\left(3y^2 - 1\right)}{4\pi k^2\left(y^2 + 1\right)^4} \tag{807}$$

The graphs of $k^2\mu$, k^2P_r, $k^2P_\perp$, $k^2(\mu + P_r)$ and $k^2(\mu + P_\perp)$ of Eqs (803) - (807) for $n = 2$ and 3 are given by Figures 217 - 226. From these graphs we find that in both cases the solution satisfies the WEC and the radial pressure P_r takes positive, zero and negative values in the interior region.

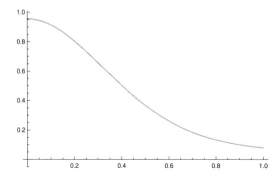

Figure 217: $k^2\mu$ of expression (803) for $n = 2$

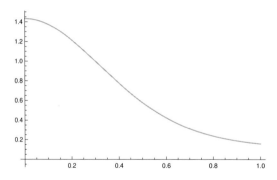

Figure 218: $k^2\mu$ of expression (803) for $n = 3$

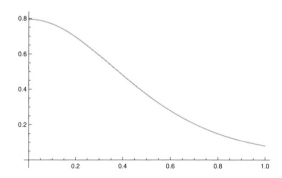

Figure 219: $k^2(\mu + P_r)$ of expression (806) for $n = 2$

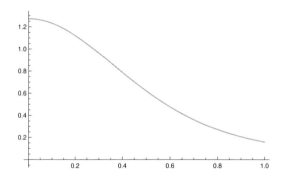

Figure 220: $k^2(\mu + P_r)$ of expression (806) for $n = 3$

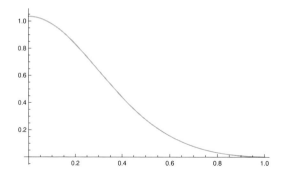

Figure 221: $k^2(\mu + P_\perp)$ of expression (807) for $n = 2$

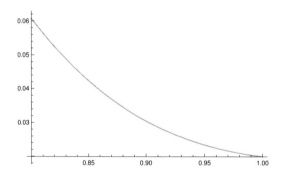

Figure 222: $k^2(\mu + P_\perp)$ of expression (807) for $n = 3$

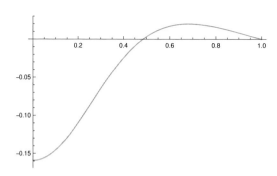

Figure 223: $k^2 P_r$ of expression (804) for $n = 2$

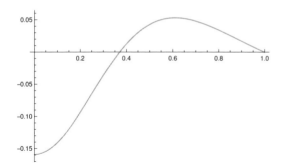

Figure 224: $k^2 P_r$ of expression (804) for $n = 3$

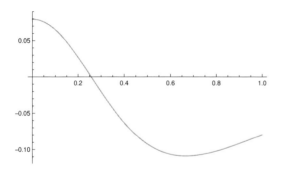

Figure 225: $k^2 P_\perp$ of expression (805) for $n = 2$

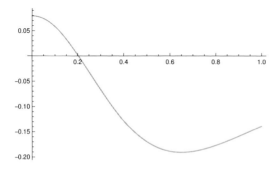

Figure 226: $k^2 P_\perp$ of expression (805) for $n = 3$

Example 2.3.2.6 : Solution with the $f(r)$ and the $h(r)$ of Eq (808)

Consider the solution with

$$f(r) = \frac{(k+r)^4}{16k^2} \quad \text{and} \quad h(r) = bke^{\frac{r-k}{k}} + (1-b)r \tag{808}$$

The non-vanishing components of the Ricci tensor $R_{\mu\nu}$ the Ricci scalar R the second order curvature invariant R^2 and the eigenvalues B_i, $i = t$, r, θ and ϕ of the Ricci tensor R_μ^ν of this solution are obtained from Eqs (5) - (12) and (808). We get

$$R_{tt} = -\frac{16kM}{(k+r)^{10}}(4(b-1)k^2 + be^{\frac{r-k}{k}}(k-r)^2)(-32bk^3Me^{\frac{r-k}{k}} + 4k^2r(8(b-1)M+k) + k^4 + 6k^2r^2 + 4kr^3 + r^4) \tag{809}$$

$$R_{rr} = \frac{1}{(k+r)^2}(-32bk^3Me^{\frac{r-k}{k}} + 4k^2r(8(b-1)M+k) + k^4 + 6k^2$$
$$r^2 + 4kr^3 + r^4)^{(-1)}(16bkMe^{\frac{r-k}{k}}(9k^2 - 2kr + r^2) - 4(4k^3(-4bM + r^2 + r) + 2k^2r(16(b-1)M + 3r) + k^4 + 4kr^3 + r^4)) \tag{810}$$

$$R_{\theta\theta} = \frac{R_{\phi\phi}}{sin^2\theta} = \frac{1}{8k^2(k+r)^2}(4k^3(-8bM + 8M + r) + 32bk^2Mr$$
$$e^{\frac{r-k}{k}} + 5k^4 - 10k^2r^2 - 12kr^3 - 3r^4) \tag{811}$$

$$R = \frac{16}{(k+r)^6}(16(2bkMe^{\frac{r-k}{k}}(5k^2 + 2kr + r^2) - 4k^2r(2(b-1)M + r) + k^4 - 4kr^3 - r^4)) \tag{812}$$

$$R^2 = \frac{32}{(k+r)^{12}}(32b^2k^2M^2e^{\frac{2(r-k)}{k}}(313k^4 - 220k^3r + 78k^2r^2 - 12k$$
$$r^3 + r^4) + 32bk^2Me^{\frac{r-k}{k}}(k^4(272(b-1)M + 19r) - 2k^3r(364(b-1)M + 3r) + 2k^2r^2(112(b-1)M - 9r) + kr^3(-24(b-1)M - 7r)$$
$$+13k^5 - r^5) + (8k^7(4(b-1)M + 7r) + 4k^6(640(b-1)^2M^2 - 72(b-1)Mr + 9r^2) - 8k^5r(1024(b-1)^2M^2 + 56(b-1)Mr + 3r^2) + 2k^4r^2(4608(b-1)^2M^2 + 96(b-1)Mr + r^2) + 8k^3r^4(52(b-1)M + 9r) + 4k^2r^5(24(b-1)M + 17r) + 19k^8 + 24kr^7 + 3r^8)) \tag{813}$$

229

$$B_t = \frac{16kM\left(4(b-1)k^2 + be^{\frac{r-k}{k}}(k-r)^2\right)}{(k+r)^6} \tag{814}$$

$$B_r = -\frac{4}{(k+r)^6}(k^4 + 4kr^3 + r^4 + 4k^3(-4(-1+b)M+r) + 2k^2r$$
$$(16(-1+b)M+3r) - 4be^{-k+rk}kM(9k^2 - 2kr + r^2)) \tag{815}$$

$$B_\theta = B_\phi = \frac{1}{(k+r)^6}(64bk^2Mre^{\frac{r-k}{k}} + 2(4k^3(-8bM+8M+r) +$$
$$5k^4 - 10k^2r^2 - 12kr^3 - 3r^4)) \tag{816}$$

From Eqs (812) and (813) we find that the invariants R and R^2 are regular for every value of the constant b. Therefore the solution is regular for every b.

The energy density μ, the radial pressure P_r, the tangential pressure $P_\perp$ and the quantities $\mu + P_r$ and $\mu + P_\perp$, which are obtained from Eqs (14) - (18) and (808), are the following in the variables y and n of Eqs (172):

$$\mu = \frac{4bne^{y-1} - 4(b-1)n - y^3 - 3y^2 - y + 1}{\pi k^2(y+1)^5} \tag{817}$$

$$P_r = \frac{(y-1)\left(((y+1)^2(y+3) - 8(b-1)n) - 8bne^{y-1}\right)}{2\pi k^2(y+1)^6} \tag{818}$$

$$P_\theta = \frac{-4bne^{y-1}(y^2 - 2y + 5) + 16(b-1)n(y-1) + (y+1)^4}{4\pi k^2(y+1)^6} \tag{819}$$

$$\mu + P_r = \frac{-4y(4(b-1)n+1) + 16bne^{y-1} - y^4 - 4y^3 - 6y^2 - 1}{2\pi k^2(y+1)^6} \tag{820}$$

$$\mu + P_\perp = \frac{1}{4\pi k^2(y+1)^6}(-4bne^{y-1}(y^2 - 6y + 1) - 32(b-1)n -$$
$$(3y^2 + 6y - 5)(y+1)^2) \tag{821}$$

The line element d^2s of the solution is obtained from Eqs (1) and (808). We get

$$d^2s = -(1 - \frac{32k^2M(bke^{\frac{r-k}{k}} + (1-b)r)}{(k+r)^4})dt^2 +$$
$$\frac{dr^2}{1 - \frac{32k^2M(bke^{\frac{r-k}{k}} + (1-b)r)}{(k+r)^4}} + \frac{(k+r)^4}{16k^2}(d^2\theta + sin^2\theta d^2\phi) \tag{822}$$

230

With numerical computer calculations we find that in the interior region the quanties μ, P_r, $P_\perp$, $\mu + P_r$ and $\mu + P_\perp$ for $n = 1$, $n = 2$, $n = 10$ and $n = 20$ take the following values :

(A) $n = 1$

μ is non negative for $b \leq \frac{5e}{4(e-1)} = 1.97747$ and non negative and monotonically decreasing for $b \leq \frac{13e}{4(5e-4)} = 1.84215$. It takes positive zero and negative values for $1.977470 \leq b < 2.5$ and it is non positive and monotonically increasing for $b \leq 2.5$.

P_r is non positive for $b \leq \frac{11e}{8(e+1)} = 1.00521$ and non positive and monotonically increasing for $b \leq \frac{35e}{4(7e+600)} = 0.950335$. It takes positive , zero or negative values for $1.00521 < b < 1.5$ and it is positive and monotonically decreasing if $b \geq 1.5$.

$P_\perp$ is non negative for $b \leq 0.698$ and non negative and monotonically decreasing for $b \leq 0.651$. It takes positive, zero or negative values for $0.698 < b < 1$ and it is non positive and monotonically increasing if $b \geq 1$.

$\mu + P_r$ takes positive, zero and negative values for $b \leq \frac{e}{16} = 0.169893$ and it is non negative for $b > 0.169893$. Also it is non negative and monotonically decreasing if $b \geq \frac{9e}{8(e+5)} = 0.396211$

$\mu + P_\perp$ is non negative and monotonically decreasing if $b \leq 1$, while for $b > 1$ itspoints take a positive or zero or nerative value.

(B) $n = 2$

μ is positive for $b \leq \frac{9e}{8(e-1)} = 1.77972$ and positive and monotonically decreasing for $b \leq \frac{23e}{4(5e-4)} = 1.6296$. For $1.77972 < b$ it takes positive zero and negative values.

P_r is non positive for $b \leq \frac{19e}{16(e+1)} = 0.868132$ and non positive and monotonically increasing for $b \leq \frac{63e}{8(7e+6)} = 0.855302$. It takes positive , zero or negative values for $0.868132 < b < 1$ and it is non negative and monotonically decreasing if $b \geq 1$.

$P_\perp$ is non negative and monotonically decreasing for $b \leq 0.5$. It takes positive, zero and negative values for $0.5 < b < \frac{31e}{8(4e+5)} = 0.706409$. Also it is non positive for $b \geq 0.706409$ and non positive and monotonically increasing for $b \geq \frac{113e}{4(28e+27)} = 0.744739$

$\mu + P_r$ takes positive, zero and negative values for $b < \frac{e}{32} = 0.0849463$ and it is non negative for $b \geq 0.0849463$. Also it is non negative and monotonically decreasing if $b \geq \frac{17e}{8(e+5)} = 0.396211$.

$\mu + P_\perp$ is non negative if $b \leq \frac{69e}{8(8e+1)} = 1.03073$ and non negative and monotonically decreasing if $b \leq \frac{205e}{4(48e+11)} = 0.984693$, while for $b > 1.03073$ its points take a positive or zero or nerative value.

(C) $n = 10$

μ is positive for $b \leq \frac{41e}{40(e-1)} = 1.62153$ and positive and monotonically decreasing for $b \leq \frac{103e}{20(5e-4)} = 1.45955$. For $b > 1.62153$ it takes positive zero and negative values.

P_r is non positive for $b \leq 0.6$ and takes positive zero or negative values for $0.6 < b < \frac{83e}{80(e+1)} = 0.758473$. It is non negative for $b \geq 0.758473$ and non negative and monotonically decreasing for $b \geq \frac{274e}{40(7e+6)} = 0.779275$

$P_\perp$ is positive and monotonically decreasing for $b < 0.1$. It takes positive, zero and negative values for $0.1 \leq b < \frac{161e}{8(4e+5)} = 0.689283$. Also it is non positive for $b \geq 0.689283$ and negative and monotonically increasing for $b \geq \frac{561e}{20(28e+27)} = 0.739453$

$\mu + P_r$ takes positive, zero and negative values for $b \leq \frac{e}{160} = 0.0169893$ and it is positive for $b > 0.0169893$. Also it is positive and monotonically decreasing if $b \geq \frac{81e}{80(e+5)} = 0.35659$.

$\mu + P_\perp$ is non negative if $b \leq \frac{65e}{8(8e+1)} = 0.970975$ and non negative and monotonically decreasing if $b \leq \frac{973e}{20(48e+11)} = 0.934738$. If $0.970975 < b \leq 1.9$ its points take positive zero or negative values, while if $b > 1.9$ it is negative and monotonically increasing.

(D) $n = 20$

μ is positive for $b \leq \frac{81e}{80(e-1)} = 1.60175$ and positive and monotonically decreasing for $b \leq \frac{203e}{40(5e-4)} = 1.4383$. For $b > 1.60175$ it takes positive zero and negative values.

P_r is non positive for $b \leq 0.55$ and takes positive zero or negative values for $0.55 < b < \frac{164e}{160(e+1)} = 0.744766$. It is non negative for $b \geq 0.744766$ and non negative and monotonically decreasing for $b \geq \frac{567e}{80(7e+6)} = 0.769772$.

$P_\perp$ is positive and monotonically decreasing for $b < 0.05$. It takes positive, zero and negative values for $0.05 \leq b < \frac{321e}{80(4e+5)} = 0.687143$. Also it is non positive for $b \geq 0.687143$ and negative and monotonically increasing for $b \geq \frac{1121e}{40(28e+27)} = 0.738808$

$\mu + P_r$ takes positive, zero and negative values for $b \leq \frac{e}{320} = 0.00849463$ and it is positive for $b > 0.00849453$. Also it is positive and monotonically decreasing if $b \geq \frac{161e}{160(e+5)} = 0.354389$.

$\mu + P_\perp$ is non negative if $b \leq \frac{129e}{16(8e+1)} = 0.963506$ and non negative and monotonically decreasing if $b \leq \frac{1933e}{40(48e+11)} = 0.928464$. If $0.963506 < b \leq 1.95$

its points take positive zero or negative values, while if $b > 1.9$ it is negative and monotonically increasing.

We find that the solution satisfies the WEC for $n = 1$ if $0.169893 \leq b \leq 1$ for $n = 2$ if $0.0849463 \leq b \leq 1.03073$ for $n = 10$ if $0.0169893 < b \leq 0.970975$ and for $n = 20$ if $0.00849453 < b \leq 0.963506$. Below we shall consider the cases $b = 0.5$ and $b = 0.9$.

Example 2.3.2.6.1 : Solution with the $f(r)$ and the $h(r)$ of Eq (823)

Consider the solution with

$$f(r) = \frac{(k+r)^4}{16k^2} \quad \text{and} \quad h(r) = \frac{k}{2}e^{\frac{r-k}{k}} + \frac{r}{2} \tag{823}$$

which is obtained from the solution of Example 2.3.2.6. for $b = 0.5$. Inserting $b = 0.5$ in expression (822) we get:

$$d^2s = -(1 - \frac{16k^2 M(ke^{\frac{r-k}{k}} + r)}{(k+r)^4})dt^2 + \frac{dr^2}{1 - \frac{16k^2 M(ke^{\frac{r-k}{k}} + r)}{(k+r)^4}} +$$

$$\frac{(k+r)^4}{16k^2}(d^2\theta + sin^2\theta d^2\phi) \tag{824}$$

which is the line element of this solution. The non-vanishing components of the Ricci tensor $R_{\mu\nu}$, the Ricci scalar R, the second order curvature invariant R^2 and the eigenvalues B_i, $i = t, r, \theta$ and ϕ of the Ricci tensor R^{ν}_{μ} are obtained from Eqs (809) - (816) for $b = 0.5$. We get:

$$R_{tt} = -\frac{8kM \left(e^{\frac{r-k}{k}}(k-r)^2 - 4k^2\right)}{(k+r)^{10}}(k^4 - 16k^3 M e^{\frac{r-k}{k}} + 4k^3 r +$$

$$2k^2 r(3r - 8M) + 4kr^3 + r^4) \tag{825}$$

$$R_{rr} = \frac{1}{(k+r)^2}(k^4 - 16k^3 M e^{\frac{r-k}{k}} + 4k^3 r + 2k^2 r(3r - 8M) + 4kr^3$$

$$+r^4)^{-1}(8kM e^{\frac{r-k}{k}}(9k^2 - 2kr + r^2) - 4(k^4 + 4k^3(2M + r) + 2k^2 r$$

$$(3r - 8M) + 4kr^3 + r^4)) \tag{826}$$

$$R_{\theta\theta} = \frac{R_{\phi\phi}}{sin^2\theta} = \frac{1}{8k^2(k+r)^2}(5k^4 + 4k^3(4M+r) + 16k^2Mre^{\frac{r-k}{k}} -$$
$$10k^2r^2 - 12kr^3 - 3r^4) \tag{827}$$

$$R = \frac{16}{(k+r)^6}(k^4 + kMe^{\frac{r-k}{k}}\left(5k^2 + 2kr + r^2\right) + 4k^2r(M-r) - 4kr^3 - r^4) \tag{828}$$

$$R^2 = \frac{32}{(k+r)^{12}}(19k^8 + 8k^7(7r - 2M) + 4k^6(160M^2 + 36Mr +$$
$$9r^2) - 8k^5r(256M^2 - 28Mr + 3r^2) + 2k^4r^2(1152M^2 - 48Mr +$$
$$r^2) + 8k^3r^4(9r - 26M) + 4k^2r^5(17r - 12M) + 8k^2M^2e^{\frac{2(r-k)}{k}}$$
$$(313k^4 - 220k^3r + 78k^2r^2 - 12kr^3 + r^4) + 16k^2Me^{\frac{r-k}{k}}(13k^5 +$$
$$k^4(19r - 136M) + 2k^3r(182M - 3r) - 2k^2r^2(56M + 9r) + kr^3$$
$$(12M - 7r) - r^5) + 24kr^7 + 3r^8) \tag{829}$$

$$B_t = \frac{8kM\left(e^{\frac{r-k}{k}}(k-r)^2 - 4k^2\right)}{(k+r)^6} \tag{830}$$

$$B_r = -\frac{4}{(k+r)^6}(k^4 + 4k^3(2M+r) - 2kMe^{\frac{r-k}{k}}(9k^2 - 2kr + r^2) +$$
$$2k^2r(3r - 8M) + 4kr^3 + r^4) \tag{831}$$

$$B_\theta = B_\phi = \frac{1}{(k+r)^6}(32k^2Mre^{\frac{r-k}{k}} + 2\left(5k^4 + 4k^3(4M+r) - 10\right.$$
$$k^2r^2 - 12kr^3 - 3r^4)) \tag{832}$$

The energy density μ, the radial pressure P_r, the tangential pressure $P_\perp$ and the quantities $\mu + P_r$ and $\mu + P_\perp$, which are obtained in the variables y and n of Eqs (172) from Eqs (817) - (821) for $b = 0.5$ are the following:

$$\mu = \frac{2ne^{y-1} + 2n - y^3 - 3y^2 - y + 1}{\pi k^2(y+1)^5} \tag{833}$$

$$P_r = \frac{(y-1)\left(-4ne^{y-1} + 4n + (y+3)(y+1)^2\right)}{2\pi k^2(y+1)^6} \tag{834}$$

$$P_\perp = \frac{-2n((y-2)y+5)e^{y-1} - 8n(y-1) + (y+1)^4}{4\pi k^2(y+1)^6} \tag{835}$$

$$\mu + P_r = \frac{16e^{y-1} - y^4 - 4y^3 - 6y^2 + 12y - 1}{2\pi k^2(y+1)^6} \tag{836}$$

$$\mu + P_\perp = \frac{-2ne^{y-1}\left(y^2 - 6y + 1\right) + 16n - \left(3y^2 + 6y - 5\right)(y+1)^2}{4\pi k^2(y+1)^6} \tag{837}$$

The graphs of $k^2\mu$, $k^2 P_r$, $k^2 P_\perp$, $k^2(\mu + P_r)$ and $k^2(\mu + P_\perp)$ of Eqs (833) - (837) for $n = 1$ and 2 are given by Figures 227 - 236. From these graphs we find that in both cases the solution satisfies the WEC and has radial pressure P_r non positive and monotonically increasing in the interior region.

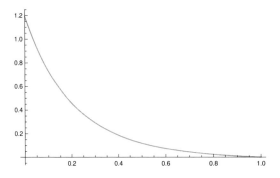

Figure 227: $k^2\mu$ of expression (833) for $n = 1$

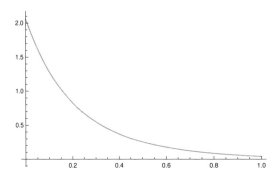

Figure 228: $k^2\mu$ of expression (833) for $n = 2$

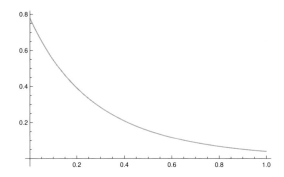

Figure 229: $k^2(\mu + P_r)$ of expression (836) for $n = 1$

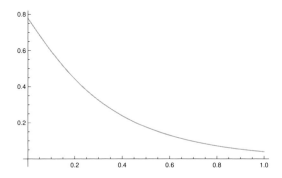

Figure 230: $k^2(\mu + P_r)$ of expression (836) for $n = 2$

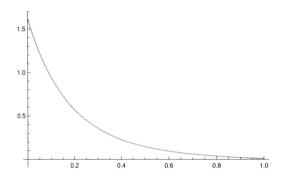

Figure 231: $k^2(\mu + P_\perp)$ of expression (837) for $n = 1$

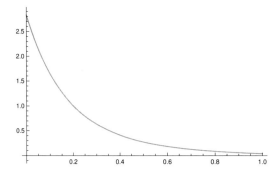

Figure 232: $k^2(\mu + P_\perp)$ of expression (837) for $n = 2$

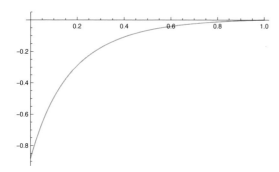

Figure 233: $k^2 P_r$ of expression (834) for $n = 1$

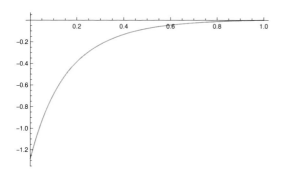

Figure 234: $k^2 P_r$ of expression (834) for $n = 2$

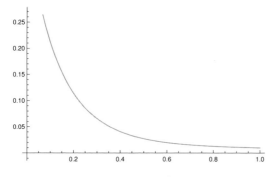

Figure 235: $k^2 P_\perp$ of expression (835) for $n = 1$

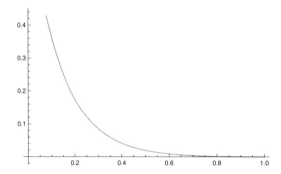

Figure 236: $k^2 P_\perp$ of expression (835) for $n = 2$

Example 2.3.2.6.2 : Solution with the $f(r)$ and the $h(r)$ of Eq (838)

Consider the solution with

$$f(r) = \frac{(k+r)^4}{16k^2} \quad \text{and} \quad h(r) = 0.9ke^{\frac{r-k}{k}} + 0.1k \tag{838}$$

The above expressions are obtained from the corresponding expressions of Eq (808) for $b = 0.9$.

The line element d^2s of this solution, which is obtained from the expression (822) for $b = 0.9$, is

$$d^2s = -(1 - \frac{16k^2 M(9ke^{\frac{r-k}{k}} + r)}{5(k+r)^4})dt^2 + \frac{dr^2}{1 - \frac{16k^2 M(9ke^{\frac{r-k}{k}}+r)}{5(k+r)^4}} +$$

$$\frac{(k+r)^4}{16k^2}(d^2\theta + sin^2\theta d^2\phi) \tag{839}$$

The non-vanishing components of the Ricci tensor $R_{\mu\nu}$, the Ricci scalar R, the second order curvature invariant R^2 and the eigenvalues B_i, $i = t,\ r,\ \theta$ and ϕ of the Ricci tensor R_μ^ν are obtained from Eqs (809 - (816) for $b = 0.9$. We get:

$$R_{tt} = \frac{4kM\left(4k^2 - 9e^{\frac{r-k}{k}}(k-r)^2\right)}{25(k+r)^{10}}(5k^4 - 72k^3 Me^{\frac{r-k}{k}} + 20k^3 r +$$

$$2k^2 r(15r - 4M) + 20kr^3 + 5r^4) \tag{840}$$

$$R_{rr} = \frac{1}{(k+r)^2}(5k^4 - 72k^3 Me^{\frac{r-k}{k}} + 20k^3 r + 2k^2 r(15r - 4M) +$$

$$20kr^3 + 5r^4)^{(-1)}(36kMe^{\frac{r-k}{k}}(9k^2 - 2kr + r^2) - 4(5k^4 + 4k^3(M + 5r) + 2k^2 r(15r - 4M) + 20kr^3 + 5r^4)) \tag{841}$$

$$R_{\theta\theta} = \frac{R\phi\phi}{sin^2\theta} = \frac{1}{40k^2(k+r)^2}(25k^4 + 4k^3(2M + 5r) + 72k^2 Mr$$

$$e^{\frac{r-k}{k}} - 50k^2 r^2 - 60kr^3 - 15r^4) \tag{842}$$

$$R = \frac{8}{5(k+r)^6}(9kMe^{\frac{r-k}{k}}(5k^2 + 2kr + r^2) + 2(5k^4 + 2k^2 r(M -$$

$$10r) - 20kr^3 - 5r^4)) \tag{843}$$

$$R^2 = \frac{32}{25(k+r)^{12}}(475k^8 - 40k^7(M - 35r) + 20k^6(8M^2 + 18Mr$$

$$+45r^2) - 8k^5 r(64M^2 - 70Mr + 75r^2) + 2k^4 r^2(288M^2 - 120Mr$$

$$+25r^2) + 40k^3 r^4(45r - 13M) + 20k^2 r^5(85r - 6M) + 162k^2 M^2$$

$$e^{\frac{2(r-k)}{k}}(313k^4 - 220k^3 r + 78k^2 r^2 - 12kr^3 + r^4) + 72k^2 Me^{\frac{r-k}{k}}(65$$

$$k^5 + k^4(95r - 68M) + 2k^3 r(91M - 15r) - 2k^2 r^2(28M + 45r) +$$

$$kr^3(6M - 35r) - 5r^5) + 600kr^7 + 75r^8) \tag{844}$$

$$B_t = \frac{4kM\left(9e^{\frac{r-k}{k}}(k-r)^2 - 4k^2\right)}{5(k+r)^6} \tag{845}$$

$$B_r = -\frac{4}{5(k+r)^6}(5k^4 + 4k^3(M + 5r) + k^2\left(30r^2 - 8Mr\right) - 9kM$$

$$e^{\frac{r-k}{k}}(9k^2 - 2kr + r^2) + 20kr^3 + 5r^4) \tag{846}$$

$$B_\theta = B_\phi = \frac{2}{5(k+r)^6}(25k^4 + 4k^3(2M + 5r) + 72k^2 Mre^{\frac{r-k}{k}} -$$

$$50k^2 r^2 - 60kr^3 - 15r^4) \tag{847}$$

The energy density μ, the radial pressure P_r, the tangential pressure $P_\perp$ and the quantities $\mu + P_r$ and $\mu + P_\perp$ are obtained in the variables y and n of Eqs (172) from Eqs (817) - (821) for $b = 0.9$. We get

$$\mu = \frac{9ne^{y-1} + n - 5\left(y^3 + 3y^2 + y - 1\right)}{5\pi k^2 (y+1)^5} \tag{848}$$

$$P_r = \frac{(y-1)\left(-18ne^{y-1} + 2n + 5(y+3)(y+1)^2\right)}{10\pi k^2 (y+1)^6} \tag{849}$$

$$P_\perp = \frac{-9ne^{y-1}\left(y^2 - 2y + 5\right) - 4n(y-1) + 5(y+1)^4}{20\pi k^2 (y+1)^6} \tag{850}$$

$$\mu + P_r = \frac{4(n-5)y + 36ne^{y-1} - 5y^4 - 20y^3 - 30y^2 - 5}{10\pi k^2 (y+1)^6} \tag{851}$$

$$\mu + P_\perp = \frac{-9ne^{y-1}\left(y^2 - 6y + 1\right) + 8n - 5\left(3y^2 + 6y - 5\right)(y+1)^2}{20\pi k^2 (y+1)^6} \tag{852}$$

The graphs of $k^2\mu$, $k^2 P_r$, $k^2 P_\perp$, $k^2(\mu + P_r)$ and $k^2(\mu + P_\perp)$ of Eqs (848) - (852) for $n = 10$ and 20 are given by Figures 237 - 246. From these graphs we find that in both cases the solution satisfies the WEC and has radial pressure P_r non negative and monotonically decreasing in the interior region..

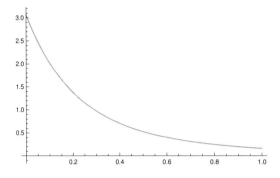

Figure 237: $k^2\mu$ of expression (848) for $n = 10$

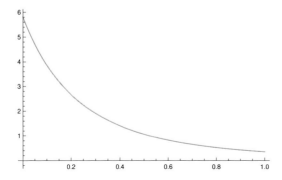

Figure 238: $k^2\mu$ of expression (848) for $n = 20$

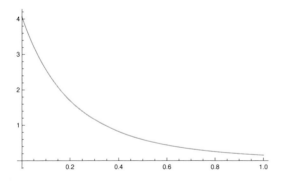

Figure 239: $k^2(\mu + P_r)$ of expression (851) for $n = 10$

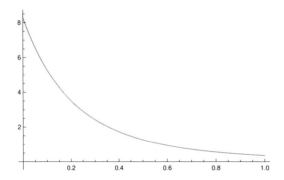

Figure 240: $k^2(\mu + P_r)$ of expression (851) for $n = 20$

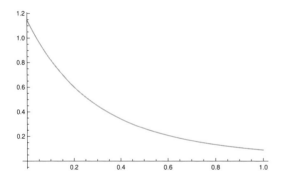

Figure 241: $k^2(\mu + P_\perp)$ of expression (852) for $n = 10$

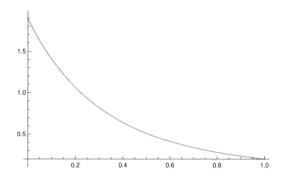

Figure 242: $k^2(\mu + P_\perp)$ of expression (852) for $n = 20$

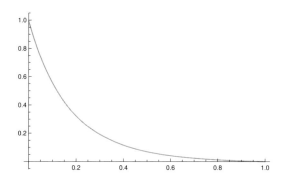

Figure 243: $k^2 P_r$ of expression (849) for $n = 10$

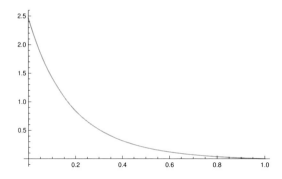

Figure 244: $k^2 P_r$ of expression (849) for $n = 20$

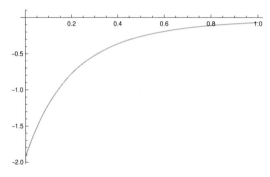

Figure 245: $k^2 P_\perp$ of expression (850) for $n = 10$

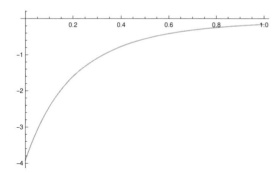

Figure 246: $k^2 P_\perp$ of expression (850) for $n = 20$

2.3.3 Perfect Fluid Solutions

As we argued before the functions $f(r)$ and $h(r)$ of a perfect fluid solution satisfy the relation (23) and the equivalent relations (24) and (25). Therefore taking a function $f(r)$, which does not vanish for $0 \leq r \leq k$ and which satisfy the matching conditions (3) and (4), substituting this function in Eq (23), solving for $h(r)$ the resulting differential equation and choosing the constants of integration such that the matching conditions (3) and (4) are satisfied we get the $f(r)$ and $h(r)$ of a perfect fluid solution. We shall present examples of such solutions.

Example 2.3.3.1 : Perfect Fluid Solution with the $f(r)$ of Eq (853)

Consider the solution with

$$f(r) = k^2 e^{\frac{2(-k+r)}{k}} \tag{853}$$

Substituting this $f(r)$ in Eq (23) we get

$$k \left(k \left(M h''(r) - 1 \right) - 4 M h'(r) \right) + 4 M h(r) = 0 \tag{854}$$

The solution of this equation is

$$h(r) = C(1) e^{\frac{2r}{k}} + C(2) r e^{\frac{2r}{k}} + \frac{k^2}{4M} \tag{855}$$

246

Choosing the constants of integration $C(1)$ and $C(2)$ such that the matching conditions $h(k) = k$ and $h'(k) = 1$ are satisfied and inserting their values in Eq (855) we get

$$h(r) = \frac{1}{4M}(e^{\frac{2(r-k)}{k}}\left(-3k^2 + 2k(4M + r) - 4Mr\right) + k^2) \tag{856}$$

The solution with the $f(r)$ and $h(r)$ of Eqs (853) and (856) is a perfect fluid solution.

The non zero components of the Ricci tensor R^ν_μ, coming from a line element of the form of Eq (1) with the $f(r)$ and $h(r)$ of Eqs (853) and (856), are the following:

$$R_{tt} = \frac{k - 2M}{2k^5}(k^2 e^{-\frac{2(r-k)}{k}} - 5k^2 + 2k(4M + r) - 4Mr) \tag{857}$$

$$R_{rr} = \frac{2k^2 e^{\frac{2(k-r)}{k}} - 8k^2 + 4k(3M + r) - 8Mr}{k^2\left(5k^2 - 2k(4M + r) + 4Mr\right) - k^4 e^{\frac{2(k-r)}{k}}} \tag{858}$$

$$R_{\theta\theta} = \frac{R_{\phi\phi}}{sin^2\theta} = 1 - \frac{2}{k^2}e^{\frac{2(r-k)}{k}}\left(2k^2 - k(3M + r) + 2Mr\right) \tag{859}$$

Also we get the following expressions for the Ricci scalar R and the second order curvature invariant R^2, which are obtained from Eqs (8), (9), (853) and (856):

$$R = \frac{k^2\left(3e^{2 - \frac{2r}{k}} - 11\right) + 2k(8M + 3r) - 12Mr}{k^4} \tag{860}$$

$$R^2 = \frac{1}{k^8}(15k^4 e^{\frac{4(k-r)}{k}} + 59k^4 - 4k^3(46M + 13r) + 4k^2(36M^2 +$$
$$46Mr + 3r^2) - 2k^2 e^{\frac{2(k-r)}{k}}(17k^2 - 28kM - 6kr + 12Mr) - 16kM$$
$$r(10M + 3r) + 48M^2 r^2 \tag{861}$$

It is obvious that R and R^2 are regular, which means that the solution is regular.

The eigenvalues B_t and $B_r = B_\theta = B_\phi$ of the Ricci tensor R^ν_μ, which are obtained from Eqs (11) - (13), (853) and (856), are given by the relations

$$B_t = \frac{k - 2M}{k^3} \tag{862}$$

$$B_r = B_\theta = B_\phi = \frac{1}{k^4}(k^2 \left(e^{\frac{2(k-r)}{k}} - 4\right) + 2k(3M + r) - 4Mr) \qquad (863)$$

while the energy density μ, the pressure $P = P_r = P_\theta = P_\phi$ and the quantity $\mu + P$, which are obtained from Eqs (14) - (18), (853) and (856), can be written in the form

$$\mu = \frac{1}{16\pi k^4}(3k^2 \left(e^{\frac{2(k-r)}{k}} - 1\right) + 2(2M - k)(5k - 3r)) \qquad (864)$$

$$P = \frac{1}{16\pi k^4}(k^2 \left(1 - e^{\frac{2(k-r)}{k}}\right) - 2(2M - k)(k - r)) \qquad (865)$$

$$\mu + P = \frac{1}{8\pi k^4}(k^2 \left(e^{\frac{2(k-r)}{k}} - 1\right) + 2(2M - k)(2k - r)) \qquad (866)$$

From Eqs (864) and (866) we find that if $2M - k \geq 0$ the energy density and the quantity $\mu + P$ are non-negative in the whole interior region. Therefore the solution satisfies the WEC. Also we find from Eq (865) that if $2M - k \geq 0$ the pressure P is non-positive in the whole interior region.

To draw graphs of μ, P and $\mu + P$ we shall express them in the variables y and n of Eq (172), in which case we get

$$\mu = -\frac{1}{16\pi k^2}(6ny - 10n - 3e^{2-2y} - 6y + 13) \qquad (867)$$

$$P = \frac{1}{16\pi k^2}(2n(y - 1) - e^{2(1-y)} - 2y + 3) \qquad (868)$$

$$\mu + P = -\frac{1}{8\pi k^2}(2n(y - 2) - e^{2(1-y)} - 2y + 5) \qquad (869)$$

The graphs of $k^2\mu$, k^2P and $k^2(\mu + P)$ for $n = 1$ and $n = 2$ are given by Figures 247 - 252.

Eliminating y from Eqs (867) and (868) we find the equation of state

$$\mu = -3P + \frac{n - 1}{4\pi k^2} \qquad (870)$$

The line element d^2s of the solution is obtained from Eqs (1), (853) and (856). We get

$$d^2s = -(1 - \frac{2M}{k^2 e^{\frac{2(-k+r)}{k}}}(\frac{1}{4M}(e^{\frac{2(r-k)}{k}}(-3k^2 + 2k(4M + r)$$
$$-4Mr) + k^2)))d^2t +$$

$$\frac{d^2r}{(1 - \frac{2M}{k^2 e^{\frac{2(-k+r)}{k}}}(\frac{1}{4M}(e^{\frac{2(r-k)}{k}}(-3k^2 + 2k(4M + r) - 4Mr) + k^2)))}$$
$$+k^2 e^{\frac{2(-k+r)}{k}}(d^2\theta + sin^2\theta d^2\phi) \qquad (871)$$

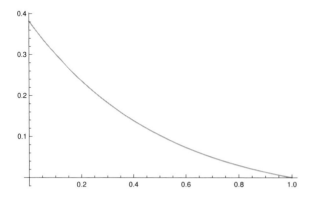

Figure 247: $k^2\mu$ of expression (867) for $n = 1$)

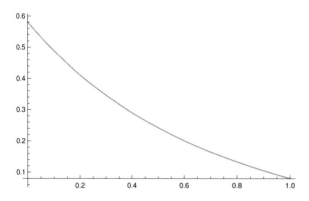

Figure 248: $k^2\mu$ of expression (867) for $n = 2$)

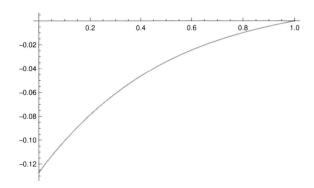

Figure 249: k^2P of expression (868) for $n = 1$

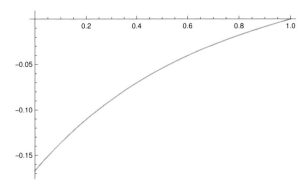

Figure 250: k^2P of expression (868) for $n = 2$

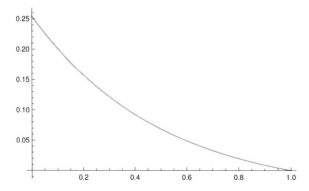

Figure 251: $k^2(\mu + P)$ of expression (869) for $n = 1$

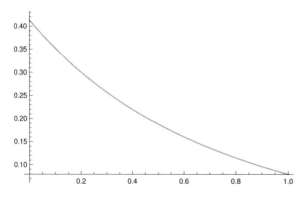

Figure 252: $k^2(\mu + P)$ of expression (869) for $n = 2$

Example 2.3.3.2 : Perfect Fluid Solution with the $f(r)$ of Eq (872)

We shall try to find perfect fluid solutions starting from an $f(r)$ of the form

$$f(r) = 2^b k^{2-b} b^{-b} (\frac{bk}{2} - k + r)^b \tag{872}$$

If we insert the above $f(r)$ in Eq (23) solve for $h(r)$ the resulting differential equation assuming that $b > 0$ and $(b - 4)b + 2 \neq 0$ which implies that $b \neq 2 + \sqrt{2}$ and write

$$\sqrt{1 + 4b} = w \tag{873}$$

we get

$$h(r) = \frac{1}{4((b-4)b+2)M}(4((b-4)b+2)M((b-2)k+2r)^{b-\frac{w}{2}+\frac{1}{2}}$$
$$(C(2)((b-2)k+2r)^w + C(1) + 2(\frac{1}{b})^b((b-4)b+2)k^{2-b}((b-2)k$$
$$+2r)^b + (b-2)^2k^2 + 4(b-2)kr + 4r^2) \tag{874}$$

where the values of the integration constants $C(1)$ and $C(2)$ are such that the matching conditions $h(k) = k$ and $h'(k) = 1$ are satisfied. From these relations we get

$$C(1) = \frac{b^{\frac{1}{2}(-2b+w-1)}k^{\frac{1}{2}(-2b+w+1)}}{8((b-4)b+2)Mw}(4((b-4)b+2)M(b+w+1) -$$
$$(b-2)k(b(2b+3w+3) - 2(w+1))) \tag{875}$$

$$C(2) = \frac{b^{\frac{1}{2}(-2b-w-1)}k^{\frac{1}{2}(-2b-w+1)}}{8((b-4)b+2)Mw}((b-2)k(b(2b-3w+3)+2(w$$
$$-1)) - 4((b-4)b+2)M(b-w+1)) \tag{876}$$

Substituting in Eq (874) expressions (875) and (876) for $C(1)$ and $C(2)$ we get

$$h(r) = \frac{1}{8((b-4)b+2)Mw}(4b^{-b}((b-4)b+2)wk^{2-b}((b-2)k +$$
$$2r)^b + b^{\frac{1}{2}(-2b-w-1)}k^{\frac{1}{2}(-2b-w+1)}((b-2)k+2r)^{b-\frac{w}{2}+\frac{1}{2}}(b^wk^w(4((b$$
$$-4)b+2)M(b+w+1) - (b-2)k(b(2b+3w+3) - 2(w+1))) +$$
$$((b-2)k(b(2b-3w+3)+2(w-1)) - 4((b-4)b+2)M(b-w+$$
$$1))((b-2)k+2r)^w) + 2(b-2)^2k^2w + 8(b-2)krw + 8r^2w) \tag{877}$$

The solution with the $f(r)$ and $h(r)$ of Eqs (872) and (877) is a perfect fluid solution.

The non vanishing components of the Ricci tensor R^ν_μ and the invariant R, as functions of w, $C(1)$ and $C(2)$, which are obtained from Eqs (5) - (8), (872) and (874), are the following:

$$R_{tt} = \frac{1}{2((b-4)b+2)^2}(\frac{1}{b})^{-2b}k^{2b-4}((b-2)k+2r)^{-2b-w-\frac{3}{2}}(((b-$$

$$4)b + 2)M((b - 2)k + 2r)^b(C(2)(w + 1)(2b + w - 1)((b - 2)k + 2$$
$$r)^w + C(1)(w - 1)(-2b + w + 1)) - (b - 2)^2 k((b - 2)k + 2r)^{\frac{w+1}{2}}$$
$$-2(b - 2)r((b - 2)k + 2r)^{\frac{w+1}{2}})(4(((b - 4)b + 2)M((b - 2)k + 2$$
$$r)^{b+\frac{1}{2}}(C(2)((b - 2)k + 2r)^w C(1) + r^2((b - 2)k + +2r)^{w/2}) + (b -$$
$$2)^2 k^2((b - 2)k + 2r)^{w/2} + 4(b - 2)kr((b - 2)k + 2r)^{w/2}) \tag{878}$$

$$R_{rr} = -2(((b - 4)b + 2)C(1)M(4b^2 - 2b(w + 3) + w^2 - 1)((b - 2)$$
$$k + 2r)^b + ((b - 4)b + 2)C(2)M(4b^2 + 2b(w - 3) + w^2 - 1)((b - 2)$$
$$k + 2r)^{b+w} + (b - 2)(b - 1)((b - 2)k + 2r)^{\frac{w+3}{2}})/((b - 2)k + 2r)^{3/2}$$
$$(4((b - 4)b + 2)C(2)M((b - 2)k + 2r)^{b+w+\frac{1}{2}} + 4((b - 4)b + 2)C(1)$$
$$M((b - 2)k + 2r)^{b+\frac{1}{2}} + ((b - 2)k + 2r)^{\frac{w}{2}+2}) \tag{879}$$

$$R_{\theta\theta} = \frac{R_{\phi\phi}}{sin^2\theta} = \frac{1}{(b - 4)b + 2}((b - 2)k + 2r)^{\frac{1}{2}(-w-3)}(2(b((b - 4)b +$$
$$2)M((b - 2)k + 2r)^b(C(2)(2b + w - 1)((b - 2)k + 2r)^w + C(1)(2b$$
$$-w - 1)) + (b - 2)(b - 1)r((b - 2)k + 2r)^{\frac{w+1}{2}}) + (b - 2)^2(b - 1)k$$
$$((b - 2)k + 2r)^{\frac{w+1}{2}}) \tag{880}$$

$$R = \frac{k^{b-2}}{b^2 - 4b + 2}(\frac{1}{b})^{-b}((b - 2)k + 2r)^{\frac{1}{2}(-2b-w-3)}(2((b^2 - 4b + 2)M$$
$$((b - 2)k + 2r)^b(C(2)(6b^2 + 4b(w - 1) + w^2 - 1)((b - 2)k + 2r)^w$$
$$+C(1)(6b^2 - 4b(w + 1) + w^2 - 1)) + (3b^2 - 10b + 8)r((b - 2)k +$$
$$2r)^{\frac{w+1}{2}}) + (b - 2)^2(3b - 4)k((b - 2)k + 2r)^{\frac{w+1}{2}}) \tag{881}$$

The expression for the invariant R^2 is very long and we shall not give it explicitly. However R^2 is regular in the interior region if $b > 2$ but $b \neq 2+\sqrt{2}$. Since the same thing happens for the invariant R, as we see from the above equation, the solution is regular if

$$b > 2 \quad \text{but} \quad b \neq 2 + \sqrt{2} \tag{882}$$

Solutions $h(r)$ of Eq (23) with a function $f(r)$ of the form of Eq (872) and $b < 0$ can also be found, as we see from Example 2.3.3.2.5 and Example 2.3.3.2.6.

The eigenvalues B_t and $B_r = B_\theta = B_\phi$ of the Ricci tensor R^ν_μ, expressed in terms of r, w, $C(1)$ and $C(2)$, which are obtained from Eqs (10), (12), (872) and (874), are given by the relations

$$B_t = \frac{k^{b-2}}{(b-4)b+2}(\frac{1}{b})^{-b}((b-2)k+2r)^{\frac{1}{2}(-2b-w-3)}(((b-4)b+2)$$
$$M((b-2)k+2r)^b(C(2)(w+1)(2b+w-1)((b-2)k+2r)^w +$$
$$C(1)(w-1)(-2b+w+1)) - (b-2)^2k((b-2)k+2r)^{\frac{w+1}{2}} - 2(b$$
$$-2)r((b-2)k+2r)^{\frac{w+1}{2}}) \tag{883}$$

$$B_r = B_\theta = B_\phi = \frac{k^{b-2}}{(b-4)b+2}(\frac{1}{b})^{-b}((b-2)k+2r)^{\frac{1}{2}(-2b-w-3)}(2(b((b-4)$$
$$b+2)M((b-2)k+2r)^b(C(2)(2b+w-1)((b-2)k+2r)^w + C(1)(2b-$$
$$w-1)) + (b-2)(b-1)r((b-2)k+2r)^{\frac{w+1}{2}}) + (b-2)^2(b-1)k((b-2)k$$
$$+2r)^{\frac{w+1}{2}}) \tag{884}$$

The quantities $k^2\mu$, $k^2P = k^2P_r = k^2P_\theta = k^2P_\phi$ and $k^2(\mu+P)$, which are obtained from Eqs (14) - (18), (872) and (877), are the following in the variables y and n of Eqs (172):

$$k^2\mu = -\frac{b^b(b+2y-2)^{\frac{1}{2}(-2b-w-3)}}{32\pi((b-4)b+2)w}(b^{\frac{1}{2}(-2b-w+1)}(b+2y-2)^b((-3b$$
$$-w+3)(-2b^3(n-1) + b^2(2n-1)(w+3) + 4bn(1-2w) + 2(w$$
$$-1)(-(b-4)b+2n-2))(b+2y-2)^w + (-3b+w+3)b^w(2b^3(n$$
$$-1) + b^2(2n-1)(w-3) - 4bn(2w+1) + 2(w+1)(-(b-4)b+$$
$$2n-2))) + 2(2-3b)(b-2)^2w(b+2y-2)^{\frac{w+1}{2}} - 4(b-2)(3b-2)$$
$$wy(b+2y-2)^{\frac{w+1}{2}}) \tag{885}$$

$$k^2P = \frac{b^b(b+2y-2)^{\frac{1}{2}(-2b-w-3)}}{64\pi((b-4)b+2)k^2w}(b^{\frac{1}{2}(-2b-w-1)}(b+2y-2)^b((-2bw$$
$$-2(b-1)b-w^2+1)(-2b^3(n-1) + b^2(2n-1)(w+3) + 4bn(1-$$
$$2w) + 2(w-1)(-(b-4)b+2n-2))(b+2y-2)^w + (-2b^2+2b$$
$$(w+1)-w^2+1)b^w(2b^3(n-1) + b^2(2n-1)(w-3) - 4bn(2w$$
$$+1) + 2(w+1)(-(b-4)b+2n-2))) - 4(b-2)^3w(b+2y-$$
$$2)^{\frac{w+1}{2}} - 8(b-2)^2wy(b+2y-2)^{\frac{w+1}{2}}) \tag{886}$$

$$k^2(\mu + P) = \frac{b^b(b + 2y - 2)^{\frac{1}{2}(-2b-w-3)}}{64\pi((b-4)b+2)k^2w}(b^{\frac{1}{2}(-2b-w-1)}(b + 2y - 2)^b$$

$$((-2bw - 2(b-1)b - w^2 + 1)(-2b^3(n-1) + b^2(2n(w+3) - 3w -$$

$$1) + 4b(-2nw + n + 2w - 2) + 4(n-1)(w-1))(b + 2y - 2)^w +$$

$$(-2b^2 + 2b(w+1) - w^2 + 1)b^w(2b^3(n-1) + b^2(2n(w-3) - 3w +$$

$$1) - 4b(2(n-1)w + n - 2) + 4(n-1)(w+1))) - 2(b^{\frac{1}{2}(-2b-w+1)}(b$$

$$+2y - 2)^b((-3b - w + 3)(-2b^3(n-1) + b^2(2n(w+3) - 3w - 1)$$

$$+4b(-2nw + n + 2w - 2) + 4(n-1)(w-1))(b + 2y - 2)^w + (-3b$$

$$+w + 3)b^w(2b^3(n-1) + b^2(2n(w-3) - 3w + 1) - 4b(2(n-1)w$$

$$+n - 2) + 4(n-1)(w+1))) + 2(2 - 3b)(b-2)^2 w(b + 2y - 2)^{\frac{w+1}{2}}$$

$$-4(b-2)(3b-2)wy(b + 2y - 2)^{\frac{w+1}{2}}) - 4(b-2)^3 w(b + 2y - 2)^{\frac{w+1}{2}}$$

$$-8(b-2)^2 wy(b + 2y - 2)^{\frac{w+1}{2}}) \tag{887}$$

With numerical computer calculations we find that for $b > 2$, $n = 1$ and $n = 2$ the energy density μ is non negative and monotonically decreasing, the pressure P is non positive and monotonically increasing and the quantity $\mu + P$ is non negative and monotonically decreasing in the whole interior region. Therefore the solution for $b > 2$, $n = 1$ and $n = 2$ satisfies the WEC. We shall consider the solutions corresponding to $b = 3$, $b = 4$, $b = 6$ and $b = \frac{15}{4}$ in Example 2.3.3.2.1, Example 2.3.3.2.2, Example 2.3.3.2.3 and Example 2.3.3.2.4 respectively. Also in Example 2.3.3.2.5 and Example 2.3.3.2.6 we shall consider the solutions we get for $b = -2$ and $b = -3$ respectively.

The line element d^2s of the solution is given by Eq (1), where $f(r)$ and $h(r)$ are given by expressions (872) and (877).

Example 2.3.3.2.1 : Perfect Fluid Solution with the $f(r)$ of Eq (888)

Consider the perfect fluid solution with

$$f(r) = \frac{(k + 2r)^3}{27k} \tag{888}$$

which is obtained from Eq (872) for

$$b = 3 \tag{889}$$

Also from Eqs (874) and (889) we get

$$h(r) = \frac{1}{4M}\left(-4C(2)M(k+2r)^{\frac{1}{2}(7+\sqrt{13})} - 4C(1)M(k+2r)^{\frac{7}{2}-\frac{\sqrt{13}}{2}}\right.$$
$$\left. -k^2 - \frac{2(k+2r)^3}{27k} + 4kr + 4r^2\right) \tag{890}$$

where according to Eqs (889), (875) and (876) we have

$$C(1) = \frac{3^{\frac{1}{2}(\sqrt{13}-7)}k^{\frac{1}{2}(\sqrt{13}-5)}((25 + 7\sqrt{13})k + 4(4 + \sqrt{13})M)}{8\sqrt{13}M} \tag{891}$$

$$C(2) = \frac{3^{\frac{1}{2}(-7-\sqrt{13})}k^{\frac{1}{2}(-5-\sqrt{13})}((7\sqrt{13} - 25)k + 4(\sqrt{13} - 4)M)}{8\sqrt{13}M} \tag{892}$$

All $C(1)$ and $C(2)$, which appear in formulas of this example, are given by the above expressions.

The non vanishing components of the Ricci tensor R^ν_μ and the Ricci scalar R, which are obtained from Eqs (878) - (881) for $b = 3$, are the following:

$$R_{tt} = \frac{729}{2}k^2(k+2r)^{-4-\sqrt{13}}(4M(k+2r)^{3/2}(C(2)(k+2r)^{\sqrt{13}} +$$
$$C(1)) - (k+2r)^{\frac{\sqrt{13}}{2}})((k+2r)^{\frac{\sqrt{13}}{2}} - 6M(k+2r)^{3/2}((\sqrt{13}-3)$$
$$C(1) - (3 + \sqrt{13})(k+2r)^{\frac{\sqrt{13}}{2}})C(2)(k+2r)^{\sqrt{13}})) \tag{893}$$

$$R_{rr} = -\frac{4}{4M(k+2r)^{3/2}(C(2)(k+2r)^{\sqrt{13}} + C(1)) - (k+2r)^{\frac{\sqrt{13}}{2}}}$$
$$\frac{1}{(k+2r)^2}(-3M(k+2r)^{3/2}((\sqrt{13}-5)C(1) - (5 + \sqrt{13})C(2)(k+$$
$$2r)^{\sqrt{13}}) - (k+2r)^{\frac{\sqrt{13}}{2}}) \tag{894}$$

$$R_{\theta\theta} = \frac{R_{\phi\phi}}{sin^2\theta} = 2(k+2r)^{-\frac{\sqrt{13}}{2}}(-3M(k+2r)^{3/2}((\sqrt{13}-5)C(1) -$$
$$(5 + \sqrt{13})C(2)(k+2r)^{\sqrt{13}}) - (k+2r)^{\frac{\sqrt{13}}{2}}) \tag{895}$$

$$R = 27k(k+2r)^{-3-\frac{\sqrt{13}}{2}}(-12M(k+2r)^{3/2}((2\sqrt{13}-9)C(1)-(9$$
$$+2\sqrt{13})C(2)(k+2r)^{\sqrt{13}})-5(k+2r)^{\frac{\sqrt{13}}{2}}) \tag{896}$$

The second order curvature invariant R^2 is obtained from Eqs (9), (888) and (890). We get

$$R^2 = 729k^2(k+2r)^{-6-\sqrt{13}}(24M(6(31+4\sqrt{13})C(2)^2M(k+$$
$$2r)^{3+2\sqrt{13}}+60C(1)C(2)M(k+2r)^{3+\sqrt{13}}-6(4\sqrt{13}-31)C(1)^2M$$
$$(k+2r)^3+3\sqrt{13}C(2)k(k+2r)^{\frac{1}{2}+\frac{3\sqrt{13}}{2}}-26C(2)k(k+2r)^{\frac{1}{2}+\frac{3\sqrt{13}}{2}}$$
$$+6\sqrt{13}C(2)r(k+2r)^{\frac{1}{2}+\frac{3\sqrt{13}}{2}}-52C(2)r(k+2r)^{\frac{1}{2}+\frac{3\sqrt{13}}{2}}-3\sqrt{13}$$
$$C(1)k(k+2r)^{\frac{1}{2}(1+\sqrt{13})}-26C(1)k(k+2r)^{\frac{1}{2}(1+\sqrt{13})}-6\sqrt{13}C(1)r$$
$$(k+2r)^{\frac{1}{2}(1+\sqrt{13})}-52C(1)r(k+2r)^{\frac{1}{2}(1+\sqrt{13})})+83(k+$$
$$2r)^{\sqrt{13}}) \tag{897}$$

The eigenvalues B_t and $B_r = B_\theta = B_\phi$ of the Ricci tensor R_μ^ν, which are obtained from the relations (883) and (884) for $b = 3$ are the following:

$$B_t = 27k(k+2r)^{-3-\frac{\sqrt{13}}{2}}((k+2r)^{\frac{\sqrt{13}}{2}}-\frac{1}{\sqrt{13}}3^{\frac{1}{2}(-5-\sqrt{13})}$$
$$k^{\frac{1}{2}(-5-\sqrt{13})}(k+2r)^{3/2}(3^{\sqrt{13}}k^{\sqrt{13}}((4+\sqrt{13})k+(1+\sqrt{13})M)+$$
$$((\sqrt{13}-4)k+(\sqrt{13}-1)M)(k+2r)^{\sqrt{13}})) \tag{898}$$

$$B_r = B_\theta = B_\phi = 54k(k+2r)^{-3-\frac{\sqrt{13}}{2}}(-(k+2r)^{\frac{\sqrt{13}}{2}}+$$
$$\frac{1}{4\sqrt{13}}3^{\frac{1}{2}(-5-\sqrt{13})}k^{\frac{1}{2}(-5-\sqrt{13})}(k+2r)^{3/2}(3^{\sqrt{13}}(17+5\sqrt{13})k^{1+\sqrt{13}}$$
$$+3^{\sqrt{13}}2(7+\sqrt{13})k^{\sqrt{13}}M+2(\sqrt{13}-7)M(k+2r)^{\sqrt{13}}+(5\sqrt{13}-$$
$$17)k(k+2r)^{\sqrt{13}})) \tag{899}$$

The quantities $k^2\mu$, k^2P and $k^2(\mu+P)$, which are obtained from Eqs (885) - (887) for $b = 3$, are the following in the variables y and n of Eqs (172):

$$k^2\mu = \frac{27(2y+1)^{-3-\frac{\sqrt{13}}{2}}}{16\pi}(-7(2y+1)^{\frac{\sqrt{13}}{2}}+\frac{1}{2\sqrt{13}}3^{\frac{1}{2}(-5-\sqrt{13})}(2y+$$
$$1)^{3/2}(((4\sqrt{13}-22)n+17\sqrt{13}-59)(2y+1)^{\sqrt{13}}+3^{\sqrt{13}}((22+4$$
$$\sqrt{13})n+17\sqrt{13}+59)) \tag{900}$$

$$k^2 P = \frac{1}{416\pi} 3^{\frac{3}{2}-\frac{\sqrt{13}}{2}} (2y+1)^{-3-\frac{\sqrt{13}}{2}} ((2\sqrt{13}n + 3\sqrt{13} - 13)(2y+$$
$$1)^{\frac{3}{2}+\sqrt{13}} - 3^{\sqrt{13}}(2\sqrt{13}n + 3\sqrt{13} + 13)(2y+1)^{3/2} + 26 \; 3^{\frac{1}{2}(3+\sqrt{13})}$$
$$(2y+1)^{\frac{\sqrt{13}}{2}}) \tag{901}$$

$$k^2(\mu + P) = \frac{1}{208\pi} 3^{\frac{1}{2}-\frac{\sqrt{13}}{2}} (2y+1)^{-3-\frac{\sqrt{13}}{2}} (-((8\sqrt{13}-26)n + 25\sqrt{13} -$$
$$91)(2y+1)^{\frac{3}{2}+\sqrt{13}} + 3^{\sqrt{13}}((26+8\sqrt{13})n + 25\sqrt{13} + 91)(2y+1)^{3/2} -$$
$$26 \; 3^{\frac{1}{2}(7+\sqrt{13})}(2y+1)^{\frac{\sqrt{13}}{2}}) \tag{902}$$

The graphs of $k^2\mu$, k^2P and $k^2(\mu + P)$ for $n = 1$ and 2 are given by Figures (253) - (258). From the Figures of $k^2\mu$, and $k^2(\mu + P)$ we conclude that the solution for $n = 1$ and 2 satisfies the WEC.

The line element d^2s of the solution is obtained from Eqs (1), (888) and 890). We get

$$d^2 s = -(1 + \frac{27k}{2(k+2r)^3}(-4C(2)M(k+2r)^{\frac{1}{2}(7+\sqrt{13})} - 4C(1)M(k$$
$$+2r)^{\frac{7}{2}-\frac{\sqrt{13}}{2}} + k^2 - \frac{2(k+2r)^3}{27k} + 4kr + 4r^2))d^2t + (1 + \frac{27k}{2(k+2r)^3}$$
$$(-4C(2)M(k+2r)^{\frac{1}{2}(7+\sqrt{13})} - 4C(1)M(k+2r)^{\frac{7}{2}-\frac{\sqrt{13}}{2}} + k^2 -$$
$$\frac{2(k+2r)^3}{27k} + 4kr + 4r^2))^{(-1)}d^2r + \frac{(k+2r)^3}{27k}(d^2\theta + sin^2\theta d^2\phi) \tag{903}$$

where $C(1)$ and $C(2)$ are given by Eqs (891) and 892).

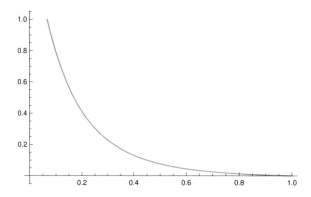

Figure 253: $k^2\mu$ of expression (900) for $n = 1$

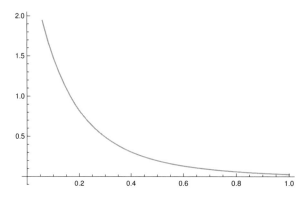

Figure 254: $k^2\mu$ of expression (900) for $n = 2$

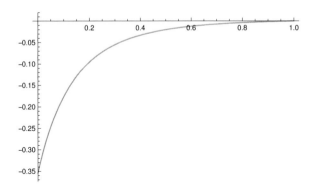

Figure 255: k^2P of expression (901) for $n = 1$

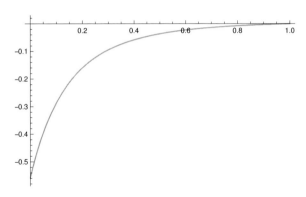

Figure 256: k^2P of expression (901) for $n = 2$

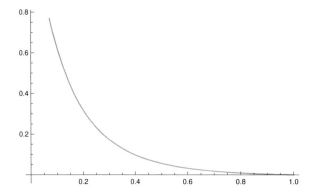

Figure 257: $k^2(\mu + P)$ of expression (902) for $n = 1$

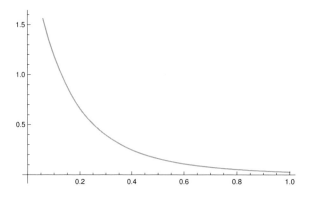

Figure 258: $k^2(\mu + P)$ of expression (902) for $n = 2$

Example 2.3.3.2.2 : Perfect Fluid Solution with the $f(r)$ of Eq (904)

Consider the perfect fluid solution with

$$f(r) = \frac{(k + r)^4}{16k^2} \tag{904}$$

which is obtained from Eq (872) for $b = 4$. Also from Eq (874) for $b = 4$ we get

$$h(r) = \frac{1}{8M}(8C(2)M(2k + 2r)^{\frac{1}{2}(9+\sqrt{17})} + 8C(1)M(2k + 2r)^{\frac{9}{2}-\frac{\sqrt{17}}{2}}$$

$$+\frac{(k+r)^4}{4k^2}+4(k+r)^2 \tag{905}$$

where according to Eqs (875) and (876) for $b = 4$

$$C(1) = \frac{2^{\sqrt{17}-11}k^{\frac{1}{2}(\sqrt{17}-7)}((-21-5\sqrt{17})k+2(5+\sqrt{17})M)}{\sqrt{17}M} \tag{906}$$

$$C(2) = \frac{2^{-11-\sqrt{17}}k^{\frac{1}{2}(-7-\sqrt{17})}((21-5\sqrt{17})k+2(\sqrt{17}-5)M)}{\sqrt{17}M} \tag{907}$$

The non vanishing components of the Ricci tensor R_μ^ν, the Ricci scalar R, the second order curvature invariant R^2 and the eigenvalues B_t and $B_r = B_\theta = B_\phi$ of the Ricci tensor R_μ^ν of the solution, which are obtained from Eqs Eqs (878) - (881), (9), (883) and (884) for $b = 4$ are the following:

$$R_{tt} = -\frac{1}{(k+r)^6}(32\sqrt{2}M(k+r)^{5/2}(2^{\sqrt{17}}C(2)(k+r)^{\sqrt{17}}+C(1))$$

$$+(2k+2r)^{\frac{\sqrt{17}}{2}}(32\sqrt{2}M(k+r)^{5/2}((\sqrt{17}-3)C(1)-2^{\sqrt{17}}(3+$$

$$\sqrt{17})C(2)(k+r)^{\sqrt{17}})+(2k+2r)^{\frac{\sqrt{17}}{2}}) \tag{908}$$

$$R_{rr} = (32\sqrt{2}M(k+r)^{5/2}((\sqrt{17}-7)C(1)-2^{\sqrt{17}}(7+\sqrt{17})C(2)(k$$

$$+r)^{\sqrt{17}})-3(2k+2r)^{\frac{\sqrt{17}}{2}})(32\sqrt{2}M(k+r)^{5/2}(2^{\sqrt{17}}C(2)(k+r)^{\sqrt{17}}$$

$$+C(1))+(2k+2r)^{\frac{\sqrt{17}}{2}})^{-1}(k+r)^{-2} \tag{909}$$

$$R_{\theta\theta} = \frac{R_{\phi\phi}}{\sin^2\theta} = (2k+2r)^{-\frac{\sqrt{17}}{2}}(3(2k+2r)^{\frac{\sqrt{17}}{2}}-32\sqrt{2}M(k+r)^{5/2}$$

$$((\sqrt{17}-7)C(1)-2^{\sqrt{17}}(7+\sqrt{17})C(2)(k+r)^{\sqrt{17}})) \tag{910}$$

$$R = \frac{128k^2(2k+2r)^{-\frac{\sqrt{17}}{2}}}{(k+r)^4}((2k+2r)^{\frac{\sqrt{17}}{2}}-16\sqrt{2}M(k+r)^{5/2}((\sqrt{17}$$

$$-6)C(1)-2^{\sqrt{17}}(6+\sqrt{17})C(2)(k+r)^{\sqrt{17}})) \tag{911}$$

$$R^2 = 2^{11-\sqrt{17}}k^4(k+r)^{-8-\sqrt{17}}(-2048M^2(3\sqrt{17}C(1)^2k^5-25C(1)^2$$

$$k^5 + 15\sqrt{17}C(1)^2k^4r - 125C(1)^2k^4r + 30\sqrt{17}C(1)^2k^3r^2 - 250$$
$$C(1)^2k^3r^2 - 15\ 2^{1+2\sqrt{17}}\sqrt{17}C(2)^2k^2r^3(k+r)^{2\sqrt{17}} - 125\ 2^{1+2\sqrt{17}}$$
$$C(2)^2k^2r^3(k+r)^{2\sqrt{17}} + 30\sqrt{17}C(1)^2k^2r^3 - 250C(1)^2k^2r^3 - (25+$$
$$3\sqrt{17})C(2)^2(2k+2r)^{2\sqrt{17}}(k^5 + 5k^4r + 10k^3r^2 + r^5) - 15\ 4^{\sqrt{17}}\sqrt{17}$$
$$C(2)^2kr^4(k+r)^{2\sqrt{17}} - 125\ 4^{\sqrt{17}}C(2)^2kr^4(k+r)^{2\sqrt{17}} + 15\sqrt{17}$$
$$C(1)^2kr^4 - 125C(1)^2kr^4 - 16C(1)C(2)(2k+2r)^{\sqrt{17}}(k+r)^5 + 3$$
$$\sqrt{17}C(1)^2r^5 - 25C(1)^2r^5) + 2^{\frac{1}{2}(13+\sqrt{17})}M(k+r)^{\frac{1}{2}(5+\sqrt{17})}((12+$$
$$\sqrt{17})C(1) - 2^{\sqrt{17}}(\sqrt{17} - 12)C(2)(k+r)^{\sqrt{17}}) + 21(2k+$$
$$2r)^{\sqrt{17}}) \tag{912}$$

$$B_t = -2^{4-\frac{\sqrt{17}}{2}}k^2(k+r)^{-4-\frac{\sqrt{17}}{2}}(32\sqrt{2}M(k+r)^{5/2}((\sqrt{17}-3)C(1)$$
$$-2^{\sqrt{17}}(3+\sqrt{17})C(2)(k+r)^{\sqrt{17}}) + (2k+2r)^{\frac{\sqrt{17}}{2}}) \tag{913}$$

$$B_r = B_\theta = B_\phi = \frac{16k^2(2k+2r)^{-\frac{\sqrt{17}}{2}}}{(k+r)^4}(3(2k+2r)^{\frac{\sqrt{17}}{2}} - 32\sqrt{2}M(k$$
$$+r)^{5/2}((\sqrt{17}-7)C(1) - 2^{\sqrt{17}}(7+\sqrt{17})C(2)(k+r)^{\sqrt{17}})) \tag{914}$$

The quantities $k^2\mu$, k^2P and $k^2(\mu + P)$, which are obtained from Eqs (885) - (887) for $b = 4$, are the following in the variables y and n of Eqs (172):

$$k^2\mu = \frac{2^{-3-\frac{\sqrt{17}}{2}}(y+1)^{-4-\frac{\sqrt{17}}{2}}}{17\pi}(\sqrt{34}(y+1)^{5/2}(((\sqrt{17}-7)n - 6\sqrt{17}$$
$$+26)(y+1)^{\sqrt{17}} + 2^{\sqrt{17}}((7+\sqrt{17})n - 6\sqrt{17} - 26)) + 85\ 2^{4+\frac{\sqrt{17}}{2}}(y$$
$$+1)^{\frac{\sqrt{17}}{2}}) \tag{915}$$

$$k^2P = -\frac{2^{-3-\frac{\sqrt{17}}{2}}(y+1)^{-4-\frac{\sqrt{17}}{2}}}{17\pi}(17\ 2^{4+\frac{\sqrt{17}}{2}}(y+1)^{\frac{\sqrt{17}}{2}} - \sqrt{34}(y+$$
$$1)^{5/2}((2n+\sqrt{17}-5)(y+1)^{\sqrt{17}} + 2^{\sqrt{17}}(-2n+\sqrt{17}+5))) \tag{916}$$

$$k^2(\mu + P) = \frac{2^{-3-\frac{\sqrt{17}}{2}}(y+1)^{-4-\frac{\sqrt{17}}{2}}}{17\pi}(\sqrt{34}(y+1)^{5/2}((2n+\sqrt{17} -$$

$$5)(y + 1)^{\sqrt{17}} + 2^{\sqrt{17}}(-2n + \sqrt{17} + 5)) + \sqrt{34}(y + 1)^{5/2}(((\sqrt{17} -$$
$$7)n - 6\sqrt{17} + 26)(y + 1)^{\sqrt{17}} + 2^{\sqrt{17}}((7 + \sqrt{17})n - 6\sqrt{17} - 26)) +$$
$$17\ 2^{6 + \frac{\sqrt{17}}{2}}(y + 1)^{\frac{\sqrt{17}}{2}}) \tag{917}$$

The graphs of $k^2\mu$, k^2P and $k^2(\mu + P)$ of Eqs (915) - (917) for $n = 1$ and $n = 2$ are given by Figures (259) - (264). It is obvious from these Figures that the solution for $n = 1$ and $n = 2$ satisfies the WEC.

The line element d^2s of the solution is obtained from Eqs (1), (904) and (905). We get

$$d^2s = -(1 - \frac{4k^2}{(k + r)^4}8C(2)M(2k + 2r)^{\frac{1}{2}(9 + \sqrt{17})} + (8C(1)M(2k +$$
$$2r)^{\frac{9}{2} - \frac{\sqrt{17}}{2}} + \frac{(k + r)^4}{4k^2} + 4(k + r)^2))d^2t + (1 - \frac{4k^2}{(k + r)^4}8C(2)M(2$$
$$k + 2r)^{\frac{1}{2}(9 + \sqrt{17})} + (8C(1)M(2k + 2r)^{\frac{9}{2} - \frac{\sqrt{17}}{2}} + \frac{(k + r)^4}{4k^2} + 4(k +$$
$$r)^2))^{(-1)}d^2r + \frac{(k + r)^4}{16k^2}(d^2\theta + sin^2\theta d^2\phi) \tag{918}$$

where $C(1)$ and $C(2)$ are given by Eqs (906) and (907).

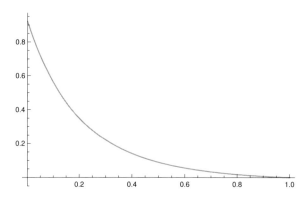

Figure 259: $k^2\mu$ of expression (915) for $n = 1$

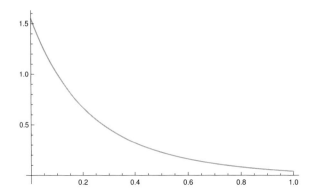

Figure 260: $k^2\mu$ of expression (915) for $n = 2$

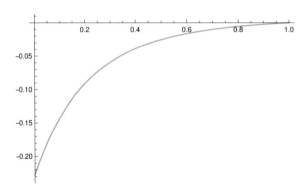

Figure 261: k^2P of expression (916) for $n = 1$

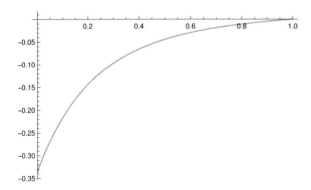

Figure 262: $k^2 P$ of expression (916) for $n = 2$

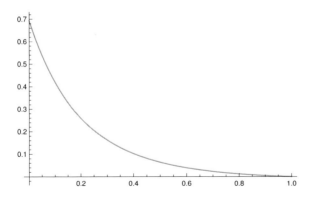

Figure 263: $k^2(\mu + P)$ of expression (917) for $n = 1$

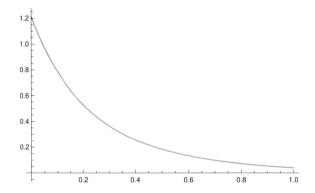

Figure 264: $k^2(\mu + P)$ of expression (917) for $n = 2$

Example 2.3.3.2.3 : Perfect Fluid Solution with the $f(r)$ of Eq (919)

Consider the perfect fluid solution with

$$f(r) = \frac{(2k + r)^6}{729k^4} \qquad (919)$$

which is obtained from Eq (872) for $b = 6$. The $h(r)$ of the solution, which is obtained from Eq (877) for $b = 6$, is

$$h(r) = \frac{1}{56M}(4(2k + r)^2 + \frac{8(2k - 7M)(2k + r)^9}{98415k^8} + \frac{28(2k + r)^6}{729k^4} + \frac{112(M - k)(2k + r)^4}{135k^3}) \qquad (920)$$

The non vanishing components of the Ricci tensor R^ν_μ, the Ricci scalar R, the second order curvatute invariant R^2 and the eigenvalues B_t and $B_r = B_\theta = B_\phi$ of the Ricci tensor R^ν_μ of the solution, which are obtained from Eqs Eqs (878) - (881), (9), (883) and (884) for $b = 6$, are the following:

$$R_{tt} = \frac{1}{297675}(\frac{8r^4(2k - 7M)^2}{k^8} - \frac{3228504075k^8}{(2k + r)^{10}} + \frac{64r^3(2k - 7M)^2}{k^7}$$
$$+ \frac{192r^2(2k - 7M)^2}{k^6} + \frac{1674039150k^5(k - M)}{(2k + r)^8} + \frac{256r(2k - 7M)^2}{k^5}$$

267

$$+\frac{128(2k-7M)^2}{k^4}-\frac{61236(2k-7M)(k-M)}{k^3(2k+r)}-$$
$$\frac{208324872k^2(k-M)^2}{(2k+r)^6}+\frac{328050(2k-7M)}{(2k+r)^3})\tag{921}$$

$R_{rr}=6(-43601k^8-115304k^7(M-r)+14k^6r(1419r-6956M)+14$
$k^5r^2(501M-640r)+4480k^4r^3(7M-r)+448k^3r^4(35M-3r)+224k^2$
$r^5(21M-r)+16kr^6(49M-r)+56Mr^7)((2k+r)^2(17279k^8+79856k^7$
$(M-r)+28k^6r(2692M-633r)+28k^5r^2(393M+80r)+1120k^4r^3(r$
$-7M)+112k^3r^4(3r-35M)+56k^2r^5(r-21M)+4kr^6(r-49M)-$
$14Mr^7))^{(-1)}\tag{922}$

$R_{\theta\theta}=\dfrac{R_\phi\phi}{sin^2\theta}=\dfrac{2}{229635k^8}(43601k^8+115304k^7(M-r)+14k^6r$
$(6956M-1419r)+14k^5r^2(640r-501M)-4480k^4r^3(7M-r)-$
$448k^3r^4(35M-3r)-224k^2r^5(21M-r)+16kr^6(r-49M)-$
$56Mr^7)\tag{923}$

$$R=\frac{4}{45}\left(\frac{2r(2k-7M)}{k^4}+\frac{32805k^4}{(2k+r)^6}+\frac{8k-28M}{k^3}-\frac{5832k(k-M)}{(2k+r)^4}\right)\tag{924}$$

$R^2=\dfrac{16}{33075}(\dfrac{13r^2(2k-7M)^2}{k^8}+\dfrac{38383326225k^8}{(2k+r)^{12}}+\dfrac{52r(2k-7M)^2}{k^7}$
$+\dfrac{52(2k-7M)^2}{k^6}-\dfrac{7812182700k^5(k-M)}{(2k+r)^{10}}-$
$\dfrac{95256(2k-7M)(k-M)}{k^3(2k+r)^3}+\dfrac{486091368k^2(k-M)^2}{(2k+r)^8}+$
$\dfrac{437400(2k-7M)}{(2k+r)^5})\tag{925}$

$B_t=\dfrac{2}{315}(\dfrac{4r(2k-7M)}{k^4}-\dfrac{32805k^4}{(2k+r)^6}+\dfrac{8(2k-7M)}{k^3}+$
$\dfrac{10206k(k-M)}{(2k+r)^4})\tag{926}$

$$B_r = B_\theta = B_\phi = \frac{2}{315}(\frac{8r(2k-7M)}{k^4} + \frac{164025k^4}{(2k+r)^6} + \frac{16(2k-7M)}{k^3}$$
$$-\frac{30618k(k-M)}{(2k+r)^4}) \tag{927}$$

The quantities $k^2\mu$, k^2P and $k^2(\mu + P)$, which are obtained from Eqs (885) - (887) for $b = 6$, are the following in the variables y and n of Eqs (172):

$$k^2\mu = \frac{1}{252\pi}(\frac{5103(n-2)}{(y+2)^4} + (4-7n)y - 14n + \frac{52488}{(y+2)^6} + 8) \tag{928}$$

$$k^2P = -\frac{1}{420\pi}(\frac{1701(n-2)}{(y+2)^4} - 7ny - 14n + 4y + \frac{21870}{(y+2)^6} + 8) \tag{929}$$

$$k^2(\mu+P) = \frac{1}{630\pi}(\frac{10206(n-2)}{(y+2)^4} + (4-7n)y - 14n + \frac{98415}{(y+2)^6} + 8) \tag{930}$$

The graphs of $k^2\mu$, k^2P and $k^2(\mu+P)$ of Eqs (928) - (930) are given by Figures (265) - (270). From the graphs of $k^2\mu$ and $k^2(\mu + P)$ we conclude that the solution for $n = 1$ and $n = 2$ satisfies the WEC

The line element d^2s of the solution is obtained from Eqs (1), (919) and 920). We get.

$$d^2s = -(1 - \frac{729k^4}{28(2k+r)^4}(\frac{8(2k-7M)(2k+r)^7}{98415k^8} + \frac{28(2k+r)^4}{729k^4} +$$
$$\frac{112(M-k)(2k+r)^2}{135k^3} + 4))d^2t + (1 - \frac{729k^4}{28(2k+r)^4}$$
$$(\frac{8(2k-7M)(2k+r)^7}{98415k^8} + \frac{28(2k+r)^4}{729k^4} + \frac{112(M-k)(2k+r)^2}{135k^3} +$$
$$4))^{(-1)}d^2r +$$
$$\frac{(2k+r)^6}{729k^4}(d^2\theta + sin^2\theta d^2\phi) \tag{931}$$

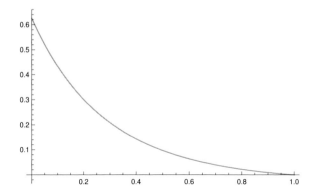

Figure 265: $k^2\mu$ of expression (928) for $n = 1$

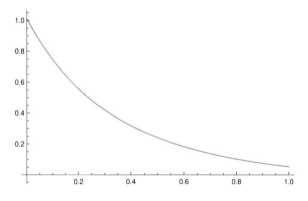

Figure 266: $k^2\mu$ of expression (928) for $n = 2$

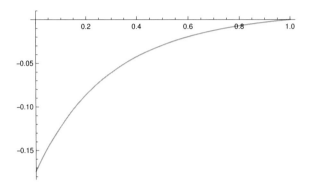

Figure 267: $k^2 P$ of expression (929) for $n = 1$

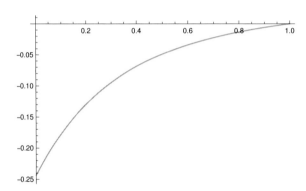

Figure 268: $k^2 P$ of expression (929) for $n = 2$

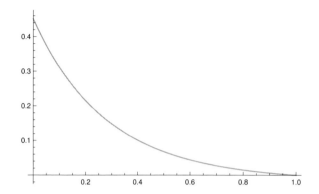

Figure 269: $k^2(\mu + P)$ of expression (930) for $n = 1$

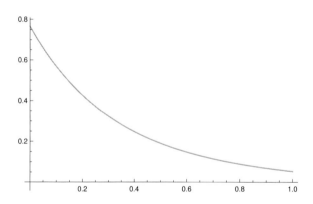

Figure 270: $k^2(\mu + P)$ of expression (930) for $n = 2$

Example 2.3.3.2.4 : Perfect Fluid Solution with the $f(r)$ of Eq (932)

Consider the perfect fluid solution with

$$f(r) = \frac{(7k + 8r)^{15/4}}{3375 \; 15^{3/4} k^{7/4}} \tag{932}$$

which is obtained from Eq (872) for $b = \frac{15}{4}$. The $h(r)$ of the solution, which is obtained from Eq (877) for $b = \frac{15}{4}$ is

$$h(r) = \frac{1}{34M}\Big(\frac{17(7k+8r)^{15/4}}{3375\ 15^{3/4}k^{7/4}} + \frac{49k^2}{2} +$$

$$\frac{(\frac{7k}{4}+2r)^{9/4}((7k-34M)(7k+8r)^4 - 10040625k^4(7k-2M))}{3796875\sqrt{2}\sqrt[4]{15}k^{21/4}} +$$

$$56kr + 32r^2\Big) \tag{933}$$

The non vanishing components of the Ricci tensor R_μ^ν, the Ricci scalar R, the second order curvature invariant R^2 and the eigenvalues B_t and $B_r = B_\theta = B_\phi$ of the Ricci tensor R_μ^ν of the solution, which are obtained from Eqs Eqs (878) - (881), (9), (883) and (884) for $b = \frac{15}{4}$, are the following:

$$R_{tt} = -\frac{315\sqrt{15}(7k+8r)^{5/2}}{1212153856k^{7/4}\left(\frac{7k}{4}+2r\right)^{13}}(972000000k^{21/4}r +$$

$$850500000k^{25/4} - 15^{3/4}(7k+8r)^{5/4}(1434375k^4(7k-2M) +$$

$$(7k-34M)(7k+8r)^4))(\frac{49}{256}k^2(7k+8r)^2 +$$

$$\frac{1}{911250000k^{21/4}}(227812500k^{21/4}r^2(7k+8r)^2 + \sqrt{2}15^{3/4}(\frac{7k}{4} +$$

$$2r)^{17/4}((7k-34M)(7k+8r)^4 - 10040625k^4(7k-2M))) \tag{934}$$

$$R_{rr} = (630(-13921875k^{21/4} + 1044848\ 15^{3/4}k^5\sqrt[4]{7k+8r} -$$

$$2\ 15^{3/4}k^4\sqrt[4]{7k+8r}(146863M + 2401r) - 1372\ 15^{3/4}k^3r\sqrt[4]{7k+8r}$$

$$(6r - 17M) - 784\ 15^{3/4}k^2r^2\sqrt[4]{7k+8r}(8r - 51M) + 8704\ 15^{3/4}M$$

$$r^4\sqrt[4]{7k+8r} - 1792\ 15^{3/4}kr^3\sqrt[4]{7k+8r}(r - 17M)))((7k+8r)^2$$

$$(56953125k^{21/4} - 4391723\ 15^{3/4}k^5\sqrt[4]{7k+8r} + 14\ 15^{3/4}k^4$$

$$\sqrt[4]{7k+8r}(89284M + 343r) + 1372\ 15^{3/4}k^3r\sqrt[4]{7k+8r}(6r - 17M)$$

$$+784\ 15^{3/4}k^2r^2\sqrt[4]{7k+8r}(8r - 51M) - 8704\ 15^{3/4}Mr^4\sqrt[4]{7k+8r} +$$

$$792\ 15^{3/4}kr^3\sqrt[4]{7k+8r}(r - 17M)))^{-1} \tag{935}$$

$$R_{\theta\theta} = \frac{R_{\phi\phi}}{sin^2\theta} = \frac{7(7k+8r)^{5/2}}{88128000000k^{21/4}(\frac{7k}{4}+2r)^{7/2}}(3564000000k^{21/4}r$$

$$+3118500000k^{25/4} - 2\ 15^{3/4}(7k+8r)^{5/4}(2390625k^4(7k-2M) -$$

$$(7k-34M)(7k+8r)^4)) \tag{936}$$

$$R = \frac{7(7k+8r)^{5/2}}{10695475200\sqrt[4]{30}\,k^{7/2}(\frac{7k}{8}+r)^{15/4}(\frac{7k}{4}+2r)^{7/2}}$$
$$(28188000000k^{21/4}r + 24664500000k^{25/4} - 2\;15^{3/4}(7k+8r)^{5/4}$$
$$(18646875k^4(7k-2M) - 11(7k-34M)(7k+8r)^4)) \tag{937}$$

$$R^2 = \frac{1}{108375\sqrt{15}\,k^7(7k+8r)^{15/2}}(-13294108800000\;15^{3/4}k^{21/4}$$
$$Mr^4\sqrt[4]{7k+8r} + 2737022400000\;15^{3/4}k^{25/4}r^3\sqrt[4]{7k+8r}(r-17M)$$
$$+1197447300000\;15^{3/4}k^{29/4}r^2\sqrt[4]{7k+8r}(8r-51M) + 49612500$$
$$15^{3/4}k^{37/4}\sqrt[4]{7k+8r}(81512654M+147833r) + 2095532775000$$
$$15^{3/4}k^{33/4}r\sqrt[4]{7k+8r}(6r-17M) - 14179833189506250\;15^{3/4}$$
$$k^{41/4}\sqrt[4]{7k+8r} + 108455444384765625k^{21/2} + 7002742183538843$$
$$\sqrt{15}k^{10}\sqrt{7k+8r} - 1372\sqrt{15}k^9\sqrt{7k+8r}(2910359710306M +$$
$$6234285337r) - 196\sqrt{15}k^8\sqrt{7k+8r}(-2904250956452M^2 -$$
$$224183209166Mr + 74685892561r^2) - 268912\sqrt{15}k^7r\sqrt{7k+8r}$$
$$(43252318M^2 - 279223487Mr + 41230894r^2) - 38416\sqrt{15}k^6r^2$$
$$\sqrt{7k+8r}(503918029M^2 - 1472600792Mr + 79533940r^2) +$$
$$43904\sqrt{15}k^5r^3\sqrt{7k+8r}(-300689183M^2 + 343263490Mr +$$
$$2927848r^2) + 12544\sqrt{15}k^4r^4\sqrt{7k+8r}(-89152165M^2 -$$
$$99546832Mr + 5855696r^2) + 1499058176\sqrt{15}k^3r^5\sqrt{7k+8r}$$
$$(2023M^2 - 476Mr + 16r^2) + 856604672\sqrt{15}k^2r^6\sqrt{7k+8r}(2r$$
$$-119M)(2r-17M) + 80835510272\sqrt{15}M^2r^8\sqrt{7k+8r} -$$
$$33285210112\sqrt{15}kMr^7\sqrt{7k+8r}(r-17M)) \tag{938}$$

$$B_t = -\frac{7}{10200\sqrt[4]{15}\,k^{7/2}(7k+8r)^{19/4}}(972000000k^{21/4}r +$$
$$850500000k^{25/4} - 15^{3/4}(7k+8r)^{5/4}(1434375k^4(7k-2M) +$$
$$(7k-34M)(7k+8r)^4)) \tag{939}$$

$$B_r = B_\theta = B_\phi = \frac{7(7k+8r)^{5/2}}{222822400\sqrt{2}\sqrt[4]{15}\,k^{7/2}(\frac{7k}{4}+2r)^{29/4}}$$

$$(3564000000k^{21/4}r + 3118500000k^{25/4} - 2 \; 15^{3/4}(7k + 8r)^{5/4}$$
$$(2390625k^4(7k - 2M) - (7k - 34M)(7k + 8r)^4)) \tag{940}$$

The quantities $k^2\mu$, k^2P and $k^2(\mu + P)$, which are obtained from Eqs (885) - (887) for $b = \frac{15}{4}$, are the following in the variables y and n of Eqs (172):

$$k^2\mu = -\frac{7}{20400\sqrt[4]{15}\pi(8y + 7)^{15/4}}(15^{3/4}\sqrt[4]{8y + 7}(34n(896y^4 +$$
$$3136y^3 + 4116y^2 + 2401y - 44299) - 7(1792y^4 + 6272y^3 + 8232y^2$$
$$+4802y - 1522973)) - 140484375) \tag{941}$$

$$k^2P = \frac{7}{4080\sqrt[4]{15}\pi(8y + 7)^{15/4}}(15^{3/4}\sqrt[4]{8y + 7}(34n(128y^4 + 448y^3$$
$$+588y^2 + 343y - 1507) - 7(256y^4 + 896y^3 + 1176y^2 + 686y -$$
$$53639)) - 5315625) \tag{942}$$

$$k^2(\mu + P) = -\frac{7}{10200\sqrt[4]{15}\pi(8y + 7)^{15/4}}(2 \; 15^{3/4}\sqrt[4]{8y + 7}(17n(y$$
$$(4y + 7)(8y(4y + 7) + 49) - 18382) - 7y(4y + 7)(8y(4y + 7) +$$
$$49)) + 4391723 \; 15^{3/4}\sqrt[4]{8y + 7} - 56953125) \tag{943}$$

The graphs of $k^2\mu$, k^2P and $k^2(\mu + P)$ of Eqs (941) - (943) are given by Figures (271) - (276). From the graphs of $k^2\mu$ and $k^2(\mu + P)$ we conclude that the solution for $n = 1$ and $n = 2$ satisfies the WEC

The line element d^2s of the solution is obtained from Eqs (1), (932) and (933).

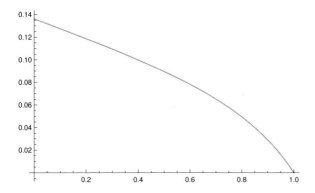

Figure 271: $k^2\mu$ of expression (941) for $n = 1$

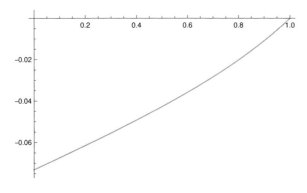

Figure 272: $k^2\mu$ of expression (941) for $n = 2$

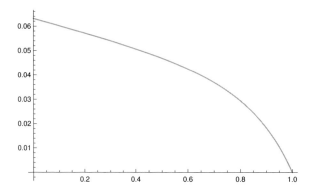

Figure 273: k^2P of expression (942) for $n = 1$

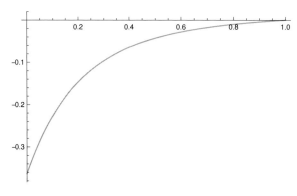

Figure 274: k^2P of expression (942) for $n = 2$

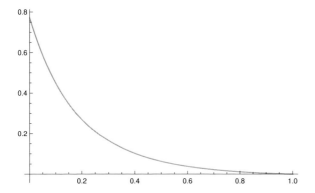

Figure 275: $k^2(\mu + P)$ of expression (943) for $n = 1$

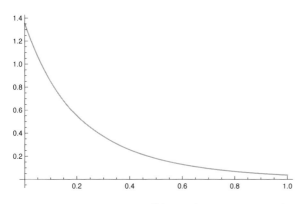

Figure 276: $k^2(\mu + P)$ of expression (943) for $n = 2$

Example 2.3.3.2.5 : Perfect Fluid Solution with the $f(r)$ of Eq (944)

Consider the solution with

$$f(r) = \frac{k^4}{(2k - r)^2} \tag{944}$$

which is obtained from Eq (872) for

$$b = -2 \tag{945}$$

278

If we substitute the $f(r)$ of Eq (944) in Eq (23) and solve for $h(r)$ the resulting differential equation we get

$$h(r) = \frac{1}{14M(r-2k)^2}((7M\sqrt{2k-r}(C(2)\cos(\tfrac{1}{2}\sqrt{7}\log(2k-r)) - C(1)$$
$$\sin(\tfrac{1}{2}\sqrt{7}\log(2k-r))) + 23k^4 - 32k^3 r + 24k^2 r^2 - 8kr^3 + r^4)) \quad (946)$$

where $C(1)$ and $C(2)$ are integration constants, which will be determined from the matching conditions (3) and (4). Imposing these conditions we get

$$C(1) = \frac{2k^{5/2}(\sqrt{7}(4k-7M)\sin(\tfrac{1}{2}\sqrt{7}\log(k)) - 7M\cos(\tfrac{1}{2}\sqrt{7}\log(k)))}{7\sqrt{7}M} \quad (947)$$

and

$$C(2) = -\frac{2k^{5/2}\cos(\tfrac{1}{2}\sqrt{7}\log(k))(\sqrt{7}M\tan(\tfrac{1}{2}\sqrt{7}\log(k)) + 4k - 7M)}{7M} \quad (948)$$

Inserting the above expressions for $C(1)$ and $C(2)$ in Eq (946) we get

$$h(r) = \frac{1}{14M(r-2k)^2}(-2k^{5/2}M\sqrt{14k-7r}\sin\left(\frac{1}{2}\sqrt{7}\log\left(\frac{k}{2k-r}\right)\right) -$$
$$2k^{5/2}(4k-7M)\sqrt{2k-r}\cos\left(\frac{1}{2}\sqrt{7}\log\left(\frac{k}{2k-r}\right)\right) + 23k^4 - 32k^3 r +$$
$$24k^2 r^2 - 8kr^3 + r^4) \quad (949)$$

The solution with the $f(r)$ and $h(r)$ of Eqs (944) and (949) is a perfect fluid solution.

The non vanishing components of the Ricci tensor R_μ^ν, the Ricci scalar R, the second order curvature invariant R^2 and the eigenvalues B_t and $B_r = B_\theta = B_\phi$ of the Ricci tensor R_μ^ν of the solution, which are obtained from Eqs (5) - (12), (944) and (949), are the following:

$$R_{tt} = -\frac{2}{49k^8(2k-r)^{3/2}}(2\sqrt{7}k^{5/2}(k-M)\sin(\frac{1}{2}\sqrt{7}\log(\frac{k}{2k-r})) + 2k^{5/2}$$
$$(3k-7M)\cos(\frac{1}{2}\sqrt{7}\log(\frac{k}{2k-r})) + (2k-r)^{7/2})(2k^{5/2}M\sqrt{14k-7r}$$
$$\sin(\frac{1}{2}\sqrt{7}\log(\frac{k}{2k-r})) + 2k^{5/2}(4k-7M)\sqrt{2k-r}\cos(\frac{1}{2}\sqrt{7}\log(\frac{k}{2k-r})) -$$
$$(r-2k)^4) \quad (950)$$

$$R_{rr} = \frac{1}{(2k-r)^{3/2}}(4\sqrt{7}k^{5/2}(k-3M)\sin(\frac{1}{2}\sqrt{7}\log(\frac{k}{2k-r})) - 4k^{5/2}$$

$$(5k-7M)\cos(\frac{1}{2}\sqrt{7}\log(\frac{k}{2k-r})) + 6(2k-r)^{7/2})(2k^{5/2}M\sqrt{14k-7r}$$

$$\sin(\frac{1}{2}\sqrt{7}\log(\frac{k}{2k-r})) + 2k^{5/2}(4k-7M)\sqrt{2k-r}\cos(\frac{1}{2}\sqrt{7}$$

$$\log(\frac{k}{2k-r})) - (r-2k)^4)^{-1} \tag{951}$$

$$R_{\theta\theta} = \frac{R_{\phi\phi}}{sin^2\theta} = \frac{1}{7(2k-r)^{7/2}}2(2\sqrt{7}k^{5/2}(k-3M)\sin(\frac{1}{2}\sqrt{7}\log(\frac{k}{2k-r})) -$$

$$2k^{5/2}(5k-7M)\cos(\frac{1}{2}\sqrt{7}\log(\frac{k}{2k-r})) + 3(2k-r)^{7/2}) \tag{952}$$

$$R = \frac{1}{7k^4(2k-r)^{3/2}}4(2\sqrt{7}k^{5/2}(2k-5M)\sin(\frac{1}{2}\sqrt{7}\log(\frac{k}{2k-r})) -$$

$$2k^{5/2}(6k-7M)\cos(\frac{1}{2}\sqrt{7}\log(\frac{k}{2\ k-r})) + 5(2k-r)^{7/2}) \tag{953}$$

$$R^2 = \frac{16}{49k^8(2k-r)^3}(-4k^{5/2}Mr^3\sqrt{14k-7r}\sin(\frac{1}{2}\sqrt{7}\log(\frac{k}{2k-r})) +$$

$$24k^{7/2}Mr^2\sqrt{14k-7r}\sin(\frac{1}{2}\sqrt{7}\log(\frac{k}{2k-r})) + 32k^{11/2}M\sqrt{14k-7r}$$

$$\sin(\frac{1}{2}\sqrt{7}\log(\frac{k}{2k-r})) - 48k^{9/2}Mr\sqrt{14k-7r}\sin(\frac{1}{2}\sqrt{7}\log(\frac{k}{2k-r})) -$$

$$4k^{5/2}(3k-7M)(2k-r)^{7/2}\cos(\frac{1}{2}\sqrt{7}\log(\frac{k}{2k-r})) + 4k^{7/2}r^3\sqrt{14k-7r}$$

$$\sin(\frac{1}{2}\sqrt{7}\log(\frac{k}{2k-r})) - 24k^{9/2}r^2\sqrt{14k-7r}\sin(\frac{1}{2}\sqrt{7}\log(\frac{k}{2k-r})) -$$

$$32k^{13/2}\sqrt{14k-7r}\sin(\frac{1}{2}\sqrt{7}\log(\frac{k}{2k-r})) + 48k^{11/2}r\sqrt{14k-7r}\sin(\frac{1}{2}\sqrt{7}$$

$$\log(\frac{k}{2k-r})) - 12\sqrt{7}k^7\sin(\sqrt{7}\log(\frac{k}{2k-r})) + 3536k^7 + 68\sqrt{7}k^6M$$

$$\sin(\sqrt{7}\log(\frac{k}{2k-r})) - 280k^6M - 12096k^6r - 77\sqrt{7}k^5M^2\sin(\sqrt{7}$$

$$\log(\frac{k}{2k-r})) + 280k^5M^2 + 18144k^5r^2 - 15120k^4r^3 + 7560k^3r^4 - 2268k^2$$
$$r^5 + k^5(52k^2 - 140kM + 63M^2)\cos(\sqrt{7}\log(\frac{k}{2k-r})) + 378kr^6 -$$
$$27r^7) \tag{954}$$

$$B_t = \frac{2}{7k^4(2k-r)^{3/2}}(2\sqrt{7}k^{5/2}(k-M)\sin(\frac{1}{2}\sqrt{7}\log(\frac{k}{2k-r})) + 2k^{5/2}$$
$$(3k - 7M)\cos(\frac{1}{2}\sqrt{7}\log(\frac{k}{2k-r})) + (2k-r)^{7/2}) \tag{955}$$

$$B_r = B_\theta = B_\phi = \frac{1}{7k^4(2k-r)^{3/2}}(4\sqrt{7}k^{5/2}(k-3M)\sin(\frac{1}{2}\sqrt{7}$$
$$\log(\frac{k}{2k-r})) - 4k^{5/2}(5k-7M)\cos(\frac{1}{2}\sqrt{7}\log(\frac{k}{2k-r})) + 6(2k-r)^{7/2}) \tag{956}$$

The energy density μ, the pressure $P = P_r = P_\theta = P_\phi$ and the quantity $\mu + P$ of the solution, which are obtained from Eqs (14) - (18), (944) and (949), are the following in the variables y and n of Eqs (172):

$$\mu = \frac{1}{14\pi k^2(2-y)^{3/2}}(-\sqrt{7}(2n-1)\sin\left(\frac{1}{2}\sqrt{7}\log\left(\frac{1}{2-y}\right)\right) - (9-7n)$$
$$\cos\left(\frac{1}{2}\sqrt{7}\log\left(\frac{1}{2-y}\right)\right) + 2(2-y)^{7/2}) \tag{957}$$

$$P = -\frac{1}{14\pi k^2(2-y)^{3/2}}(-\sqrt{7}(n-1)\sin\left(\frac{1}{2}\sqrt{7}\log\left(\frac{1}{2-y}\right)\right) + (2-y)^{7/2}$$
$$- \cos\left(\frac{1}{2}\sqrt{7}\log\left(\frac{1}{2-y}\right)\right)) \tag{958}$$

$$\mu + P = \frac{1}{14\pi k^2(2-y)^{3/2}}(-\sqrt{7}n\sin(\frac{1}{2}\sqrt{7}\log(\frac{1}{2-y})) - (8-7n)$$
$$\cos(\frac{1}{2}\sqrt{7}\log(\frac{1}{2-y})) + (2-y)^{7/2}) \tag{959}$$

The graphs of $k^2\mu$, k^2P and $k^2(\mu + P)$ of Eqs (957) - (959) for $n = 1$ are given by Figures (277) - (279). From the Figures (277) and (279) we conclude that the solution for $n = 1$ satisfies the WEC

The line element d^2s of the solution is obtained from Eqs (1), (944) and 949). We get

$$d^2s = -(1 - \frac{1}{7k^4}(-2k^{5/2}M\sqrt{14k - 7r}\sin(\frac{1}{2}\sqrt{7}\log(\frac{k}{2k - r})) - 2k^{5/2}$$
$$(4k - 7M)\sqrt{2k - r}\cos(\frac{1}{2}\sqrt{7}\log(\frac{k}{2k - r})) + 23k^4 - 32k^3r + 24k^2r^2 -$$
$$8kr^3 + r^4)d^2t + (1 - \frac{1}{7k^4}(-2k^{5/2}M\sqrt{14k - 7r}\sin(\frac{1}{2}\sqrt{7}\log(\frac{k}{2k - r})) -$$
$$2k^{5/2}(4k - 7M)\sqrt{2k - r}\cos(\frac{1}{2}\sqrt{7}\log(\frac{k}{2k - r})) + 23k^4 - 32k^3r + 24k^2r^2$$
$$-8kr^3 + r^4)^{-1}d^2r + \frac{k^4}{(2k - r)^2}(d^2\theta + sin^2\theta d^2\phi) \tag{960}$$

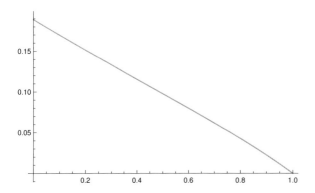

Figure 277: $k^2\mu$ of expression (957) for $n = 1$

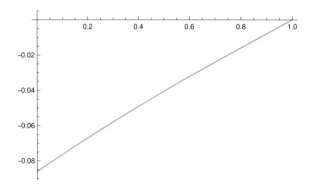

Figure 278: $k^2 P$ of expression (958) for $n = 1$

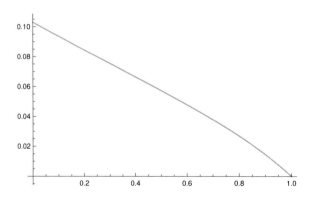

Figure 279: $k^2(\mu + P)$ of expression (959) for $n = 1$

Example 2.3.3.2.6 : Perfect Fluid Solution with the $f(r)$ of Eq (961)

Consider the solution with

$$f(r) = \frac{27k^5}{(5k - 2r)^3} \tag{961}$$

which is obtained from Eq (872) for

$$b = -3 \tag{962}$$

283

Substituting the $f(r)$ of Eq (961) in Eq (23) and solving for $h(r)$ the resulting differential equation we get

$$h(r) = \frac{1}{92M(5k-2r)^3}(46M\sqrt{5k-2r}(C(2)\cos(\frac{1}{2}\sqrt{11}\log(5k-2r)) -$$
$$C(1)\sin(\frac{1}{2}\sqrt{11}\log(5k-2r))) + 4367k^5 - 6250k^4r + 5000k^3r^2 -$$
$$2000k^2r^3 + 400kr^4 - 32r^5) \tag{963}$$

where $C(1)$ and $C(2)$ are integration constants. These constants will take the values for which the matching conditions (3) and (4) are satisfied. These values are the following:

$$C(1) = \frac{9\sqrt{\frac{3}{11}}k^{7/2}}{46M}(\sqrt{11}(55k - 92M)\sin\left(\frac{1}{2}\sqrt{11}\log(3k)\right) + (35k -$$
$$184M)\cos\left(\frac{1}{2}\sqrt{11}\log(3k)\right)) \tag{964}$$

$$C(2) = \frac{9\sqrt{3}k^{7/2}}{506M}(\cos\left(\frac{1}{2}\sqrt{11}\log(3k)\right)(\sqrt{11}(35k - 184M)$$
$$\tan(\frac{1}{2}\sqrt{11}\log(3k)) - 605k + 1012M)) \tag{965}$$

Substituting the above expressions of $C(1)$ and $C(2)$ in Eq (963) we get

$$h(r) = \frac{1}{1012M(5k-2r)^3}(9\sqrt{33}k^{7/2}(35k - 184M)\sqrt{5k-2r}\sin(\frac{1}{2}\sqrt{11}$$
$$\log(\frac{3k}{5k-2r})) - 99tk^{7/2}(55k - 92M)\sqrt{15k-6r}\cos(\frac{1}{2}\sqrt{11}\log(\frac{3k}{5k-2r}))$$
$$+11(4367k^5 - 6250k^4r + 5000k^3r^2 - 2000k^2r^3 + 400kr^4 - 32r^5)) \tag{966}$$

The solution with the $f(r)$ and $h(r)$ of Eqs (961) and (966) is a perfect fluid solution.

The non vanishing components of the Ricci tensor R_μ^ν, the Ricci scalar R, the second order curvature invariant R^2 and the eigenvalues B_t and $B_r = B_\theta = B_\phi$ of the Ricci tensor R_μ^ν of the solution, which are obtained from Eqs (5) - (12), (961) and (966), are the following:

$$R_{tt} = \frac{5}{93325122k^{10}(5k-2r)^{3/2}}((54\sqrt{33}k^{7/2}(25k - 23M)\sin(\frac{1}{2}\sqrt{11}$$

$$\log(\frac{3k}{5k-2r})) + 594\sqrt{3}k^{7/2}(10k - 23M)\cos(\frac{1}{2}\sqrt{11}\log(\frac{3k}{5k-2r})) +$$

$$11(5k-2r)^{9/2})(9\sqrt{33}k^{7/2}(35k - 184M)\sqrt{5k-2r}\sin(\frac{1}{2}\sqrt{11}$$

$$\log(\frac{3k}{5k-2r})) - 99k^{7/2}(55k - 92M)\sqrt{15k-6r}\cos(\frac{1}{2}\sqrt{11}\log(\frac{3k}{5k-2r})) +$$

$$11(5k-2r)^5)) \tag{967}$$

$$R_{rr} = \frac{10}{(5k-2r)^{3/2}}(135\sqrt{33}k^{7/2}(17k - 46M)\sin(\frac{1}{2}\sqrt{11}\log(\frac{3k}{5k-2r})) -$$

$$297\sqrt{3}k^{7/2}(35k - 46M)\cos(\frac{1}{2}\sqrt{11}\log(\frac{3k}{5k-2r})) + 44(5k-2r)^{9/2})(-9$$

$$\sqrt{33}k^{7/2}(35k - 184M)\sqrt{5k-2r}\sin(\frac{1}{2}\sqrt{11}\log(\frac{3k}{5k-2r})) + 99k^{7/2}(55k -$$

$$92M)\sqrt{15k-6r}\cos(\frac{1}{2}\sqrt{11}\log(\frac{3k}{5k-2r})) - 11(5k-2r)^5)^{-1} \tag{968}$$

$$R_{\theta\theta} = \frac{R\phi\phi}{sin^2\theta} = \frac{5}{253(5k-2r)^{9/2}}(135\sqrt{33}k^{7/2}(17k - 46M)\sin(\frac{1}{2}\sqrt{11}$$

$$\log(\frac{3k}{5k-2r})) - 297\sqrt{3}k^{7/2}(35k - 46M)\cos(\frac{1}{2}\sqrt{11}\log(\frac{3k}{5k-2r})) +$$

$$44(5k-2r)^{9/2}) \tag{969}$$

$$R = \frac{5}{6831k^5(5k-2r)^{3/2}}(27\sqrt{33}k^{7/2}(305k - 736M)\sin(\frac{1}{2}\sqrt{11}$$

$$\log(\frac{3k}{5k-2r})) - 297\sqrt{3}k^{7/2}(85k - 92M)\cos(\frac{1}{2}\sqrt{11}\log(\frac{3k}{5k-2r})) +$$

$$143(5k-2r)^{9/2}) \tag{970}$$

$$R^2 = -\frac{1}{4242051k^{10}(5k-2r)^3}(2782080\sqrt{33}k^{7/2}Mr^4\sqrt{5k-2r}\sin(\frac{1}{2}\sqrt{11}$$

$$\log(\frac{3k}{5k-2r})) - 27820800\sqrt{33}k^{9/2}Mr^3\sqrt{5k-2r}\sin(\frac{1}{2}\sqrt{11}\log(\frac{3k}{5k-2r}))$$

$$+104328000\sqrt{33}k^{11/2}Mr^2\sqrt{5k-2r}\sin(\frac{1}{2}\sqrt{11}\log(\frac{3k}{5k-2r})) +$$

$$108675000\sqrt{33}k^{15/2}M\sqrt{5k-2r}\sin(\frac{1}{2}\sqrt{11}\log(\frac{3k}{5k-2r}))-173880000$$

$$\sqrt{33}k^{13/2}Mr\sqrt{5k-2r}\sin(\frac{1}{2}\sqrt{11}\log(\frac{3k}{5k-2r}))+2970\sqrt{3}k^{7/2}(1205k-$$

$$2392M)(5k-2r)^{9/2}\cos(\frac{1}{2}\sqrt{11}\log(\frac{3k}{5k-2r}))+4816800\sqrt{33}k^{9/2}r^4$$

$$\sqrt{5k-2r}\sin(\frac{1}{2}\sqrt{11}\log(\frac{3k}{5k-2r}))-48168000\sqrt{33}k^{11/2}r^3\sqrt{5k-2r}$$

$$\sin(\frac{1}{2}\sqrt{11}\log(\frac{3k}{5k-2r}))+180630000\sqrt{33}k^{13/2}r^2\sqrt{5k-2r}\sin(\frac{1}{2}\sqrt{11}$$

$$\log(\frac{3k}{5k-2r}))+188156250\sqrt{33}k^{17/2}\sqrt{5k-2r}\sin(\frac{1}{2}\sqrt{11}$$

$$\log(\frac{3k}{5k-2r}))-301050000\sqrt{33}k^{15/2}r\sqrt{5k-2r}\sin(\frac{1}{2}\sqrt{11}\log(\frac{3k}{5k-2r}))+$$

$$461402325\sqrt{11}k^9\sin(\sqrt{11}\log(\frac{3k}{5k-2r}))-111485376875k^9-2115660060$$

$$\sqrt{11}k^8M\sin(\sqrt{11}\log(\frac{3k}{5k-2r}))+8827825500k^8M+392519531250k^8r+$$

$$2110227552\sqrt{11}k^7M^2\sin(\sqrt{11}\log(\frac{3k}{5k-2r}))-9023999400k^7M^2-$$

$$628031250000k^7r^2+586162500000k^6r^3-351697500000k^5r^4+$$

$$140679000000k^4r^5-37514400000k^3r^6+6431040000k^2r^7-6561k^7$$

$$(173225k^2-314180kM-71944M^2)\cos(\sqrt{11}\log(\frac{3k}{5k-2r}))-$$

$$643104000kr^8+28582400r^9) \tag{971}$$

$$B_t=\frac{5}{6831k^5(5k-2r)^{3/2}}(54\sqrt{33}k^{7/2}(25k-23M)\sin(\frac{1}{2}\sqrt{11}\log(\frac{3k}{5k-2r}))$$

$$+594\sqrt{3}k^{7/2}(10k-23M)\cos(\frac{1}{2}\sqrt{11}\log(\frac{3k}{5k-2r}))+11(5k-2r)^{9/2}) \tag{972}$$

$$B_r=B_\theta=B_\phi=\frac{5}{6831k^5(5k-2r)^{3/2}}(135\sqrt{33}k^{7/2}(17k-46M)\sin(\frac{1}{2}\sqrt{11}$$

$$\log(\frac{3k}{5k-2r}))-297\sqrt{3}k^{7/2}(35k-46M)\cos(\frac{1}{2}\sqrt{11}\log(\frac{3k}{5k-2r}))+$$

$$44(5k-2r)^{9/2}) \tag{973}$$

In the variables y and n defined by Eqs (172) the energy density μ, the pressure $P = P_r = P_\theta = P_\phi$ and the quantity $\mu + P$, which are obtained from Eqs (14) - (18), (961) and (966), are the following:

$$\mu = \frac{5}{109296\pi k^2 (5-2y)^{3/2}}(-27\sqrt{33}(322n - 205)\sin(\frac{1}{2}\sqrt{11}\log(\frac{3}{5-2y}))$$
$$+297\sqrt{3}(92n - 125)\cos(\frac{1}{2}\sqrt{11}\log(\frac{3}{5-2y})) + 121(5-2y)^{9/2}) \qquad (974)$$

$$P = -\frac{5}{109296\pi k^2 (5-2y)^{3/2}}(-81\sqrt{33}(46n - 45)\sin(\frac{1}{2}\sqrt{11}\log(\frac{3}{5-2y}))$$
$$+55(5-2y)^{9/2} - 4455\sqrt{3}\cos(\frac{1}{2}\sqrt{11}\log(\frac{3}{5-2y}))) \qquad (975)$$

$$\mu + P = \frac{5}{18216\pi k^2 (5-2y)^{3/2}}(-9\sqrt{33}(92n - 35)\sin(\frac{1}{2}\sqrt{11}\log(\frac{3}{5-2y}))$$
$$+99\sqrt{3}(46n - 55)\cos(\frac{1}{2}\sqrt{11}\log(\frac{3}{5-2y})) + 11(5-2y)^{9/2}) \qquad (976)$$

The graphs of $k^2\mu$, $k^2 P$ and $k^2(\mu + P)$ of Eqs (974) - (976) for $n = 1$ and $n = 2$ are given by Figures (280) - (285). From the Figures of $k^2\mu$ and $k^2(\mu + P)$ we conclude that the solution for $n = 1$ and $n = 2$ satisfies the WEC

Substituting the expressions for $f(r)$ and $h(r)$ of Eqs (961) and (966) in the expression for $d^2 s$ of Eq (1) we get the line element of the solution.

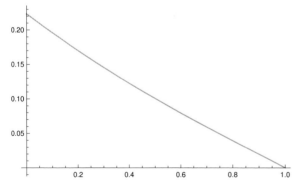

Figure 280: $k^2\mu$ of expression (974) for $n = 1$

287

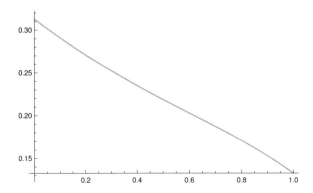

Figure 281: $k^2\mu$ of expression (974) for $n = 2$

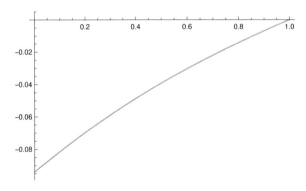

Figure 282: k^2P of expression (975) for $n = 1$

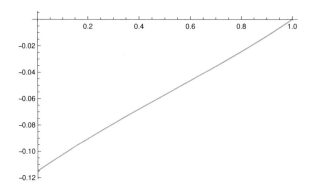

Figure 283: $k^2 P$ of expression (975) for $n = 2$

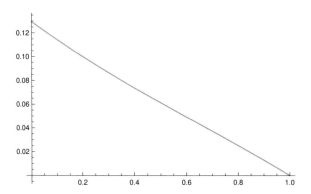

Figure 284: $k^2(\mu + P)$ of expression (976) for $n = 1$

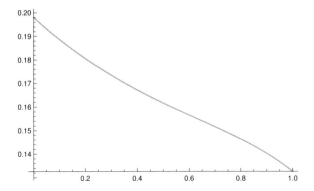

Figure 285: $k^2(\mu + P)$ of expression (976) for $n = 2$

Example 2.3.3.3: Perfect Fluid Solution with the $f(r)$ of Eq (977)

Consider the solution with

$$f(r) = k^2 \left(\frac{1}{b^2} - 1\right) \sinh^2\left(b\left(\frac{r}{k} + p\right)\right) \tag{977}$$

After several calculations we find that the above $f(r)$ together with the function

$$h(r) = \frac{k}{b^2 n} \sinh(b(\frac{r}{k} + p))((b - (b^2 - 1)(n - 1)\tanh^{-1}(\tanh(b(1 - \frac{r}{k}))))$$
$$\cosh(b(\frac{r}{k} + p)) - ((b^2 - 1)n + 1)\sinh(b(\frac{r}{k} + p))) \tag{978}$$

where $n = 2M/k$ and b and p arbitrary constants satisfies Eq (23). If the constants b and p satisfy the relation

$$\tanh(b(p + 1)) = b \tag{979}$$

the functions $f(r)$ and $h(r)$ satisfy the matching conditions Eqs (3) and (4). Therefore the line element d^2s of Eq (1) with the $f(r)$ and $h(r)$ of Eqs (977) and (978) is the line element of a perfect fluid solution, which matches to Schwarzschild's solution if relation (979) is satisfied.

Eq (979) can be written in the form

$$p = \frac{1}{2b}Log\frac{1 + b}{1 - b} - 1 \tag{980}$$

290

The non vanishing components of the Ricci tensor R^{ν}_{μ}, the Ricci scalar R, the second order curvature invariant R^2 and the eigenvalues B_t and $B_r = B_\theta = B_\phi$ of the Ricci tensor R^{ν}_{μ} of this solution, which are obtained from Eqs (5) - (12), (977) and (978), are the following:

$$R_{tt} = \frac{b^2(n-1)}{(b^2-1)k^2}((b-(b^2-1)(n-1)\tanh^{-1}(\tanh(b(1-\frac{r}{k}))))$$
$$\coth(b(\frac{r}{k}+p)) + b^2(-n+1) + n - 2) \tag{981}$$

$$R_{rr} = b^2((b^2(-n) + b^2 + n - 3)\sinh(b(\frac{r}{k}+p)) - 2(b^2-1)(n-1)$$
$$\tanh^{-1}(\tanh(b-\frac{br}{k}))\cosh(b(\frac{r}{k}+p)) + 2b\cosh(b(\frac{r}{k}+p)))(k^2((b^2(n-1)$$
$$-n+2)\sinh(b(\frac{r}{k}+p)) + (b^2-1)(n-1)\tanh^{-1}(\tanh(b-\frac{br}{k}))$$
$$\cosh(b(\frac{r}{k}+p)) - b\cosh(b(\frac{r}{k}+p))))^{(-1)} \tag{982}$$

$$R_{\theta\theta} = \frac{R_{\phi\phi}}{sin^2\theta} = -\sinh(b(\frac{r}{k}+p))((b^2(n-1)-n+3)\sinh(b(\frac{r}{k}+p)) +$$
$$2(b^2-1)(n-1)\tanh^{-1}(\tanh(b-\frac{br}{k}))\cosh((\frac{r}{k}+p)) -$$
$$2b\cosh(b(\frac{r}{k}+p))) \tag{983}$$

$$R = \frac{2b^2}{(b^2-1)\,k^2}\left(3\left(\left(b^2-1\right)(n-1)\tanh^{-1}\left(\tanh\left(b-\frac{br}{k}\right)\right)-b\right)\right.$$
$$\coth\left(b\left(\frac{r}{k}+p\right)\right) + b^2n - b^2 - n + 4\right) \tag{984}$$

$$R^2 = \frac{b^4}{8(-1+b^2)^2k^4(Sinh(b(p+r/k)))^6}((10b(-10b^2(n-1)+10n-13)$$
$$\sinh(2b(\frac{r}{k}+p)) + 8b(b^2(n-1) - n + 4)\sinh(4b(\frac{r}{k}+p)) + 2b(-2b^2(n-$$
$$1) + 2n - 5)\sinh(6b(\frac{r}{k}+p)) + 12(b^2-1)^2(n-1)^2\tanh^{-1}(\tanh(b-$$

$$\frac{br}{k}))^2(-4\cosh(2b(\frac{r}{k}+p)) + \cosh(4b(\frac{r}{k}+p)) + 11)\cosh^2(b(\frac{r}{k}+p)) + 2$$

$$(b^2-1)(n-1)\tanh^{-1}(\tanh(b-\frac{br}{k}))(5(10b^2(n-1) - 10n + 13)\sinh(2b$$

$$(\frac{r}{k}+p)) + 4(b^2(-n) + b^2 + n - 4)\sinh(4b(\frac{r}{k}+p)) + (2b^2(n-1) - 2n +$$

$$5)\sinh(6b(\frac{r}{k}+p)) - 45b\cosh(2b(\frac{r}{k}+p)) + 6b\cosh(4b(\frac{r}{k}+p)) - 3b$$

$$\cosh(6b(\frac{r}{k}+p)) - 54b) + (46b^4(n-1)^2 + b^2(4(61-23n)n - 107) + 2n$$

$$(23n-76) + 151)\cosh(2b(\frac{r}{k}+p)) - 2(2b^4(n-1)^2 + b^2(-4(n-5)n -$$

$$13) + 2(n-8)n + 23)\cosh(4b(\frac{r}{k}+p)) + (2b^4(n-1)^2 + b^2(-4(n-3)n$$

$$9)\cosh(6b(\frac{r}{k}+p)) + 2(-22b^4(n-1)^2 + b^2(4n(11n-27) + 91) - 22n^2 +$$

$$64n - 57))) \tag{985}$$

$$B_t = -\frac{b^2(n-1)}{k^2} \tag{986}$$

$$B_r = B_\theta = B_\phi = \frac{b^2}{(b^2-1)k^2}(2((b^2-1)(n-1)\tanh^{-1}(\tanh(b-\frac{br}{k})) - b)$$

$$\coth(b(\frac{r}{k}+p)) + b^2n - b^2 - n + 3) \tag{987}$$

From Eqs (984) and (985) we find that the invariants R and R^2 and therefore the solution are regular if $b^2 \neq 1$ and $Sinh(b(p+\frac{r}{k})) \neq 0$ in the interior region.

The quantities $k^2\mu$, $k^2P = k^2P_r = k^2P_\theta = k^2P_\phi$ and $k^2(\mu + P)$, which are obtained from Eqs (14) - (18), (977) and (978), are given in the variables $n = \frac{2M}{k}$ and $y = \frac{r}{k}$ by the expressions:

$$k^2\mu = \frac{b^2}{8\pi(b^2-1)}(3\left((b^2-1)(n-1)\tanh^{-1}(\tanh(b(1-y))) - b\right)$$

$$\coth(b(p+y)) + 2b^2n - 2b^2 - 2n + 5) \tag{988}$$

$$k^2P = \frac{b^2}{8\pi(b^2-1)}((b-(b^2-1)(n-1)\tanh^{-1}(\tanh(b(1-y))))$$

$$\coth(b(p+y)) - 1) \tag{989}$$

$$k^2(\mu + P) = \frac{b^2}{4\pi\,(b^2 - 1)}\left(\left(\left(b^2 - 1\right)(n - 1)\tanh^{-1}(\tanh(b(1 - y))) - b\right)\right.$$
$$\coth(b(p + y)) + b^2 n - b^2 - n + 2) \tag{990}$$

Using Eq (989) to eliminate the variable y from Eq (988) we get the relation

$$\mu = -3P + \frac{b^2(n - 1)}{4\pi k^2} \tag{991}$$

which is the equation of state of our solution.

Given a constant b we can use Eq (980) to find the corresponding p. For example for $b = 0.76$ we find $p = 0.310809$. The graphs of $k^2\mu$, $k^2 P$ and $k^2(\mu + P)$ of Eqs (988) - (990) for $b = 0.76$, $p = 0.310809$ and $n = 1$ and 2 are given by Figures (286) - (291). From the graphs of $k^2\mu$ and $k^2(\mu + P)$ we find that the solution with these values of the constants satisfies the WEC.

The line element d^2s of the solution is obtained from Eqs (1), where $f(r)$ and $h(r)$ are obtained from Eqs (977) and (978) respectively. We get.

$$d^2s = -(1 + \frac{1}{b^2 - 1}(-(b^2 - 1)(n - 1)\tanh^{-1}(\tanh(b - \frac{br}{k}))\coth(b(\frac{r}{k} +$$
$$p)) + b^2(-n) + b\coth(b(\frac{r}{k} + p)) + n - 1))d^2t + (1 + \frac{1}{b^2 - 1}(-(b^2 - 1)$$
$$(n - 1)\tanh^{-1}(\tanh(b - \frac{br}{k}))\coth(b(\frac{r}{k} + p)) + b^2(-n) + b\coth(b(\frac{r}{k} +$$
$$p)) + n - 1))^{(-1)}d^2r + k^2(\frac{1}{b^2} - 1)\sinh^2(b(\frac{r}{k} + p))(d^2\theta + \sin^2\theta d^2\phi) \tag{992}$$

where $n = \frac{2M}{k}$.

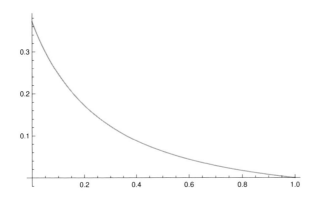

Figure 286: $k^2\mu$ of expression (988) for $b = 0.76$, $p = 0.310809$ and $n = 1$

d

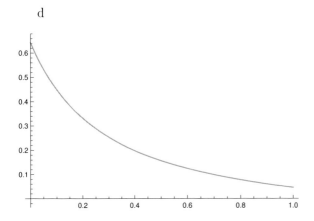

Figure 287: $k^2\mu$ of expression (988) for $b = 0.76$, $p = 0.310809$ and $n = 2$

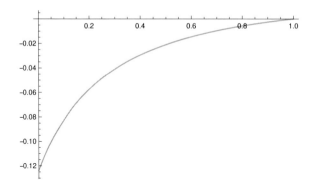

Figure 288: $k^2 P$ of expression (989) for $b = 0.76$, $p = 0.310809$ and $n = 1$

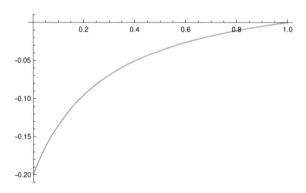

Figure 289: $k^2 P$ of expression (989) for $b = 0.76$, $p = 0.310809$ and $n = 2$

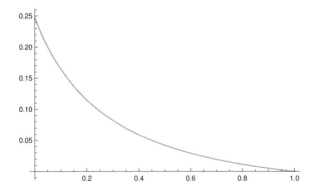

Figure 290: $k^2(\mu + P)$ of expression (990) for $b = 0.76$, $p = 0.310809$ and $n = 1$

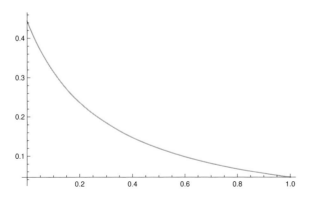

Figure 291: $k^2(\mu + P)$ of expression (990) for $b = 0.76$, $p = 0.310809$ and $n = 2$

3 Interior Solutions to the Solution of Kerr

To find interior solutions to the solution of Kerr we consider a metric which in in Boyer-Lindquist coordinates [35] has the form

$$g_{\mu\nu} = \{[-T, 0, 0, -a(1 - x^2)(1 - T)], [0, \frac{F(r) + a^2x^2}{F(r) + H(r) + a^2}, 0, 0],$$

296

$$[0, 0, F(r) + a^2 x^2, 0], [-a(1 - x^2)(1 - T), 0, 0, (1 - x^2)(F(r) +$$
$$a^2 x^2 + a^2(1 - x^2)(2 - T))] \tag{993}$$

where a is a constant,

$$x = \cos\theta, \qquad T = 1 + \frac{H(r)}{F(r) + a^2 x^2} \tag{994}$$

and $F(r)$ and $H(r)$ are functions to be determined. The above $g_{\mu\nu}$ has the form of a metric we have considered before [44] and becomes Kerr's metric if $F(r) = r^2$ and $H(r) = -2Mr$.

To study the matching problem consider two spacetimes one of which is Kerr's spacetime, which are described by the same coordinate system, and which are separated by a surface $r = k$, where k is a constant. Let g_{ij}^3 be the three metric of the surface. The notation P^+ means that P is calculated in the exterior region and the notation P^- that it is calculated in the interior region. The notation $P^+|_S$ ($P^-|_S$) means that the quantity P is calculated in the exterior (interior) region and evaluated at the surface. Also we use the notation $[P] = P^+|_S - P^-|_S$, which means that $[P]$ denotes the discontinuity of P at the surface.

The Darmois conditions for the matching of the interior and the exterior regions are [36] continuity of the first fundamental form

$$[g_{ij}^3] = 0 \tag{995}$$

and continuity of the extrinsic curvature K_{ij} (second fundamental form)

$$[K_{ij}] = 0 \tag{996}$$

In our case relations (995) are satisfied with Kerr's solution as exterior solution if the functions $F(r)$ and $H(r)$ are continuous across the surface that is if

$$F(k) = k^2 \quad \text{and} \quad H(k) = -2kM \tag{997}$$

and the relations (996) are satisfied if the derivatives with respect to r of the functions $F(r)$ and $H(r)$ are continuous across the surface [28], [32] that is if

$$F'(k) = 2k \quad \text{and} \quad H'(k) = -2M \tag{998}$$

Also we find that if relations (997) and (998) are satisfied the interior metric (993) and (994) and the exterior Kerr metric as well as their first deriverives in coordinates are continuous at the matching surface $r = k$, which means that we have also matching according to the matching conditions of Lichnerowicz [37]. The coordinates we use are admissible.

For $a = 0$ Kerr's solution becomes Schwarzschild's solution, while the metric of Eq (993) with $F(r) = f(r)$ and $H(r) = -2Mh(r)$ becomes the metric of Eq (1). Therefore in the Schwarzschild's case the matching conditions of Darmois and of Lichnerowicz are those of Eqs (3) and (4).

It is obvious that as far as the matching conditions is concern the same functions $F(r)$ and $f(r)$ and the same functions $H(r)$ and $-2Mh(r)$ can be used for the case of Kerr and the case of Schwarzschild respectively. This happens in Example 3.1.1.1 and Example 2.3.1.7 where we have written $H(r) = -2Mh(r)$ and we have teken $h(r) = r + kC(p)(1 - \frac{r}{k})^p$. Also in Example 3.1.2.1 we write $H(r) = -2Mh(r)$ with $h(r)$ the $h(r)$ of Example 2.2.1 for $q = 0$.

In Boyer-Lindquist coordinates the matching surface $r = k$ is an oblate spheroid [38]. We can easily write the line element coming from the metric of Eq (993). We get

$$d^2 s = -(1 + \frac{H(r)}{F(r) + a^2 cos^2\theta})d^2 t + \frac{2asin^2\theta H(r)}{F(r) + a^2 cos^2\theta}dtd\phi +$$
$$\frac{F(r) + a^2 cos^2\theta}{F(r) + H(r) + a^2}d^2 r + (F(r) + a^2 cos^2\theta)d^2\theta +$$
$$sin^2\theta(F(r) + a^2 - \frac{a^2 sin^2\theta H(r)}{F(r) + a^2 cos^2\theta})d^2\phi \qquad (999)$$

We shall consider two cases namely Case A with $F(r) = r^2$ and Case B with $F(r) \neq r^2$

3.1 Case A : Interior Solutions to the Solution of Kerr with $F(r) = r^2$

We shall write
$$H(r) = -2Mh(r) \qquad (1000)$$

in which case the metric (993) matches to Kerr's metric at the matching surface $r = k$ if the matching conditions

$$h(k) = k \quad \text{and} \quad h'(k) = 1 \qquad (1001)$$

are satisfied. The non-vanishing components of the Ricci tensor $R_{\mu\nu}$ the Ricci scalar R and the second order curvature invariant R^2 coming from the metric of Eqs (993), (994) and (1000) for $F(r) = r^2$ are the following

$$R_{tt} = \frac{1}{(a^2x^2 + r^2)^3}(2M\left(h(r) - rh'(r)\right)\left(a^2\left(x^2 - 2\right) + 2Mh(r) - r^2\right) -$$

$$-2Mh(r)\left(h(r) - rh'(r)\right) - M\left(a^2x^2 + r^2\right)h''(r)\left(a^2 - 2Mh(r) + r^2\right))$$
$$(1002)$$

$$R_{t\phi} = \frac{aM\left(x^2 - 1\right)}{(a^2x^2 + r^2)^3}(4\left(rh'(r) - h(r)\right)\left(a^2 - Mh(r) + r^2\right) -$$

$$\left(a^2x^2 + r^2\right)h''(r)\left(a^2 - 2Mh(r) + r^2\right))$$
$$(1003)$$

$$R_{rr} = \frac{M\left((a^2x^2 + r^2)h''(r) - 2rh'(r) + 2h(r)\right)}{(a^2x^2 + r^2)(a^2 - 2Mh(r) + r^2)}$$
$$(1004)$$

$$R_{\theta\theta} = -\frac{2M\left(h(r) - rh'(r)\right)}{a^2x^2 + r^2}$$
$$(1005)$$

$$R_{\phi\phi} = \frac{M(x^2 - 1)}{(a^2x^2 + r^2)^3}$$
$$(2(rh'(r) - h(r))((a^2 + r^2)(a^2(x^2 - 2) - r^2) - 2a^2M(x^2 - 1)h(r)) - a^2(x^2 - 1)(a^2x^2 + r^2)h''(r)(a^2 - 2Mh(r) + r^2))$$
$$(1006)$$

$$R = \frac{2Mh''(r)}{a^2x^2 + r^2}$$
$$(1007)$$

$$R^2 = \frac{1}{(a^2x^2 + r^2)^6}((a^2x^2 + r^2)^4h''(r)^2 + 4(5r^2 - 3a^2x^2)(a^2x^2 + r^2)^2h'(r)^2$$
$$-4(a^2x^2 + r^2)^2h''(r)(2r(a^2x^2 + r^2)h'(r) + h(r)(a^2x^2 - 3r^2)) + 64rh(r)$$
$$(2a^4x^4 + a^2r^2x^2 - r^4)h'(r) + 8h(r)^2(7a^4x^4 - 34a^2r^2x^2 + 7r^4))$$
$$(1008)$$

The eigenvalues of the Ricci tensor R_μ^ν are the following:

$$B_1 = \frac{M\left(a^2x^2h''(r) + r^2h''(r) - 2rh'(r) + 2h(r)\right)}{\left(a^2x^2 + r^2\right)^2} \tag{1009}$$

$$B_2 = \frac{2M\left(rh'(r) - h(r)\right)}{\left(a^2x^2 + r^2\right)^2} \tag{1010}$$

$$B_r = \frac{M\left(\left(a^2x^2 + r^2\right)h''(r) - 2rh'(r) + 2h(r)\right)}{\left(a^2x^2 + r^2\right)^2} \tag{1011}$$

$$B_\theta = \frac{2M\left(rh'(r) - h(r)\right)}{\left(a^2x^2 + r^2\right)^2} \tag{1012}$$

To find the eigenvalue B_t of the timelike eigenvector $(u_t)^\mu$ of the Ricci tensor R_μ^ν we consider the eigenvalue equation $R_\mu^\nu (u_i)^\mu = B_i(u_i)^\nu$ Writing for the eigenvectors $(u_i)^\mu$, $i = t$ and ϕ which corresponds to the eigenvalues B_t and B_ϕ

$$(u_i)^\mu = \begin{pmatrix} b_i \\ 0 \\ 0 \\ c_i \end{pmatrix}$$

we get the relations

$$(R_t^t - B_i)b_i + R_t^\phi c_i = 0 \quad and \quad R_\phi^t b_i + (R_\phi^\phi - B_i)c_i = 0 \tag{1013}$$

Therefore we have

$$\frac{c_i}{b_i} = -\frac{R_t^t - B_i}{R_t^\phi} = -\frac{R_\phi^t}{R_\phi^\phi - B_i} \tag{1014}$$

Then we get $(u_i)_\mu (u_i)^\mu = b_i^2 V_i(r, x)$, where

$$V_i(r, x) = g_{tt} - 2\frac{R_\phi^t}{R_\phi^\phi - B_i}g_{t\phi} + \left(\frac{R_\phi^t}{R_\phi^\phi - B_i}\right)^2 g_{\phi\phi} \tag{1015}$$

If $V_i(r, x)$ is negative (positive) in the interior region $0 \le r \le k$ the eigenvalue B_i is eigenvalue of a timelike (spacelike) eigenvector $(u_i)^\mu$. For $F(r) = r^2$, as in our case , and arbitrary $h(r)$ we get

$$V_1(r, x) = -\frac{(r^2 + a^2x^2)(a^2 + r^2 - 2Mh(r))}{(a^2 + r^2)^2} \tag{1016}$$

$$V_2(r, x) = \frac{r^2 + a^2 x^2}{a^2(1 - x^2)} \tag{1017}$$

Therefore we have $B_2 = B_\phi$, while we can always chose a such that $V_1(r, x) \leq 0$, which means that $B_1 = B_t$. We have $V_1(r, x) \leq 0$ if

$$a^2 + r^2 - 2Mh(r) \geq 0 \tag{1018}$$

from which for $r = k$ we get $a^2 + k^2 - 2Mk \geq 0$ since for $r = k$ we have $h(k) = k$. Therefore we get $k \geq M + (M^2 - a^2)^{1/2}$ or $k \leq M - (M^2 - a^2)^{1/2}$, which means that the matching occurs outside or on the outer horizon of the exterior solution of Kerr or inside or on the inner horizon of Kerr. Therefore if relation (1018) holds we have

$$B_t = B_1 = B_r = \frac{M\left(a^2 x^2 h''(r) + r^2 h''(r) - 2rh'(r) + 2h(r)\right)}{\left(a^2 x^2 + r^2\right)^2} \tag{1019}$$

and

$$B_\phi = B_2 = B_\theta = \frac{2M\left(rh'(r) - h(r)\right)}{\left(a^2 x^2 + r^2\right)^2} \tag{1020}$$

The energy density μ, the radial pressure P_r, the tangential pressure $P_\perp$ and the quantities $\mu + P_r$ and $\mu + P_\perp$ are given by the expressions:

$$\mu = \frac{M\left(rh'(r) - h(r)\right)}{4\pi \left(a^2 x^2 + r^2\right)^2} \tag{1021}$$

$$P_r = -\frac{M\left(rh'(r) - h(r)\right)}{4\pi \left(a^2 x^2 + r^2\right)^2} \tag{1022}$$

$$P_\perp = -\frac{M\left(\left(a^2 x^2 + r^2\right) h''(r) - 2rh'(r) + 2h(r)\right)}{8\pi \left(a^2 x^2 + r^2\right)^2} \tag{1023}$$

$$\mu + P_r = 0 \tag{1024}$$

$$\mu + P_\perp = -\frac{M\left(\left(a^2 x^2 + r^2\right) h''(r) - 4rh'(r) + 4h(r)\right)}{8\pi \left(a^2 x^2 + r^2\right)^2} \tag{1025}$$

Eq (1024) is the equation of state of the solution. Therefore we find that in the framework of our model interior solutions to Kerr's solution with $F(r) =$

r^2 have the same equation of state with interior solutions to Schwarzschild's solution with $f(r) = r^2$.

We can show that the energy-momentum tensor $T_{\mu\nu}$ of the solutions with the metric of Eqs (993), (994) and (1000) with $F(r) = r^2$ has for arbitrary $h(r)$ the form of the energy-momentum tensor of an anisotropic fluid solution. To do that we consider the normalized eigenvectors $(u_\mu)_\nu$ $\mu, \nu = t, r, \theta, \phi$ of the Ricci tensor, which are given by the relations

$$(u_t)_\mu = \sqrt{\frac{a^2 - 2Mh(r) + r^2}{a^2 x^2 + r^2}}(-\delta_{t\mu} + a(1 - x^2)\delta_{\phi\mu}) \qquad (1026)$$

$$(u_r)_\mu = \sqrt{\frac{a^2 x^2 + r^2}{a^2 - 2Mh(r) + r^2}}\delta_{r\mu} \qquad (1027)$$

$$(u_\theta)_\mu = \sqrt{a^2 x^2 + r^2}\delta_{\theta\mu} \qquad (1028)$$

$$(u_\phi)_\mu = \sqrt{\frac{1 - x^2}{a^2 x^2 + r^2}}(-a\delta_{t\mu} + (r^2 + a^2)\delta_{\phi\mu}) \qquad (1029)$$

From the expressions for $g_{\mu\nu}$, $R_{\mu\nu}$, R, μ, P_r, $P_\perp$, $(u_t)_\mu$ and $(u_r)_\mu$ given by Eqs (993), (1002)- (1007), (1021) - (1023), (1026) and (1027)we find that the energy-momentum tensor $T_{\mu\nu}$ of all solutions with $F(r) = r^2$ and arbitrary $h(r)$ is given by Eq (32), which is the energy-momentum tensor of an anisotropic fluid solution. Therefore all solutions which have metric of the form of Eq (993) with $F(r) = r^2$ are anisotropic fluid solutions for arbitrary $h(r)$.

In a perfect fluid solution with $F(r) = r^2$, which is interior to the solution of Kerr, the following relation should hold

$$B_r - B_\theta = \frac{M\left((a^2 x^2 + r^2)h''(r) - 4rh'(r) + 4h(r)\right)}{(a^2 x^2 + r^2)^2} = 0 \qquad (1030)$$

where Eqs (1011) and (1012) were used. Since the above relation should hold for every value of x we get the relations

$$-rh'(r) + h(r) = 0 \quad \text{and} \quad h''(r) = 0 \qquad (1031)$$

whose solution which satisfy the matching conditions (1001) is the expression $h(r) = r$. Therefore since $F(r) = r^2$ we get Kerr's solution and we conclude that in our model there is no perfect fluid solution with $F(r) = r^2$ interior to the solution of Kerr.

We can show that in our model with $F(r) = r^2$ solutions which are regular and satisfy the WEC do not exist. To do that we shall use Eqs (1007), (1008), (1021) and (1025). From Eqs (1007) and (1008) we find that the solution is regular if $x \neq 0$. Let us assume that for $r \to 0$ we have

$$h(r) \to cr^b \tag{1032}$$

where c and b are constants and b is the smallest power of r in the series expansion of $h(r)$ in the neighborhood of $r = 0$. Then for $x = 0$ and $h(r) = cr^b$ Eq (1008) becomes

$$R^2 = 4c^2 M^2 (56 - 76b + 41b^2 - 10b^3 + b^4) r^{-8+2b} \tag{1033}$$

Therefore R^2 is regular if

$$b \geq 4 \tag{1034}$$

We easily find that for this value of b the invariant R is also regular, which means that a regular solution has $b \geq 4$.

For $h(r) = cr^b$ we get from Eq (1021)

$$\mu = \frac{(b-1)cMr^b}{4\pi \left(a^2 x^2 + r^2\right)^2} \tag{1035}$$

Therefore since $b \geq 4$ in the neighborhood of $r = 0$ we have $\mu \geq 0$ only if $c > 0$. But then we get from Eq (1025) for $b \geq 4$ and $c > 0$

$$\mu + P_\perp = -\frac{(b-1)cMr^{b-2} \left(a^2 b x^2 + (b-4)r^2\right)}{8\pi \left(a^2 x^2 + r^2\right)^2} < 0 \tag{1036}$$

Therefore for all $h(r)$ we cannot have μ and $\mu + P_\perp$ simultaneously positive in the neighborhood of $r = 0$, which means in our model there is no regular solution which satisfy the WEC. Others have reached at the same conclusion [39]. We can however find solutions which satisfy the WEC but which have Kerr's ring singularity and also non singular solutions with the energy density only non negative in the whole interior region. Of course in order to have Kerr's ring singularity only, $h(r)$ $h'(r)$ and $h''(r)$ must be regular in the interior region. We shall study in Case A1 solutions with $F(r) = r^2$ and Kerr's ring singularity which satisfy the WEC and in Case A2 regular solutions with $F(r) = r^2$ which do not satisfy WEC.

3.1.1 Case A1 : Interior Solutions with $F(r) = r^2$ and Kerr's Ring Singularity which satisfy the WEC

Let us take

$$h(r) = r + L(r) \tag{1037}$$

Then the matching conditions for $L(r)$, which come from Eqs (1001) and (1037) are

$$L(k) = 0, \text{ and } L'(k) = 0 \tag{1038}$$

The non-vanishing components of the Ricci tensor $R_{\mu\nu}$ the Ricci scalar R the second order curvature invariant R^2 and the eigenvalues B_i, $i = t, r, \theta$ and ϕ of the Ricci tensor R^ν_μ of the solution expressed in terms of the function $L(r)$ are easily obtained from (1002) - (1012), (1019), (1020) and (1037). Also from Eqs (1021) - (1025) and (1037) we obtain the energy density μ, the radial pressure P_r, the tangential pressure $P_\perp$ and the quantities $\mu + P_r$ and $\mu + P_\perp$. We get

$$\mu = \frac{M \left(r L'(r) - L(r) \right)}{4\pi \left(a^2 x^2 + r^2 \right)^2} \tag{1039}$$

$$P_r = -\frac{M \left(r L'(r) - L(r) \right)}{4\pi \left(a^2 x^2 + r^2 \right)^2} \tag{1040}$$

$$P_\perp = -\frac{M \left((a^2 x^2 + r^2) L''(r) - 2r L'(r) + 2L(r) \right)}{8\pi \left(a^2 x^2 + r^2 \right)^2} \tag{1041}$$

$$\mu + P_r = 0 \tag{1042}$$

$$\mu + P_\perp = -\frac{M \left((a^2 x^2 + r^2) L''(r) - 4r L'(r) + 4L(r) \right)}{8\pi \left(a^2 x^2 + r^2 \right)^2} \tag{1043}$$

The solution satisfies the WEC $\mu \geq 0$ and $\mu + P_\perp \geq 0$ if in the interior region $0 \leq r \leq k$ we have

$$L(r) \leq 0, \; L'(r) \geq 0, \; L''(r) \leq 0 \tag{1044}$$

Of course $L(r)$ must satisfy the matching conditions (1038). Relations (1038) and (1044) are satisfied by any function $L(r)$ which is obtained from any function $L(y)$ which in the range $0 \leq y \leq 1$ satisfies the relations

$$L(y) \leq 0, \; L'(y) \leq 0, \; L''(y) \leq 0 \text{ with } L(0) = L'(0) = 0 \tag{1045}$$

if in the function $L(y)$ we replace y by $1 - \frac{r}{k}$. Prime in relations (1045) means derivative with respect to y. Since we want the solution to have only the ring singularity of Kerr we shall take $L(y)$, $L'(y)$ and $L''()$ non-singular in the range $0 \leq y \leq 1$. The functions

$$y^p \quad \text{and} \quad sinh^q y \, cosh^w y \tag{1046}$$

where $p \geq 2$, $q \geq 2$ and w arbitrary real constant multiplied by negative real constants and also products of such functions multiplied by negative real constants can be used as functions $L(y)$ since they satisfy relations (1045) and since these functions and there first and second derivatives with respect to y are non-singular in the interior region $0 \leq y \leq 1$. If in these expressions we replace y by $1 - \frac{r}{k}$ we get acceptable functions $L(r)$. In addition $L(r)$ which satisfy relations (1044) can be formed from linear combinations of terms, constructed as we described above, some of which are multiplied with negative and some with positive constants provided that some of these constants are not independent. For example the expression

$$L(r) = kb_p(1 - \frac{r}{k})^p + kb_q(1 - \frac{r}{k})^q \tag{1047}$$

with $b_p \leq 0$ and $b_q \geq 0$ and $p < q$ satisfies the relations (1044) if

$$-b_p \geq \frac{q(q-1)}{p(p-1)} b_q \tag{1048}$$

The line element d^2s of the solutions is obtained from Eqs (993), (994) and (1000) for $F(r) = r^2$. We get

$$d^2s = -(1 - \frac{2Mh(r)}{r^2 + a^2cos^2\theta})d^2t - \frac{4Masin^2\theta h(r)}{r^2 + a^2cos^2\theta}dtd\phi +$$
$$\frac{r^2 + a^2cos^2\theta}{r^2 + a^2 - 2Mh(r)}d^2r + (r^2 + a^2cos^2\theta)d^2\theta +$$
$$sin^2\theta(r^2 + a^2 + \frac{2Ma^2sin^2\theta h(r)}{r^2 + a^2cos^2\theta})d^2\phi \tag{1049}$$

The function $h(r)$ is obtained as explained before. For example it can be of the form

$$h(r) = r + k\sum_p C(p)(1 - \frac{r}{k})^p + k\sum_{v,w} C(v,w)sinh^v(1 - \frac{r}{k})$$

$$cosh^{w}(1 - \frac{r}{k}) + k \sum_{q,i,j} C(q,i,j)(1 - \frac{r}{k})^{q} sinh^{i}(1 - \frac{r}{k})$$

$$cosh^{j}(1 - \frac{r}{k}) \tag{1050}$$

where the constants p, v, q and i and satisfy the relations $p \geq 2$, $v \geq 2$, $q \geq 2$ and $i \geq 2$ but are otherwise arbitrary the constants w and j are arbitrary and the constants $C(p)$, $C(v,w)$ and $C(q,i,j)$ are arbitrary negative numbers. In addition relation (1018) should hold, which can always be done for proper choice of a. These solutions match to the solution of Kerr on the oblate spheroid $r = k$, satisfy the WEC and have arbitrary number of parameters. The only singularity of these solutions is Kerr's ring singularity.

It is well known that if a solution satisfies the WEC and in addition the relations $\mu - P_i \geq 0 \quad i = r, r, \theta, \phi$ hold the solution satisfies the dominant energy conditions (DEC) . In our case we have

$$\mu - P_{\theta} = \mu - P_{\phi} = \mu - P\perp = \frac{M L''(r)}{8\pi(r^2 + a^2 x^2)} \tag{1051}$$

which is non-positive since $L''(r)$ is non-positive. Also a solution satisfies the strong energy conditions (SEC) if $\mu + P_i \geq 0 \quad i = r, r, \theta, \phi$ and $\mu + Pr + R_{\theta} + P_{\phi} \geq)$ hold. In our case we have

$$\mu + P_r + P_{\theta} + P_{\phi} = -\frac{M\left((a^2 x^2 + r^2) L''(r) - 2r L'(r) + 2L(r)\right)}{4\pi\left(a^2 x^2 + r^2\right)^2} \tag{1052}$$

which is non-negative. Therefore the interior solutions with $F = r^2$ and the ring singularity of Kerr, which satisfy the WEC satisfy also the SEK but not the DEC.

We shall present below some Examples.

Example 3.1.1.1: Solution with $F(r) = r^2$ and the $h(r)$ of Eq (1053)
Consider the solution with

$$h(r) = r + kC(p)(1 - \frac{r}{k})^{p} \tag{1053}$$

where $p \geq 2$ and $C(p) < 0$. In this case we get the following expressions for the non vanishing components of the Ricci tensor R_{μ}^{ν}, the Ricci scalar R, the second order curvature invariant R^2 and the eigenvalues $B_t = B_r$ and $B_\theta = B_\phi$

$$R_{tt} = \frac{kMC(p)}{(k-r)^2(a^2x^2 + r^2)^3}(1 - \frac{r}{k})^p((1-p)p$$
$$(a^2x^2 + r^2)(a^2 - 2M(kC(p)(1 - \frac{r}{k})^p + r) + r^2) + 2(k - r)(k +$$
$$(p-1)r)(a^2(x^2 - 2) + 2kMC(p)(1 - \frac{r}{k})^p + r(2M - r))) \qquad (1054)$$

$$R_{t\phi} = \frac{aMksin^2\theta C(p)}{(k-r)^2(a^2x^2 + r^2)^3}(1 - \frac{r}{k})^p$$
$$((p-1)p(a^2x^2 + r^2)(a^2 - 2kMC(p)(1 - \frac{r}{k})^p + r(r - 2M)) + 4$$
$$(k - r)(k + (p-1)r)(a^2 - kMC(p)(1 - \frac{r}{k})^p + r(r - M))) \qquad (1055)$$

$$R_{rr} = \frac{kMC(p)((p-1)(a^2px^2 + (p-2)r^2) + 2k^2 + 2k(p-2)r)}{(k-r)^2(a^2x^2 + r^2)(a^2 - 2kMC(p)(1 - \frac{r}{k})^p + r(r - 2M))}$$
$$(1 - \frac{r}{k})^p \qquad (1056)$$

$$R_{\theta\theta} = -\frac{2kMC_p(k + (p-1)r)}{(k - r)(a^2x^2 + r^2)}(1 - \frac{r}{k})^p \qquad (1057)$$

$$R_{\phi\phi} = -\frac{Mk\sin^2\theta C(p)}{(k-r)^2(a^2x^2 + r^2)^3}(1 - \frac{r}{k})^p(2(k - r)(k + (p-1)r)$$
$$(-a^4(x^2 - 2) + 2a^2kM(x^2 - 1)C(p)(1 - \frac{r}{k})^p + a^2r(x^2(2M - r)$$
$$-2M + 3r) + r^4) - a^2(p-1)p(x^2 - 1)(a^2x^2 + r^2)(a^2 - 2kMC(p)$$
$$(1 - \frac{r}{k})^p + r(r - 2M))) \qquad (1058)$$

$$R = \frac{2M(p-1)pC(p)}{k(a^2x^2 + r^2)}(1 - \frac{r}{k})^{p-2} \qquad (1059)$$

$$R^2 = \frac{4M^2}{(a^2x^2 + r^2)^6}\left(\frac{(p-1)^2p^2C(p)^2(a^2x^2+r^2)^4}{k^2}(1-\frac{r}{k})^{2(p-2)} + \right.$$

$$4(5r^2 - 3a^2x^2)(a^2x^2+r^2)^2(pC(p)(1-\frac{r}{k})^{p-1}-1)^2 +$$

$$8(7a^4x^4 - 34a^2r^2x^2 + 7r^4)(kC(p)(1-\frac{r}{k})^p + r)^2 + 64r(2a^4$$

$$x^4 + a^2r^2x^2 - r^4)(1 - pC(p)(1-\frac{r}{k})^{p-1})(kC(p)(1-\frac{r}{k})^p + r)$$

$$-\frac{1}{k}4(p-1)pC(p)(a^2x^2+r^2)^2(1-\frac{r}{k})^{p-2}(2(a^2x^2+r^2)(1-pC(p)$$

$$\left. (1-\frac{r}{k})^{p-1}) + (a^2x^2 - 3r^2)(kC(p)(1-\frac{r}{k})^p + r))\right) \tag{1060}$$

$$B_t = B_r = \frac{kMC(p)}{(k-r)^2(a^2x^2+r^2)^2}(1-\frac{r}{k})^p$$

$$((p-1)(a^2px^2 + (p-2)r^2) + 2k^2 + 2k(p-2)r) \tag{1061}$$

$$B_\theta = B_\phi = \frac{2kMC(p)(k+(p-1)r)}{(r-k)(a^2x^2+r^2)^2}(1-\frac{r}{k})^p \tag{1062}$$

If we substitute the expression (1053) for $h(r)$ in Eqs (1021)- (1023) and (1025) and write

$$r = ky, \quad M = \frac{kn}{2} \quad \text{and} \quad a = ku \tag{1063}$$

we get

$$k^2\mu = -k^2 P_r = -\frac{nC(p)(1-y)^{p-1}((p-1)y+1)}{8(u^2x^2+y^2)^2} \tag{1064}$$

$$k^2 P_\perp = -\frac{nC(p)(1-y)^{p-2}(u^2(p-1)px^2 + (p-2)y((p-1)y+2)+2)}{16\pi(u^2x^2+y^2)^2}$$
$$\tag{1065}$$

$$k^2(\mu + P_\perp) = -\frac{nC(p)(1-y)^{p-2}}{16\pi(u^2x^2+y^2)^2}$$

$$(u^2(p-1)px^2 + (p^2-5p+4)y^2 + 4(p-2)y + 4) \tag{1066}$$

The graphs of $k^2\mu$, $k^2P_\perp$ and $k^2(\mu+P_\perp)$ for $(p=2, C(p)=-1, u=3, n=1)$ are given in Figures 292, 293 and 294. From these graphs we find that the solution with these values of the constants satisfies the WEC.

Using Eqs (1063) and (1053) we find that expression (1018) for $(p=2, C(p)=-1, u=3, n=1)$ takes the form

$$2y^2 - 3y + 10 \geq 0 \tag{1067}$$

For $0 \leq y \leq 1$ we get $2y^2 - 3y + 10 > 0$, which means that for this solution we have $V_1(r,x) < 0$.

The line element d^2s of the solution is obtained from Eqs (1049) and (1053) . We get

$$d^2s = -(1 - \frac{2M(r + kC(p)(1 - \frac{r}{k})^p)}{r^2 + a^2cos^2\theta})d^2t - \\ \frac{4Masin^2\theta(r + kC(p)(1 - \frac{r}{k})^p)}{r^2 + a^2cos^2\theta}dtd\phi + \\ \frac{r^2 + a^2cos^2\theta}{r^2 + a^2 - 2M(r + kC(p)(1 - \frac{r}{k})^p)}d^2r + (r^2 + a^2cos^2\theta)d^2\theta + \\ sin^2\theta(r^2 + a^2 + \frac{2Ma^2sin^2\theta(r + kC(p)(1 - \frac{r}{k})^p)}{r^2 + a^2cos^2\theta})d^2\phi \tag{1068}$$

where, as we mentioned before, p and $C(p)$ are arbitrary real constants satisfying the relations $p \geq 2$ and $C(p) < 0$.

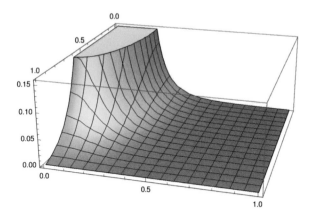

Figure 292: $k^2\mu$ of expression (1064) for ($p = 2$, $C(p) = -1$, $u = 3$, $n = 1$)

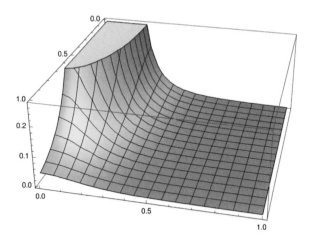

Figure 293: $k^2 P_\perp$ of expression (1065) for ($p = 2$, $C(p) = -1$, $u = 3$, $n = 1$)

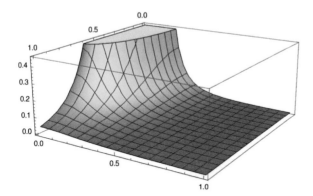

Figure 294: $k^2(\mu + P_\perp)$ of expression (1066) for ($p = 2$, $C(p) = -1$, $u = 3$, $n = 1$)

Example 3.1.1.2: Solution with $F(r) = r^2$ and the $h(r)$ of Eq (1069)
Consider the solution with

$$h(r) = r + kC(v, w) sinh^v(1 - \frac{r}{k}) cosh^w(1 - \frac{r}{k}) \qquad (1069)$$

where $v \geq 2$, $C(v, w) < 0$ and w arbitrary real number. In this case we get the following expressions for the non vanishing components of the Ricci tensor $R_{\mu\nu}$, the Ricci scalar R, the second order curvature invariant R^2 and the eigenvalues $B_t = B_r$ and $B_\theta = B_\phi$ of the Ricci tensor R_μ^ν:

$$R_{tt} = \frac{MC(v, w)}{4k(a^2x^2 + r^2)^3} sinh^{v-2}(1 - \frac{r}{k}) cosh^{w-2}(1 - \frac{r}{k})((a^2x^2 + r^2)$$

$$((2vw + v + w) sinh^2(2 - \frac{2r}{k}) + 4(v - 1)v cosh^4(1 - \frac{r}{k}) + 4(w - 1)w$$

$$sinh^4(1 - \frac{r}{k}))(2kM sinh^v(1 - \frac{r}{k}) cosh^w(1 - \frac{r}{k})C(v, w) - a^2 +$$

$$r(2M - r)) + 4k sinh(1 - \frac{r}{k}) cosh(1 - \frac{r}{k})(2rv cosh^2(1 - \frac{r}{k}) +$$

$$2rw sinh^2(1 - \frac{r}{k}) + k sinh(2 - \frac{2r}{k}))(2kM sinh^v(1 - \frac{r}{k})$$

$$\cosh^w(1 - \frac{r}{k})C(v, w) + a^2(x^2 - 2) + r(2M - r)) \tag{1070}$$

$$R_{t\phi} = -\frac{aM\sin^2\theta C(v, w)}{4k(a^2x^2 + r^2)^3}\sinh^{v-2}(1 - \frac{r}{k})\cosh^{w-2}(1 - \frac{r}{k})$$

$$((-a^2x^2 - r^2)((2vw + v + w)\sinh^2(2 - \frac{2r}{k}) + 4(v - 1)v\cosh^4(1 - \frac{r}{k}) +$$

$$4(w - 1)w\sinh^4(1 - \frac{r}{k}))(-2kM\sinh^v(1 - \frac{r}{k})\cosh^w(1 - \frac{r}{k})$$

$$C(v, w) + a^2 + r(r - 2M)) + 8k\sinh(1 - \frac{r}{k})\cosh(1 - \frac{r}{k})$$

$$(2rv\cosh^2(1 - \frac{r}{k}) + 2rw\sinh^2(1 - \frac{r}{k}) + k\sinh(2 - \frac{2r}{k}))$$

$$(kM\sinh^v(1 - \frac{r}{k})\cosh^w(1 - \frac{r}{k})C(v, w) - a^2 + r(M - r)) \tag{1071}$$

$$R_{rr} = \frac{M}{-2M(k\sinh^v(1 - \frac{r}{k})\cosh^w(1 - \frac{r}{k})C(v, w) + r) + a^2 + r^2}$$

$$\frac{1}{k(a^2x^2 + r^2)}(\frac{1}{4}(a^2x^2 + r^2)\sinh^{v-2}(1 - \frac{r}{k})\cosh^{w-2}(1 - \frac{r}{k})C(v, w)((2vw$$

$$+v + w)\sinh^2(2 - \frac{2r}{k}) + 4(v - 1)v\cosh^4(1 - \frac{r}{k}) + 4(w - 1)w\sinh^4(1 -$$

$$\frac{r}{k})) + 2k(k\sinh^v(1 - \frac{r}{k})\cosh^w(1 - \frac{r}{k})C(v, w) + r) - 2kr(1 - \sinh^{v-1}(1$$

$$-\frac{r}{k})\cosh^{w-1}(1 - \frac{r}{k})C(v, w)(v\cosh^2(1 - \frac{r}{k}) + w\sinh^2(1 - \frac{r}{k}))) \tag{1072}$$

$$R_{\theta\theta} = -\frac{MC(v, w)}{(a^2x^2 + r^2)}\sinh^{v-1}(1 - \frac{r}{k})\cosh^{w-1}(1 - \frac{r}{k})$$

$$(2rv\cosh^2(1 - \frac{r}{k}) + 2rw\sinh^2(1 - \frac{r}{k}) + k\sinh(2 - \frac{2r}{k})) \tag{1073}$$

$$R_{\phi\phi} = -\frac{Mu\sin^2 C(v, w)}{4k(a^2x^2 + r^2)^3}\sinh^{v-2}(1 - \frac{r}{k})\cosh^{w-2}(1 - \frac{r}{k})$$

$$(4k\sinh(1 - \frac{r}{k})\cosh(1 - \frac{r}{k})(2r\,v\cosh^2(1 - \frac{r}{k}) +$$

$$2rw \sinh^2(1 - \frac{r}{k}) + k \sinh(2 - \frac{2r}{k}))(2a^2 kM(x^2 - 1)$$

$$\sinh^v(1 - \frac{r}{k}) \cosh^w(1 - \frac{r}{k}) C(v, w) - a^4(x^2 - 2) + a^2 r(x^2(2M - r) -$$

$$2M + 3r) + r^4) - a^2(x^2 - 1)(a^2 x^2 + r^2)((2vw + v + w) \sinh^2(2 - \frac{2r}{k}) +$$

$$4(v - 1)v \cosh^4(1 - \frac{r}{k}) + 4(w - 1)w \sinh^4(1 - \frac{r}{k}))$$

$$(-2kM \sinh^v(1 - \frac{r}{k}) \cosh^w(1 - \frac{r}{k}) C(v, w) + a^2 + r(r - 2M))) \qquad (1074)$$

$$R = \frac{2kMC(v, w)}{(a^2 x^2 + r^2)} \sinh^{v-2}(1 - \frac{r}{k}) \cosh^{w-2}(1 - \frac{r}{k})$$

$$((2vw + v + w) \sinh^2(2 - \frac{2r}{k}) + 4(v - 1)v \cosh^4(1 - \frac{r}{k}) +$$

$$4(w - 1)w \sinh^4(1 - \frac{r}{k})) \qquad (1075)$$

$$R^2 = \frac{4M^2}{k^2(a^2 x^2 + r^2)^6} (\frac{1}{16}(a^2 x^2 + r^2)^4 \sinh^{2(v-2)}(1 - \frac{r}{k}) \cosh^{2(w-2)}(1 - \frac{r}{k})$$

$$C(v, w)^2((2vw + v + w) \sinh^2(2 - \frac{2r}{k}) + 4(v - 1)v \cosh^4(1 - \frac{r}{k}) + 4$$

$$(w - 1)w \sinh^4(1 - \frac{r}{k}))^2 + 8k^2(7a^4 x^4 - 34a^2 r^2 x^2 + 7r^4)(k \sinh^v(1 - \frac{r}{k})$$

$$\cosh^w(1 - \frac{r}{k}) C(v, w) + r)^2 - \frac{1}{16}(a^2 x^2 + r^2)^4 \sinh^{2(v-2)}(1 - \frac{r}{k})$$

$$\cosh^{2(w-2)}(1 - \frac{r}{k}) C(v, w)^2((2vw + v + w) \sinh^2(2 - \frac{2r}{k}) + 4(v - 1)v$$

$$\cosh^4(1 - \frac{r}{k}) + 4(w - 1)w \sinh^4(1 - \frac{r}{k}))^2 + 8k^2(7a^4 x^4 - 34a^2 r^2 x^2 + 7r^4)$$

$$(k \sinh^v(1 - \frac{r}{k}) \cosh^w(1 - \frac{r}{k}) C(v, w) + r)^2 - k(a^2 x^2 + r^2)^2 \sinh^{v-2}(1 - \frac{r}{k})$$

$$\cosh^{w-2}(1 - \frac{r}{k}) C(v, w)((2vw + v + w) \sinh^2(2 - \frac{2r}{k}) +$$

$$4(v - 1)v \cosh^4(1 - \frac{r}{k}) + 4(w - 1)w \sinh^4(1 - \frac{r}{k}))((a^2 x^2 - 3r^2)$$

$$(k \sinh^v(1 - \frac{r}{k}) \cosh^w(1 - \frac{r}{k}) C(v, w) + r) + 2r(a^2 x^2 + r^2)(1 - \sinh^{v-1}$$

$$(1 - \frac{r}{k}) \cosh^{w-1}(1 - \frac{r}{k}) C(v, w)(v \cosh^2(1 - \frac{r}{k}) +$$

$$w\sinh^2(1 - \frac{r}{k})))))) \tag{1076}$$

$$B_t = B_r = \frac{MC(v,w)}{k(a^2x^2 + r^2)^2}\sinh^{v+2}(1 - \frac{r}{k})\cosh^{w-2}(1 - \frac{r}{k})(\coth^2(1 - \frac{r}{k})$$
$$((2vw + v + w)(a^2x^2 + r^2) + 2k^2) + (v - 1)v(a^2x^2 + r^2)\coth^4(1 - \frac{r}{k}) +$$
$$(w - 1)w(a^2x^2 + r^2) + 2krv\coth^3(1 - \frac{r}{k}) + 2krw\coth(1 - \frac{r}{k})) \tag{1077}$$

$$B_\theta = B_\phi = -\frac{MC(v,w)}{(a^2x^2 + r^2)^2}(\sinh^{v-1}(1 - \frac{r}{k})\cosh^{w-1}(1 - \frac{r}{k})$$
$$(2rv\cosh^2(1 - \frac{r}{k}) + 2rw\sinh^2(1 - \frac{r}{k}) + k\sinh(2 - \frac{2r}{k}))) \tag{1078}$$

The energy density μ, the radial pressure P_r and the tangential pressure $P_\perp$ are obtained from Eqs (1021)- (1023) and (1069). If we substitute expressions (1063) we get

$$k^2\mu = -k^2P_r = -\frac{nC(v,w)}{16\pi(u^2x^2 + y^2)^2}\sinh^{v-1}(1 - y)\cosh^{w-1}(1 - y)$$
$$(2vy\cosh^2(1 - y) + 2wy\sinh^2(1 - y) + \sinh(2 - 2y)) \tag{1079}$$

$$k^2P_\perp = -\frac{nC(v,w)}{64\pi k^2(u^2x^2 + y^2)^2}\sinh^v(1 - y)\cosh^w(1 - y)(4csch^2(2 - 2y)$$
$$(u^2x^2 + y^2)((2vw + v + w)\sinh^2(2 - 2y) + 4(v - 1)v\cosh^4(1 - y) +$$
$$4(w - 1)w\sinh^4(1 - y)) + 8vy\coth(1 - y) +$$
$$8wy\tanh(1 - y) + 8) \tag{1080}$$

which imply

$$k^2(\mu + P_\perp) = -\frac{nC(v,w)}{16\pi k^2(u^2x^2 + y^2)^2}\sinh^v(1 - y)\cosh^w(1 - y)(csch^2(2 -$$
$$2y)(u^2x^2 + y^2)((2vw + v + w)\sinh^2(2 - 2y) + 4(v - 1)v\cosh^4(1 - y) +$$
$$4(w - 1)w\sinh^4(1 - y)) + 4vy\coth(1 - y) + 4wy\tanh(1 - y) + 4)(1081)$$

We give the graphs of $k^2\mu$, $k^2P_\perp$ and $k^2(\mu + P_\perp)$ for $(C(v,w) = -1$, $v = 2$, $w = 0$, $u = 3$, $n = 1$) by Figures 295, 296 and 297. It is obvious from these graphs that the solution for these values of the constants satisfies the WEC.

Using Eqs (1063) and (1069) we find that expression (1018) for $(C(v,w) = -1$, $v = 2$, $w = 0$, $u = 3$, $n = 1$) takes the form

$$sinh^2(1-y) + y(y-1) + 9 \geq 0 \qquad (1082)$$

For $0 \leq y \leq 1$ we get $sinh^2(1-y) + y(y-1) + 9 > 0$, which means that for this solution we have $V_1(r,x) < 0$.

The line element d^2s of the solution is obtained from Eqs (1049) and (1069) . We get

$$d^2s = -(1 - \frac{2M(r + kC(v,w)sinh^v(1 - \frac{r}{k})cosh^w(1 - \frac{r}{k}))}{r^2 + a^2cos^2\theta})d^2t -$$
$$\frac{4Masin^2\theta(r + kC(v,w)sinh^v(1 - \frac{r}{k})cosh^w(1 - \frac{r}{k}))}{r^2 + a^2cos^2\theta}dtd\phi +$$
$$\frac{r^2 + a^2cos^2\theta}{r^2 + a^2 - 2M(r + kC(v,w)sinh^v(1 - \frac{r}{k})cosh^w(1 - \frac{r}{k}))}d^2r +$$
$$(r^2 + a^2cos^2\theta)d^2\theta + sin^2\theta(r^2 + a^2 +$$
$$\frac{2Ma^2sin^2\theta(r + kC(v,w)sinh^v(1 - \frac{r}{k})cosh^w(1 - \frac{r}{k}))}{r^2 + a^2cos^2\theta})d^2\phi \qquad (1083)$$

where as we said before $C(v,w)$ and v are arbitrary constants satisfying the relations $C(v,w) < 0$ and $v \geq 2$ and w is an arbitrary real constant.

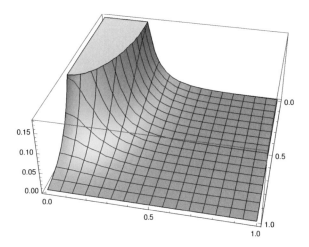

Figure 295: $k^2\mu$ of expression (1079) for $(C(v,w) = -1,\ v = 2,\ w = 0,\ u = 3,\ n = 1$)

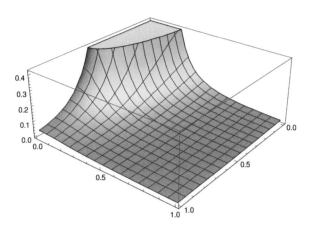

Figure 296: $k^2 P_\perp$ of expression (1080) for $(C(v,w) = -1,\ v = 2,\ w = 0,\ u = 3,\ n = 1$)

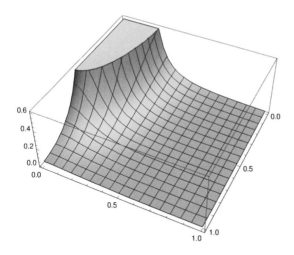

Figure 297: $k^2(\mu + P_\perp)$ of expression (1081) for $(C(v,w) = -1, v = 2, w = 0, u = 3, n = 1)$

Example 3.1.1.3: Solution with $F(r) = r^2$ and the $h(r)$ of Eq (1084)
Consider the solution with

$$h(r) = r + kC(p,v)(1 - \frac{r}{k})^p Sinh^v(1 - \frac{r}{k}) \qquad (1084)$$

In this case we get the following expressions for the non vanishing components of the Ricci tensor $R_{\mu\nu}$, the Ricci scalar R, the second order curvature invariant R^2 and the eigenvalues $B_t = B_r$ and $B_\theta = B_\phi$ of the Ricci tensor R^ν_μ:

$$R_{tt} = \frac{M\left(1 - \frac{r}{k}\right)^p \sinh^{v-2}\left(1 - \frac{r}{k}\right) C(p,v)}{(k-r)^2 \left(a^2x^2 + r^2\right)^3} \left(\frac{a^2x^2 + r^2}{k}(\sinh^2(1 - \frac{r}{k})(k^2\right.$$

$$(p^2 - p + v) - 2krv + r^2v) + kpv(k-r)\sinh(2 - \frac{2r}{k}) + (v-1)v(k-r)^2$$

$$\cosh^2(1 - \frac{r}{k}))(2kM(1 - \frac{r}{k})^p \sinh^v(1 - \frac{r}{k})C(p,v) - a^2 + r(2M - r)) +$$

$$(2(k-r)\sinh(1 - \frac{r}{k})(k(k + (p-1)r)\sinh(1 - \frac{r}{k}) + rv(k-r)\cosh(1 -$$

$$\frac{r}{k}))(2kM(1 - \frac{r}{k})^p \sinh^v(1 - \frac{r}{k})C(p,v) + a^2(x^2 - 2) +$$

$$r(2M - r)))) \qquad (1085)$$

$$R_{t\phi} = \frac{aM\left(x^2-1\right)\left(1-\frac{r}{k}\right)^p \sinh^{v-2}\left(1-\frac{r}{k}\right)C(p,v)}{k(k-r)^2\left(a^2x^2+r^2\right)^3}(4k(k-r)\sinh(1-$$

$$\frac{r}{k})(k(k+(p-1)r)\sinh(1-\frac{r}{k})+rv(k-r)\cosh(1-\frac{r}{k}))(kM(1-\frac{r}{k})^p$$

$$\sinh^v(1-\frac{r}{k})C(p,v)-a^2+r(M-r))-(a^2x^2+r^2)(\sinh^2(1-\frac{r}{k})(k^2$$

$$(p^2-p+v)-2krv+r^2v)+kpv(k-r)\sinh(2-\frac{2r}{k})+(v-1)v(k-r)^2$$

$$\cosh^2(1-\frac{r}{k}))(-2M(k(1-\frac{r}{k})^p\sinh^v(1-\frac{r}{k})C(p,v)+r)+a^2+$$

$$r^2))$$
(1086)

$$R_{rr} = \frac{M}{(-2M(k(1-\frac{r}{k})^p\sinh^v(1-\frac{r}{k})C(p,v)+r)+a^2+r^2)}$$

$$\frac{1}{(a^2x^2+r^2)}(\frac{1}{k(k-r)^2}((a^2x^2+r^2)(1-\frac{r}{k})^p\sinh^{v-2}(1-\frac{r}{k})C(p,v)$$

$$(\sinh^2(1-\frac{r}{k})(k^2(p^2-p+v)-2krv+r^2v)+kpv(k-r)\sinh(2-\frac{2r}{k})+$$

$$(v-1)v(k-r)^2\cosh^2(1-\frac{r}{k})))+2(k(1-\frac{r}{k})^p\sinh^v(1-\frac{r}{k})C(p,v)+r)$$

$$+\frac{2r}{r-k}((1-\frac{r}{k})^p\sinh^{v-1}(1-\frac{r}{k})(-C(p,v))(kp\sinh(1-\frac{r}{k})+v(k-r)$$

$$\cosh(1-\frac{r}{k}))+k-r))$$
(1087)

$$R_{\theta\theta} = -\frac{2M(1-\frac{r}{k})^p\sinh^{v-1}(1-\frac{r}{k})C(p,v)}{(k-r)(a^2x^2+r^2)}(k(k+(p-1)r)\sinh(1-\frac{r}{k})$$

$$+rv(k-r)\cosh(1-\frac{r}{k}))$$
(1088)

$$R\phi\phi = \frac{M\left(x^2-1\right)\left(1-\frac{r}{k}\right)^p\sinh^{v-2}\left(1-\frac{r}{k}\right)C(p,v)}{k(k-r)^2\left(a^2x^2+r^2\right)^3}(a^2(1-x^2)(a^2x^2+$$

$$r^2)(\sinh^2(1-\frac{r}{k})(k^2(p^2-p+v)-2krv+r^2v)+kpv(k-r)\sinh(2-\frac{2r}{k})$$

$$+(v-1)v(k-r)^2\cosh^2(1-\frac{r}{k}))(-2M(k(1-\frac{r}{k})^p\sinh^v(1-\frac{r}{k})C(p,v)+$$

$$r) + a^2 + r^2) + 2k(k-r)\sinh(1 - \frac{r}{k})(k(k+(p-1)r)\sinh(1 - \frac{r}{k}) + rv$$

$$(k-r)\cosh(1 - \frac{r}{k}))(2a^2kM(x^2-1)(1 - \frac{r}{k})^p \sinh^v(1 - \frac{r}{k})C(p,v) - a^4$$

$$(x^2-2) + a^2r(2M(x^2-1) - r(x^2-3)) + r^4)) \tag{1089}$$

$$R = \frac{2M\left(1 - \frac{r}{k}\right)^p \sinh^{v-2}\left(1 - \frac{r}{k}\right)C(p,v)}{k(k-r)^2\left(a^2x^2 + r^2\right)}(\sinh^2(1 - \frac{r}{k})(k^2(p^2 - p + v) -$$

$$2krv + r^2v) + kpv(k-r)\sinh(2 - \frac{2r}{k}) + (v-1)v(k-r)^2$$

$$\cosh^2(1 - \frac{r}{k})) \tag{1090}$$

$$R^2 = \frac{4M^2}{(a^2x^2 + r^2)^6}\left(\frac{1}{k^2(k-r)^4}(a^2x^2 + r^2)^4(1 - \frac{r}{k})^{2p}\sinh^{2(v-2)}(1 - \frac{r}{k})\right.$$

$$C(p,v)^2(\sinh^2(1 - \frac{r}{k})(k^2(p^2 - p + v) - 2krv + r^2v) + kpv(k-r)$$

$$\sinh(2 - \frac{2r}{k}) + (v-1)v(k-r)^2\cosh^2(1 - \frac{r}{k}))^2 + 8(7a^4x^4 - 34a^2r^2x^2 +$$

$$7r^4)(k(1 - \frac{r}{k})^p\sinh^v(1 - \frac{r}{k})C(p,v) + r)^2 + \frac{4(5r^2 - 3a^2x^2)(a^2x^2 + r^2)^2}{(k-r)^2}$$

$$((1 - \frac{r}{k})^p\sinh^{v-1}(1 - \frac{r}{k})C(p,v)(kp\sinh(1 - \frac{r}{k}) + v(k-r)\cosh(1 - \frac{r}{k}))$$

$$-k + r)^2 + 64r(2a^4x^4 + a^2r^2x^2 - r^4)(k(1 - \frac{r}{k})^p\sinh^v(1 - \frac{r}{k})C(p,v) + r)$$

$$(1 - \frac{(1 - \frac{r}{k})^p\sinh^{v-1}(1 - \frac{r}{k})C(p,v)}{k-r}(kp\sinh(1 - \frac{r}{k}) + v(k-r)\cosh(1 -$$

$$\frac{r}{k}))) - \frac{1}{k(k-r)^2}(\sinh^2(1 - \frac{r}{k})(k^2(p^2 - p + v) - 2krv + r^2v) + kpv(k -$$

$$r)\sinh(2 - \frac{2r}{k}) + (v-1)v(k-r)^2\cosh^2(1 - \frac{r}{k}))((a^2x^2 - 3r^2)(k(1 - \frac{r}{k})^p$$

$$\sinh^v(1 - \frac{r}{k})C(p,v) + r) + 2r(a^2x^2 + r^2)(1 - \frac{1}{k-r})(1 - \frac{r}{k})^p\sinh^{v-1}(1$$

$$-\frac{r}{k})C[p,v](kp\sinh(1 - \frac{r}{k}) + v(k-r)\cosh(1 - \frac{r}{k})))) \tag{1091}$$

$$B_t = B_r = \frac{M\left(1 - \frac{r}{k}\right)^p \sinh^{v-2}\left(1 - \frac{r}{k}\right)C(p,v)}{k(k-r)^2\left(a^2x^2 + r^2\right)^2}(\sinh^2(1 - \frac{r}{k})(k^2(a^2x^2$$

$$((p-1)p+v)+r^2((p-3)p+v+2))-2krv(a^2x^2+r^2)+r^2v(a^2x^2+$$
$$r^2)+2k^4+2k^3(p-2)r)+kv(k-r)\sinh(2-\frac{2r}{k})(a^2px^2+r(k+(p-1)$$
$$r))+(v-1)v(k-r)^2(a^2x^2+r^2)\cosh^2(1-\frac{r}{k})) \tag{1092}$$

$$B_\theta = B_\phi = \frac{2M\left(1-\frac{r}{k}\right)^p \sinh^{v-1}\left(1-\frac{r}{k}\right)C(p,v)}{(r-k)\left(a^2x^2+r^2\right)^2}(k(k+(p-1)r)\sinh(1$$
$$-\frac{r}{k})+rv(k-r)\cosh(1-\frac{r}{k})) \tag{1093}$$

The energy density μ, the radial pressure P_r and the tangential pressure $P_\perp$ are obtained from Eqs (1021)- (1023) and (1084). Substituting the expressions (1063) we get

$$k^2\mu = -k^2 P_r = \frac{n(1-y)^{p-1}\sinh^{v-1}(1-y)C(p,v)}{8\pi\left(u^2x^2+y^2\right)^2}((-py+y-1)\sinh(1$$
$$-y)+v(y-1)y\cosh(1-y)) \tag{1094}$$

$$k^2 P_\perp = -\frac{n(1-y)^{p-2}\sinh^{v-2}(1-y)C(p,v)}{32\pi\left(u^2x^2+y^2\right)^2}(2\sinh^2(1-y)(p^2(u^2x^2+y^2)$$
$$-p(u^2x^2+y(3y-2))+(y-1)^2(u^2vx^2+vy^2+2))+v(y-1)((v-1)(y$$
$$-1)(u^2x^2+y^2)-2\sinh(2-2y)(pu^2x^2+(p-1)y^2+y))+(v-1)v(y$$
$$-1)^2\cosh(2-2y)(u^2x^2+y^2)) \tag{1095}$$

and we find that

$$k^2(\mu+P_\perp) = \frac{n(1-y)^{p-2}\sinh^{v-2}(1-y)C[p,v]}{32\pi\left(u^2x^2+y^2\right)^2}(-2\sinh^2(1-y)(p^2(u^2x^2$$
$$+y^2)-p(u^2x^2+y(5y-4))+(y-1)^2(u^2vx^2+vy^2+4))+v(y-1)$$
$$(2\sinh(2-2y)(pu^2x^2+(p-2)y^2+2y)+(1-v)(y-1)(u^2x^2+y^2))+$$
$$(1-v)v(y-1)^2\cosh(2-2y)(u^2x^2+y^2)) \tag{1096}$$

The graphs of $k^2\mu$, $k^2 P_\perp$ and $k^2(\mu+P_\perp)$ for $(C(p,v)=-1$, $p=2$, $v=2$, $u=3$, $n=1$) are given by Figures 298, 299 and 300. It is obvious from these graphs that the solution for these values of the constants satisfies the WEC.

Using Eqs (1063) and (1084) we find that expression (1018) for $(C(p, v) = -1, p = 2, v = 2, u = 3, n = 1)$ takes the form

$$(y - 1)^2 sinh^2(1 - y) + y(y - 1) + 9 \geq 0 \tag{1097}$$

For $0 \leq y \leq 1$ we get $(y - 1)^2 sinh^2(1 - y) + y(y - 1) + 9 > 0$, which means that for this solution we have $V_1(r, x) < 0$.

The line element d^2s of the solution is obtained from Eqs (1049) and (1084) . We get

$$d^2 s = -(1 - \frac{2M(r + kC(v, w)(1 - \frac{r}{k})^p sinh^v(1 - \frac{r}{k}))}{r^2 + a^2 cos^2\theta})d^2 t -$$
$$\frac{4Masin^2\theta(r + kC(v, w)(1 - \frac{r}{k})^p sinh^v(1 - \frac{r}{k}))}{r^2 + a^2 cos^2\theta} dtd\phi +$$
$$\frac{r^2 + a^2 cos^2\theta}{r^2 + a^2 - 2M(r + kC(v, w)(1 - \frac{r}{k})^p sinh^v(1 - \frac{r}{k}))} d^2 r +$$
$$(r^2 + a^2 cos^2\theta)d^2\theta + sin^2\theta(r^2 + a^2 +$$
$$\frac{2Ma^2 sin^2\theta(r + kC(v, w)(1 - \frac{r}{k})^p sinh^v(1 - \frac{r}{k}))}{r^2 + a^2 cos^2\theta})d^2\phi \tag{1098}$$

where as we said before the constants $C(v, w)$, p and v satisfy the relations $C(v, w) < 0$, $p \geq 2$ and $v \geq 2$ but are otherwise arbitrary.

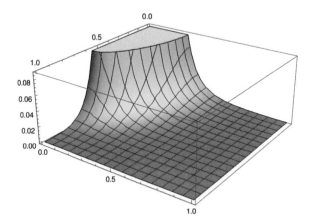

Figure 298: $k^2\mu$ of expression (1094) for $(C(p, v) = -1, p = 2, v = 2, u = 3, n = 1)$

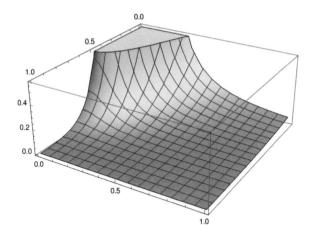

Figure 299: $k^2 P_\perp$ of expression (1095) for ($C(p, v) = -1$, $p = 2$, $v = 2$, $u = 3$, $n = 1$)

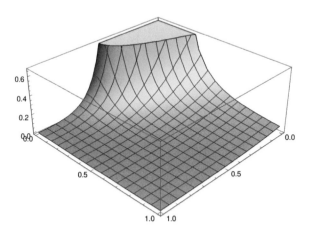

Figure 300: $k^2(\mu + P_\perp)$ of expression (1096) for ($C(p, v) = -1$, $p = 2$, $v = 2$, $u = 3$, $n = 1$)

3.1.2 Case A2: Regular Interior Solutions with $F(r) = r^2$ which have in the whole interior region the energy density μ non-negative but not the quantity $\mu + P_\perp$

We argued before that it is possible to find in our model with $F(r) = r^2$ regular interior solutions, which however do not satisfy the WEC. Solution of this type is the solution of Example 3.1.2.1

Example 3.1.2.1 : Solution with $F(r) = r^2$ and the $h(r)$ of Eq (1099)
Consider the solution with

$$h(r) = \frac{k^{1-b}}{b}(\frac{r}{k})^p((p-1)(k^b - r^b) + bk^b) \tag{1099}$$

where $b > 0$ and $p > 0$ since $h(r)$ must be regular in the interior region. The $h(r)$ of Eq (38) for $q = 0$ becomes the above $h(r)$. The non-vanishing components of the Ricci tensor $R_{\mu\nu}$, the Ricci scalar R and the second order curvature invariant R^2 of this solution are the following :

$$R_{tt} = \frac{M(p-1)k^{1-2b}(b+p-1)(\frac{r}{k})^p}{b^2 r^2 (a^2 x^2 + r^2)^3}$$
$$(-a^4 bx^2 k^b(pk^b - (b+p)r^b) + a^2(2kMx^2(\frac{r}{k})^p$$
$$(k^b(b+p-1) - (p-1)r^b)(pk^b - (b+p)r^b) + br^2 k^b(r^b(x^2(b+p+2) +$$
$$b+p-4) - k^b((p+2)x^2 + p-4))) - r^2((p-2)k^b - (b+p-2)r^b)$$
$$(br^2 k^b - 2kM(\frac{r}{k})^p(k^b(b+p-1) - (p-1)r^b))) \tag{1100}$$

$$R_{t\phi} = -\frac{aM(p-1)(1-x^2)k^{1-2b}(b+p-1)(\frac{r}{k})^p}{b^2 r^2 (a^2 x^2 + r^2)^3}(-a^4 bx^2 k^b(pk^b -$$
$$(b+p)r^b) + a^2(2kMx^2(\frac{r}{k})^p(k^b(b+p-1) - (p-1)r^b)(pk^b -$$
$$(b+p)r^b) + br^2 k^b(r^b(x^2(b+p) + b+p-4) - (k^b(b+p-1) -$$
$$(p-1)r^b)(pk^b - (b+p)r^b) + br^2 k^b(r^b(x^2(b+p) + b+p-4) -$$
$$(b+p-2)r^b) + br^2 k^b((b+p-4)r^b - (p-4)k^b)))) \tag{1101}$$

$$R_{rr} = -\frac{kM(p-1)(b+p-1)(\frac{r}{k})^p}{a^2 x^2 + r^2}$$

$$(k^b(a^2px^2 + (p-2)r^2) - r^b(a^2x^2(b+p) + r^2(b+p-2)))$$
$$(r^2(2kM(\frac{r}{k})^p(k^b(b+p-1) - (p-1)r^b) - b(a^2+r^2)k^b)^{-1} \quad (1102)$$

$$R_{\theta\theta} = \frac{2Mk^{1-b}}{b(a^2x^2+r^2)}(p-1)(b+p-1)(k^b-r^b)(\frac{r}{k})^p \quad (1103)$$

$$R_{\phi\phi} = -\frac{Mk^{1-2b}}{b^2r^2(a^2x^2+r^2)^3}(-1+p)(-1+b+p)(r/k)^p(1-x^2)$$
$$(-a^6bx^2(x^2-1)k^b(pk^b - (b+p)r^b) + a^4(2kM(x-1)x^2(x+1)$$
$$(\frac{r}{k})^p(k^b(b+p-1) - (p-1)r^b)(pk^b - (b+p)$$
$$r^b) + br^2k^b(k^b(-px^4 + p + 2x^2 - 4) + r^b(x^4(b+p) - b - p - 2$$
$$x^2 + 4))) + a^2r^2(2kM(x-1)(x+1)(\frac{r}{k})^p(k^b$$
$$b+p-1) - (p-1)r^b)((p-2)k^b - (b+p-2)r^b) + br^2k^b(k^b(-(p-2)$$
$$x^2 + p - 6) + r^b(x^2(b+p-2) - b - p + 6))) - 2br^6k^b(k^b-r^b) \quad (1104)$$

$$R = \frac{2Mk^{1-b}}{br^2(a^2x^2+r^2)}(p-1)(b+p-1)(\frac{r}{k})^p(pk^b - (b+p)r^b) \quad (1105)$$

$$R^2 = \frac{4M^2k^{2-2b}}{b^2r^4(a^2x^2+r^2)^6}(\frac{r}{k})^{2p}(k^{2b}(b+p-1)^2(a^8(p-1)^2p^2x^8 + 4a^6p(p$$
$$((p-4)p-1)+1)r^2x^6 + 2a^4(p(3(p-5)(p-1)p+62)+28)r^4x^4 + 4a^2$$
$$(p(p(p((p-8)p+19)+11)-68)r^6x^2 + (p(p(p((p-10)p+41)-76)+56)$$
$$r^8) - 2(p-1)k^b(b+p-1)r^b(a^8(p-1)px^8(b+p-1)(b+p) + 2a^6r^2x^6$$
$$(b^2(2(p-2)p-1) + 2bp(2(p-3)p-1) + b + 2p(p(p((p-4)p-1)+1))$$
$$+2a^4r^4x^4(b^2(3(p-3)p+1) + b(3p(p(2p-9)+5)+31) + p(3(p-5)$$
$$(p-1)p+62)+28) + 2a^2r^6x^2(b^2(2(p-4)p+5) + b(2p(2(p-6)p+$$
$$19)+11) + 2(p(p(p((p-8)p+19)+11)-68)) + r^8(b^2(p-3)(p-2) +$$
$$b(p-2)(p(2p-11)+19) + p(p(p((p-10)p+41)-76)+56))(p-1)^2r^{2b}$$
$$(a^8x^8(b+p-1)^2(b+p)^2 + 4a^6r^2x^6(b+p)(b^3 + b^2(3p-4) + b(p(3p-8)$$
$$-1) + p((p-4)p-1)+1) + 2a^4r^4x^4(6(2b-3)p^3 + 3(6(b-3)b+5)p^2$$

$$+6b(b(2b-9)+5)p+b(3(b-5)(b-1)b+62)+3p^4+62p+28)+4a^2r^6$$
$$x^2(b^4+4b^3(p-2)+b^2(6(p-4)p+19)+b(2p(2(p-6)p+19)+11)+$$
$$p(p((p-8)p+19)+11)-68)+r^8(b^4+2b^3(2p-5)+b^2(6(p-5)p+$$
$$41)+2b(p-2)(p(2p-11)+19)+p(p((p-10)p+41)-76)+$$
$$56)))$$
$$\tag{1106}$$

From Eqs (1105) and (1106) we find that the solution is regular if

$$p\geq 8 \quad\text{and}\quad b>0 \tag{1107}$$

since for these values of p the invariants R and R^2 are regular.

The eigenvalues of the Ricci tensor R^ν_μ can be obtained from Eqs (1019), (1020) and (1099). We get

$$B_t=B_1=B_r=\frac{M(p-1)k^{1-b}(b+p-1)}{b\left(a^2rx^2+r^3\right)^2}$$
$$\left(\frac{r}{k}\right)^p\left(\left(k^b-r^b\right)\left(a^2px^2+(p-2)r^2\right)+br^b\left(-a^2x^2-r^2\right)\right) \tag{1108}$$

$$B_\phi=B_2=B_\theta=\frac{2M(p-1)k^{1-b}(b+p-1)\left(k^b-r^b\right)\left(\frac{r}{k}\right)^p}{b\left(a^2x^2+r^2\right)^2} \tag{1109}$$

The energy density μ, the radial pressure P_r, the tangential pressure $P_\perp$ and the quantities $\mu+P_r$ and $\mu+P_\perp$ are obtained from Eqs (1021) - (1025) and (1099). If we introduce the variables y, n and u by the relations (1063) we get

$$k^2\mu=-k^2P_r=\frac{n(p-1)(b+p-1)\left(1-y^b\right)y^p}{8\pi b\left(u^2x^2+y^2\right)^2} \tag{1110}$$

$$k^2P_\perp=\frac{n(p-1)(b+p-1)y^{p-2}}{16\pi b(u^2x^2+y^2)^2}(y^b(u^2x^2(b+p)+$$
$$y^2(b+p-2))-pu^2x^2-(p-2)y^2) \tag{1111}$$

$$k^2(\mu+P_\perp)=-\frac{n(p-1)(b+p-1)y^{p-2}}{16\pi b\left(u^2x^2+y^2\right)^2}$$
$$(y^2\left(-(b+p-4)y^b+p-4\right)-u^2x^2\left((b+p)y^b-p\right)) \tag{1112}$$

It is obvious from Eq (1110) that the energy density μ is non-negative in the interior region. However from Eq (1112) we find that as $y \to 0$ we have $\mu + P_\perp \leq 0$. Therefore the solution does not satisfy the WEC. In Figures (301), (302) and (303) we give the graphs of $k^2\mu$, $k^2 P_\perp$ and $k^2(\mu + P_\perp)$ for ($p = 8$, $n = 1$, $b = 2$, $u = 0.8$).

Using Eqs (1063) and (1099) we find that expression (1018) for ($p = 8$, $n = 1$, $b = 2$, $u = 0.8$) takes the form

$$0.64 + y^2 - \frac{9y^8}{2} + \frac{7y^{10}}{2} \geq 0 \tag{1113}$$

For $0 \leq y \leq 1$ we get $0.64 + y^2 - \frac{9y^8}{2} + \frac{7y^{10}}{2} > 0$, which means that for this solution we have $V_1(r, x) < 0$.

The line element of the solution is obtained from Eqs (999), (1000) and (1099) for $F(r) = r^2$. We get

$$
d^2 s = -(1 - \frac{2Mk^{1-b}((p-1)(k^p - r^p) + bk^p)}{b(a^2 cos^2\theta + r^2)}(\frac{r}{k})^p)d^2 t -
$$
$$
\frac{4aM \sin^2\theta k^{1-b}((p-1)(k^p - r^p) + bk^p)}{b(a^2 cos^2\theta + r^2)}(\frac{r}{k})^p dt d\phi +
$$
$$
\frac{b(a^2 \cos^2\theta + r^2)}{b(a^2 + r^2) - 2Mk^{1-b}(\frac{r}{k})^p((p-1)(k^p - r^p) + bk^p)}d^2 r + (r^2 + a^2 cos^2\theta)d^2\theta
$$
$$
+ \sin^2\theta(\frac{2a^2 M \sin^2\theta k^{1-b}((p-1)(k^p - r^p) + bk^p)}{b(a^2 cos^2\theta + r^2)}(\frac{r}{k})^p + a^2 +
$$
$$
r^2)d^2\phi \tag{1114}
$$

where p and b can take any values consistent with relations Eqs (1107).

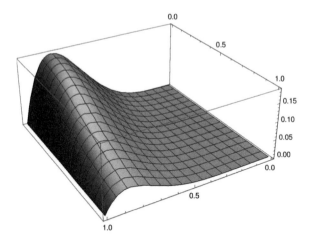

Figure 301: $k^2\mu$ of expression (1110) for ($p = 8$, $n = 1$, $b = 2$, $u = 0.8$)

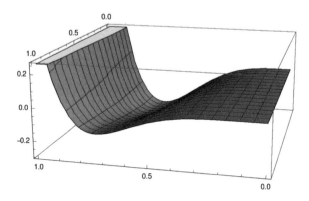

Figure 302: $k^2 P_\perp$ of expression (1111) for ($p = 8$, $n = 1$, $b = 2$, $u = 0.8$)

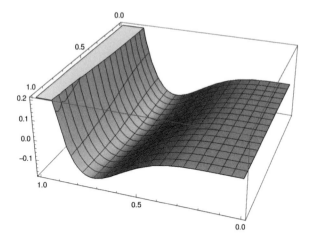

Figure 303: $k^2(\mu + P_\perp)$ of expression (1112) for $(p = 8, n = 1, b = 2, u = 0.8)$

3.2 Case B : Interior Solutions to the Solution of Kerr with $F(r) \neq r^2$.

In this most general case the non-vanishing components of the Ricci tensor $R_{\mu\nu}$ coming from the metric of Eqs (993) and (994) are the following:

$$R_{tt} = \frac{1}{2\left(a^2x^2 + F(r)\right)^4}((a^2x^2 + F(r))(F'(r)H'(r)(a^2(x^2 - 2) - F(r)) +$$
$$(a^2 + F(r))H''(r)(a^2x^2 + F(r))) + H(r)(a^2(-(a^2x^2(F''(r) + 2x^2 - 6) +$$
$$x^2F'(r)H'(r) + (x^2 - 2)F'(r)^2)) + F(r)(a^2(-((x^2 + 1)F''(r) -$$
$$6x^2 + 2)) - F'(r)H'(r) + F'(r)^2) + H''(r)(a^2x^2 + F(r))^2 - F(r)^2F''(r))$$
$$+H(r)^2(-F''(r)(a^2x^2 + F(r)) + 4a^2x^2 + F'(r)^2)) \tag{1115}$$

$$R_{t\phi} = \frac{a(x^2 - 1)}{2(a^2x^2 + F(r))^4}((a^2 + F(r))(a^2x^2 + F(r))(H''(r)(a^2x^2 + F(r)) -$$
$$2F'(r)H'(r)) + H(r)^2(-F''(r)(a^2x^2 + F(r)) + 4a^2x^2 + F'(r)^2) + H(r)$$
$$(6a^4x^2 - (a^2 + F(r))F''(r)(a^2x^2 + F(r)) - a^2x^2F'(r)H'(r) + 2a^2F'(r)^2 +$$

328

$$H''(r)(a^2x^2 + F(r))^2 + 6a^2x^2F(r) - 2a^2F(r) - F(r)F'(r)H'(r) +$$
$$2F(r)F'(r)^2 - 2F(r)^2)) \tag{1116}$$

$$R_{rr} = \frac{1}{2(a^2 + F(r) + H(r))(a^2x^2 + F(r))^2}(a^2(-x^2(F''(r)(a^2(x^2 + 1) + H$$
$$H(r)) + a^2(x^2H''(r) - 2x^2 - 2)) + x^2F'(r)H'(r) + F'(r)^2) + F(r)(-F''(r)$$
$$(a^2(3x^2 + 1) + H(r)) - 2a^2(x^2H''(r) - 3x^2 + 1) + F'(r)(F'(r) + H'(r)))$$
$$-F(r)^2(2F''(r) + H''(r)) \tag{1117}$$

$$R_{\theta\theta} = \frac{1}{2(x^2 - 1)(a^2x^2 + F(r))^2}(a^2(a^2x^2(F''(r) - 2) + x^2F'(r)H'(r) +$$
$$(x^2 - 1)F'(r)^2) + F(r)(F''(r)(a^2(x^2 + 1) + H(r)) + 2a^2(1 - 3x^2) +$$
$$F'(r)H'(r)) + H(r)(a^2x^2(F''(r) - 4) - F'(r)^2) +$$
$$F(r)^2(F''(r) - 2)) \tag{1118}$$

$$R_{\phi\phi} = \frac{1}{2(a^2x^2 + F(r))^4}((x^2 - 1)(a^8x^4(x^2(F''(r) - 2) + (x^2 - 1)H''(r)) -$$
$$a^6x^2(x^2 - 2)F'(r)H'(r) + F(r)^3(F''(r)(3a^2x^2 + a^2 + H(r)) + a^2((x^2 - 1)$$
$$H''(r) - 6x^2 - 2) + F'(r)H'(r)) - a^2(x^2 - 1)H(r)^2(a^2x^2(F''(r) - 4) -$$
$$F'(r)^2) + a^4H(r)(a^2x^2((x^4 - x^2 + 1F''(r) + (x^2 - 1)x^2H''(r) - 2(x^4 - 2$$
$$x^2 + 3)) - (x^2 - 1)x^2F'(r)H'(r) + (x^2 - 2)F'(r)^2) + a^2F(r)$$
$$(a^4x^2((x^2 + 3)x^2(F''(r) - 2) + (x^4 + x^2 - 2)H''(r)) + a^2(-x^4 + 2x^2 + 2)$$
$$F'(r)H'(r) + H(r)(a^2(2x^4F''(r) + F''(r) + 2(x^2 - 1)x^2H''(r) - 2x^4 - 8$$
$$x^2 + 2) - (x^2 - 1)F'(r)H'(r) + (x^2 - 3)F'(r)^2) - (x^2 - 1)H(r)^2F''(r)) +$$
$$F(r)^2(a^4(3(x^2 + 1)x^2(F''(r) - 2) + (2x^4 - x^2 - 1)H''(r)) + 3a^2F'(r)H'(r)$$
$$+H(r)(a^2((2x^2 + 1)F''(r) + (x^2 - 1)H''(r) - 8x^2 + 4) - F'(r)^2)) + F(r)^4$$
$$(F''(r) - 2))) \tag{1119}$$

The Ricci scalar R and the second order curvature invariant R^2 are given by the expressions

$$R = \frac{1}{2(a^2x^2 + F(r))^3}(a^2(-(2a^2x^2((x^2+1)(F''(r)-2) + x^2H''(r)) +$$
$$(x^2-2)F'(r)^2)) + F(r)(F'(r)^2 - 2(F''(r)(3a^2x^2 + a^2 + H(r)) + 2a^2(x^2$$
$$H''(r) - 4x^2 + 1))) + H(r)(F'(r)^2 - 2a^2x^2(F''(r)-2)) - 2F(r)^2(2F''(r)$$
$$+H''(r) - 2))$$

$$(1120)$$

$$R^2 = \frac{1}{4(a^2x^2 + F(r))^6}(8F(r)^3(F''(r)(H''(r)(a^2(x^2-1) - H(r)) + 2a^2(1-$$
$$3x^2)) + F''(r)^2(a^2(3x^2+1) + 2H(r)) + 2a^2x^2(H''(r)^2 + 2) + F'(r)H'(r)$$
$$(F''(r) - 2H''(r)) - F'(r)^2(F''(r)+1)) + a^4(4a^2x^4(a^2(2F''(r)(x^2(x^2-1)$$
$$H''(r) - 2(x^4+1)) + (x^4+1)F''(r)^2 + x^4H''(r)^2 - 4(x^2-1)x^2H''(r) + 4$$
$$(x^4+1)) - 12x^2H'(r)^2) - 8a^2x^4F'(r)H'(r)((2x^2-3)F''(r) + 2x^2H''(r) -$$
$$4x^2 + 6) - 4x^2F'(r)^2(a^2((x^4-x^2+2)F''(r) + (x^2-1)x^2H''(r) - 2(x^4-$$
$$x^2+2)) - 5x^2H'(r)^2) + 4(3x^2-4)x^2F'(r)^3H'(r) + (3x^4 - 4x^2+4)F'(r)^4)$$
$$2a^2H(r)(4a^4x^4(F''(r)(x^2H''(r) + 2x^2 + 2) - 2F''(r)^2 - 4x^2 + 4) - 4a^2x^2$$
$$F'(r)^2((2x^2-5)F''(r) + 2x^2H''(r) - x^2 + 2) - 4a^2x^4F'(r)(3F''(r) + 26)$$
$$H'(r) + 22x^2F'(r)^3H'(r) + 5(x^2-2)F'(r)^4) + H(r)^2(4a^4x^4(3F''(r)^2 + 44)$$
$$-8a^2x^2F'(r)^2(4F''(r) + 29) + 27F'(r)^4) + 4F(r)^4(2F''(r)^2 + H''(r)^2 + 4))$$
$$+F(r)^2(-4F'(r)^2(a^2(3(x^2+1)F''(r) + (x^2-1)(H''(r)-2)) - 5H'(r)^2) -$$
$$8a^2F'(r)H'(r)(-3F''(r) + x^2H''(r) + 4x^2 - 2) + 8H(r)(a^2(F''(r)(-3x^2$$
$$H''(r) - 6x^2 + 2) + (4x^2+2)F''(r)^2 + 16x^2 - 4) + F'(r)^2(-F''(r) +$$
$$2H''(r) - 1) + 3F'(r)F''(r)H'(r)) + 4(a^4(F''(r)(6(x^2-1)x^2H''(r) - 20x^4$$
$$-8x^2 + 4) + (7x^4 + 4x^2+1)F''(r)^2 + 6x^4H''(r)^2 - 4(x^2-1)x^2H''(r) + 4$$
$$(6x^4 - 4x^2+1)) - 12a^2x^2H'(r)^2) + 12H(r)^2F''(r)^2 - 4F'(r)^3H'(r) + 3$$
$$F'(r)^4) + 2F(r)(a^2(4a^2x^2(a^2(3x^2F''(r)((x^2-1)H''(r) - 2(x^2+1)) + (2x^4$$
$$+x^2+1)F''(r)^2 + 2x^4H''(r)^2 - 4(x^2-1)x^2H''(r) + 4(x^4 + 2x^2 - 1)) - 12$$
$$x^2H'(r)^2) - 4a^2x^2F'(r)H'(r)(3(x^2-2)F''(r) + 6x^2H''(r) + 4) - 4F'(r)^2$$
$$(a^2((x^4 + x^2+1)F''(r) + (x^2-1)x^2H''(r) + x^4 - 6x^2 + 2) - 5x^2H'(r)^2)$$
$$+4(x^2-2)F'(r)^3H'(r) + (x^2+2)F'(r)^4) + 4H(r)^2F''(r)(3a^2x^2F''(r) -$$
$$4F'(r)^2) + H(r)(4a^4x^2(x^2(-F''(r))(3H''(r) + 8) + 2(x^2+2)F''(r)^2 - 4$$

$$(x^2 - 4)) - 4a^2 F'(r)^2((x^2 + 5)F''(r) - 2(2x^2 H''(r) + x^2 - 1)) +$$
$$8a^2 x^2 F'(r)(3F''(r) + 13)H'(r) - 22F'(r)^3 H'(r) + 5F'(r)^4))) \qquad (1121)$$

It is obvious from Eqs (1120) and (1121) that a sufficient condition for R and R^2 to be regular in the interior region and therefore the solution to be regular in the interior region is to have

$$F(r) > 0 \text{ for } 0 \leq r \leq k \qquad (1122)$$

and

$$F(r), \ F'(r), \ F(r)''(r), \ H(r), \ H'(r), \ H''(r) \quad \text{regular for} \quad 0 \leq r \leq k \quad (1123)$$

The eigenvalues B_1, B_2, B_r and B_θ of the Ricci tensor R^ν_μ are given by the relations

$$B_1 = -\frac{1}{4(a^2 x^2 + F(r))^3}((a^2 x^2 + F(r))^2(F''(r) + H''(r) - 2) + \sqrt{S(r,x)})$$
$$\qquad (1124)$$
$$B_2 = -\frac{1}{4(a^2 x^2 + F(r))^3}((a^2 x^2 + F(r))^2(F''(r) + H''(r) - 2) - \sqrt{S(r,x)})$$
$$\qquad (1125)$$

$$B_r = \frac{1}{2(a^2 x^2 + F(r))^3}(a^2(-x^2(F''(r)(a^2(x^2 + 1) + H(r)) + a^2(x^2 H''(r)$$
$$-2(x^2 + 1))) + x^2 F'(r)H'(r) + F'(r)^2) + F(r)(-F''(r)(a^2(3x^2 + 1) +$$
$$H(r)) - 2a^2(x^2 H''(r) - 3x^2 + 1) + F'(r)(F'(r) + H'(r))) -$$
$$F(r)^2(2F''(r) + H''(r))) \qquad (1126)$$

$$B_\theta = -\frac{1}{2(a^2 x^2 + F(r))^3}(a^2(a^2 x^2(F''(r) - 2) + x^2 F'(r)H'(r) + (x^2 - 1)$$
$$F'(r)^2) + F(r)(F''(r)(a^2(x^2 + 1) + H(r)) + 2a^2(1 - 3x^2) + F'(r)H'(r))$$
$$+H(r)(a^2 x^2(F''(r) - 4) - F'(r)^2) + F(r)^2(F''(r) - 2) \qquad (1127)$$

where $S(r,x)$ is obtained from the relation

$$S(r, x) = a^4(x^2(F''(r)^2 x^2 + H''(r)^2 x^2 + 4x^2 - 4(x^2 - 2)H''(r) + 2F''(r)$$
$$((x^2 - 2)H''(r) - 2x^2))a^4 - 4F'(r)H'(r)(H''(r)x^2 - 2x^2 + (x^2 - 2)$$
$$F''(r) + 4)a^2 + 4F'(r)^2 H'(r)^2)x^4 - 4a^2 H(r)(x^2(-F''(r)^2 + (H''(r)x^2 -$$
$$2x^2 + 8)F''(r) + 4(-H''(r)x^2 + x^2 - 3))a^4 - 2x^2 F'(r)H'(r)$$
$$(F''(r) - 4)a^2 - F'(r)^2(H''(r)x^2 - 2x^2 + (x^2 - 2)F''(r) + 4)a^2 +$$
$$2F'(r)^3 H'(r))x^2 + 4H(r)^2(F'(r)^2 - a^2 x^2(F''(r) - 4))^2 + F(r)^4$$
$$(-F''(r) + H''(r) + 2)^2 + 4F(r)^3((H''(r)^2 x^2 + 4x^2 + 2(x^2 + 1)H''(r))a^2$$
$$+(a^2 x^2 + H(r))F''(r)^2 + F'(r)H'(r)(F''(r) - H''(r) - 2) - F''(r)$$
$$((4x^2 + (x^2 + 1)H''(r))a^2 + H(r)(H''(r) + 2))) + 2F(r)^2(3x^2(F''(r)^2 x^2 +$$
$$H''(r)^2 x^2 + 4x^2 + 4H''(r) - 2F''(r)(2x^2 + H''(r)))a^4 + 2F'(r)H'(r)(-3$$
$$H''(r)x^2 - 2x^2 + (x^2 + 2)F''(r) - 4)a^2 + 2F'(r)^2 H'(r)^2 + 2H(r)^2 F''(r)^2$$
$$+2H(r)((-F''(r)(3H''(r) + 10)x^2 + (2x^2 + 1)F''(r)^2 + 4(H''(r)x^2 + 3$$
$$x^2 - 1))a^2 + 2F'(r)H'(r)F''(r) + F'(x)^2(-F''(r) + H''(r) + 2))) + 4F(r)$$
$$(a^2(x^2(F''(r)^2 x^2 + H''(r)^2 x^2 + 4x^2 - 2(x^2 - 3)H''(r) + F''(r)$$
$$((x^2 - 3)H''(r) - 4x^2))a^4 - F'(r)H'(r)(3H''(r)x^2 - 2$$
$$x^2 + (x^2 - 4)F''(r) + 8)a^2 + 2F'(r)^2 H'(r)^2)x^2 + 2H(r)^2(a^2 x^2$$
$$(F''(r) - 4) - F'(r)^2)F''(r) + H(r)(x^2((x^2 + 2)F''(r)^2 - (3H''(r)x^2 +$$
$$6x^2 + 8)F''(r) + 8(H''(r)x^2 + x^2 + 1))a^4 + 4x^2 F'(r)H'(r)(F''(r) - 2)a^2$$
$$+2F'(r)^2(H''(r)x^2 - F''(r) + 2)a^2 - 2F'(r)^3 H'(r)))) \tag{1128}$$

We expect one of the eigenvalues B_1 and B_2 to correspond to a timelike eigenvector $(u_t)^\mu$ of the Ricci tensor R_μ^ν, which we call B_t, and the other to correspond to a spacelike eigenvector $(u_\phi)^\mu$, which we call B_ϕ. Proceeding as in the case with $F(r) = r^2$ we get $(u_i)_\mu (u_i)^\mu = ((u_i)^t)^2 V_i(r, x)$, where $V_i(r, x)$ is given by Eq (1015). Explicitly we have in this case :

$$V_1(r, x) = -\frac{1}{a^2 x^2 + F(r)}(4a^2(x^2 - 1)(a^2(x^2 + 1)F(r) + a^2(a^2 x^2 + (x^2 - 1)$$
$$H(r)) + F(r)^2)(H(r)(a^2 x^2(F''(r) - 6) + F(r)(F''(r) + 2) - 2F'(r)^2)$$
$$-(a^2 x^2 + F(r))(H''(r)(a^2 x^2 + F(r)) - 2F'(r)H'(r)))^2(a^2(x^2(a^2(a^2$$
$$x^2(x^2 F''(r) + (x^2 - 2)H''(r) - 2x^2) - 2(x^2 - 2)F'(r)H'(r)) - \sqrt{S(r, x)})$$

$$+2H(r)(a^2x^2(F''(r)+2x^2-6)+(x^2-2)F'(r)^2))+F(r)(-\sqrt{S(r,x)}+$$
$$3a^4x^4F''(r)+a^4x^4H''(r)-4a^4x^2H''(r)-6a^4x^4+4a^2F'(r)H'(r)+2H(r)$$
$$(a^2((x^2+1)F''(r)-6x^2+2)-F'(r)^2))+F(r)^2(F''(r)(3a^2x^2+2H(r))+$$
$$a^2(-((x^2+2)H''(r)+6x^2))+2F'(r)H'(r))+F(r)^3(F''(r)-H''(r)-$$
$$2))^{(-2)}-4a^2(x^2-1)H(r)((a^2x^2+F(r))(H''(r)(a^2x^2+F(r))-2F'(r)$$
$$H'(r))-H(r)(a^2x^2(F''(r)-6)+F(r)(F''(r)+2)-2F'(r)^2))(a^2(x^2(a^2$$
$$(a^2(x^2F''(r)+(x^2-2)H''(r)-2x^2)-2(x^2-2)F'(r)H'(r))-$$
$$\sqrt{S(r,x)})+2H(r)(a^2x^2(F''(r)+2x^2-6)+(x^2-2)F'(r)^2))+F(r)$$
$$(-\sqrt{S(r,x)}+3a^4x^4F''(r)+a^4x^4H''(r)-4a^4x^2H''(r)-6a^4x^4+$$
$$4a^2F'(r)H'(r)+2H(r)(a^2((x^2+1)F''(r)-6x^2+2)-F'(r)^2))+$$
$$F(r)^2(F''(r)(3a^2x^2+2H(r))+a^2(-((x^2+2)H''(r)+6x^2))+$$
$$2F'(r)H'(r))+F(r)^3(F''(r)-H''(r)-2))^{(-1)}+a^2x^2+$$
$$F(r)+H(r)) \tag{1129}$$

$$V_2(r,x)=-\frac{1}{a^2x^2+F(r)}(4a^2(x^2-1)(a^2(x^2+1)F(r)+a^2(a^2$$
$$x^2+(x^2-1)H(r))+F(r)^2)(H(r)(a^2x^2(F''(r)-6)+$$
$$F(r)(F''(r)+2)-2F'(r)^2)-(a^2x^2+F(r))(H''(r)(a^2x^2+F(r))-$$
$$2F'(r)H'(r)))^2(a^2(x^2(\sqrt{S(r,x)}+a^2(a^2x^2(x^2F''(r)+$$
$$(x^2-2)H''(r)-2x^2)-2(x^2-2)F'(r)H'(r)))+2H(r)(a^2x^2(F''(r)+$$
$$2x^2-6)+(x^2-2)F'(r)^2))+F(r)(\sqrt{S(r,x)}+3a^4x^4F''(r)+$$
$$a^4x^4H''(r)-4a^4x^2H''(r)-6a^4x^4+4a^2F'(r)H'(r)+2H(r)$$
$$(a^2((x^2+1)F''(r)-6x^2+2)-F'(r)^2)+F(r)^2(F''(r)(3a^2x^2+2$$
$$H(r))+a^2(-((x^2+2)H''(r)+6x^2))+2F'(r)H'(r))+F(r)^3(F''(r)-$$
$$H''(r)-2))^{(-2)}-4a^2(x^2-1)H(r)((a^2x^2+F(r))(H''(r)(a^2x^2+F(r))$$
$$-2F'(r)H'(r))-H(r)(a^2x^2(F''(r)-6)+F(r)(F''(r)+2)-2F'(r)^2))$$
$$(a^2(x^2(\sqrt{S(r,x)}+a^2(a^2x^2(x^2F''(r)+(x^2-2)H''(r)-$$
$$2x^2)-2(x^2-2)F'(r)H'(r)))+2H(r)(a^2x^2(F''(r)+2$$
$$x^2-6)+(x^2-2)F'(r)^2))+F(r)(\sqrt{S(r,x)}+3$$
$$a^4x^4F''(r)+a^4x^4H''(r)-4a^4x^2H''(r)-6a^4x^4+$$

$$4a^2 F'(r)H'(r) + 2H(r)(a^2((x^2+1)F''(r) - 6x^2 + 2) - F'(r)^2)) +$$
$$F(r)^2(F''(r)(3a^2x^2 + 2H(r)) + a^2(-((x^2+2)H''(r) + 6x^2)) + 2F'(r)$$
$$H'(r)) + F(r)^3(F''(r) - H''(r) - 2))^{(-1)} + a^2x^2 + F(r) + H(r)) \quad (1130)$$

We shall try to find solutions with $F(r) \neq r^2$, which in the interior region satisfy the relations

$$V_1(r,x) \leq 0 \quad \text{and} \quad V_2(r,x) \geq 0 \qquad (1131)$$

We do that because these relations, which imply that $B_1 = B_t$ and $B_2 = B_\phi$, hold if $F(r) = r^2$ as we see from Eqs (1016) and (1017). For these solutions we get

$$\mu = -\frac{1}{8\pi}(B_1 - \frac{R}{2}) = \frac{1}{32\pi(a^2x^2 + F(r))^3}(\sqrt{S(r,x)} - a^4x^4 F''(r) -$$
$$2a^4x^2 F''(r) - a^4x^4 H''(r) + 2a^4x^4 + 4a^4x^2 - a^2x^2 F'(r)^2 + 2a^2 F'(r)^2 +$$
$$F(r)(F'(r)^2 - 2(F''(r)(2a^2x^2 + a^2 + H(r)) + a^2(x^2 H''(r) - 6x^2 + 2))) +$$
$$H(r)(F'(r)^2 - 2a^2x^2(F''(r) - 2)) - F(r)^2(3F''(r) + H''(r) - 2)) \quad (1132)$$

$$P_\phi = \frac{1}{8\pi}(B_2 - \frac{R}{2}) = \frac{1}{32\pi(a^2x^2 + F(r))^3}(\sqrt{S(r,x)} + a^4x^4 F''(r)2a^4x^2$$
$$F''(r) + a^4x^4 H''(r) - 2a^4x^4 - 4a^4x^2 + a^2x^2 F'(r)^2 - 2a^2 F'(r)^2 +$$
$$F(r)(2(F''(r)(2a^2x^2 + a^2 + H(r)) + a^2(x^2 H''(r) - 6x^2 + 2)) - F'(r)^2) +$$
$$H(r)(2a^2x^2(F''(r) - 2) - F'(r)^2) + F(r)^2(3F''(r) + H''(r) - 2)) \quad (1133)$$

The P_r and P_θ are obtained from Eqs (1120), (1126)) and (1127). We get

$$P_r = \frac{1}{32\pi(a^2x^2 + F(r))^3}(a^2x^2 F'(r)(F'(r) + 2H'(r)) + F(r)(-4a^2x^2 +$$
$$2F'(r)H'(r) + F'(r)^2) - H(r)(4a^2x^2 + F'(r)^2) - 4F(r)^2) \qquad (1134)$$

$$P_\theta = \frac{1}{32(a^2x^2 + F(r))^3}(H(r)(4a^2x^2 + F'(r)^2) + a^2x^2(2a^2x^2(F''(r) +$$
$$H''(r) - 2) - 2F'(r)H'(r) - F'(r)^2) + F(r)(4a^2x^2(F''(r) + H''(r) - 1) -$$
$$2F'(r)H'(r) - F'(r)^2) + 2F(r)^2(F''(r) + H''(r)))) \qquad (1135)$$

Also we can calculate the quantities $\mu + P_r$, $\mu + P_\theta$ and $\mu + P_\phi$. We get

$$\mu + P_r = -\frac{1}{32\pi(a^2x^2 + F(r))^3}(-\sqrt{S(r,x)} + a^2(x^2(F''(r)(a^2(x^2 + 2) +$$
$$2H(r)) + a^2(x^2H''(r) - 2(x^2 + 2))) - 2x^2F'(r)H'(r) - 2F'(r)^2) +$$
$$2F(r)(F''(r)(2a^2x^2 + a^2 + H(r)) + a^2(x^2H''(r) - 4x^2 + 2) - F'(r)H'(r)$$
$$-F'(r)^2) + F(r)^2(3F''(r) + H''(r) + 2)) \tag{1136}$$

$$\mu + P_\theta = \frac{1}{32\pi(a^2x^2 + F(r))^3}(\sqrt{S(r,x)} + a^4x^4F''(r) - 2a^4x^2F''(r) +$$
$$a^4x^4H''(r) - 2a^4x^4 + 4a^4x^2 - 2a^2x^2F'(r)H'(r) - 2a^2x^2F'(r)^2 + 2a^2$$
$$F'(r)^2 + 2F(r)(-(a^2 + H(r))F''(r) + a^2(x^2H''(r) + 4x^2 - 2) - F'(r)$$
$$H'(r)) + H(r)(2F'(r)^2 - 2a^2x^2(F''(r) - 4)) + F(r)^2(-F''(r) +$$
$$H''(r) + 2)) \tag{1137}$$

$$\mu + P_\phi = \frac{\sqrt{S(r,x)}}{16\pi\,(a^2x^2 + F(r))^3} \tag{1138}$$

We want to find regular solutions which satisfy the WEC, or violate these conditions as little as possible. Our work will be based on numerical computer calculations, figures of interesting quantities and estimation of the maximum violation of the WEC.

We could not find regular solutions with $F(r) \neq r^2$, which satisfy the WEC. We found however regular solutions which violate slightly these conditions. To draw figures of the interesting quantities we shall assume that the functions $F(r) = F(r,k)$ and $H(r) = H(r, M, k)$ under the substitutions (1063)) behave as follows

$$F(r,k) = F(y,k) = k^2G(y) \text{ and } H(r, M, k) = H(y, n, k) = k^2Z(y, n) \tag{1139}$$

where the functions G and Z do not depend on k. Then we get

$$F'(r,k) = kG'(y) \quad \text{and} \quad F''(r,k) = G''(y) \tag{1140}$$

$$H'(r, M, k) = kZ'(y, n) \quad \text{and} \quad H''(r, M, k) = Z''(y, n) \tag{1141}$$

where prime on a function of r (of y) means derivative with respect to r (to y) of this function. Using these relations we find from the explicit expressions of V_1, V_2, μ, P_r, P_θ, P_ϕ, $\mu+P_r$, $\mu+P_\theta$ and $\mu+P_\phi$ that after the substitutions (1063) the functions V_1, V_2, $k^2\mu$, k^2P_r, k^2P_ϕ, $k^2(\mu+P_r)$, $k^2(\mu+P_\theta)$ and $k^2(\mu+P_\phi)$ are independent of k. We shall use this information in figures of V_1, V_2, $k^2\mu$, k^2P_r, k^2P_θ, k^2P_ϕ, $k^2(\mu+P_r)$, $k^2(\mu+P_\theta)$ and $k^2(\mu+P_\phi)$ we shall present.

To find if perfect fluid solutions exist, which are interior solutions to Kerr's solution if $F(r) \neq r^2$ we consider the eigenvalues B_r and B_θ, which are given by Eqs (1126) and (1127). For a perfect fluid solution the relation $B_r - B_\theta = 0$ should holds. Using Eqs (1126) and (1127) this relation gives

$$-H(r)(4a^2x^2 + F'(r)^2) + a^2x^2(F'(r)(F'(r) + 2H'(r)) - a^2x^2(F''(r) +$$
$$H''(r) - 2)) + F(r)(-2a^2x^2(F''(r) + H''(r)) + 2F'(r)H'(r) + F'(r)^2) -$$
$$F(r)^2(F''(r) + H''(r) + 2) = 0 \tag{1142}$$

Since the coefficients of the various powers of x of this equation should vanish we get the relations

$$F''(r) + H''(r) - 2 = 0 \tag{1143}$$

$$-2F'(r)H'(r) - F'(r)^2 + 4F(r) + 4H(r) = 0 \tag{1144}$$

$$F(r)F'(r)\left(F'(r) + 2H'(r)\right) - H(r)F'(r)^2 - 4F(r)^2 = 0 \tag{1145}$$

where Eqs (1144) and (1145) were simplified with the help of Eq (1143). Solving the system and imposing the matching conditions we get the relations

$$F(r) = r^2 \text{ and } H(r) = -2Mr \tag{1146}$$

which give the solution of Kerr. Therefore there is no perfect fluid solution with $F(r) \neq r^2$ interior to the solution of Kerr.

For $r = k$ and $x = 1$ relations (997) and (1129) give

$$V_1(k,1) = -\frac{a^2 + F(k) + H(k)}{a^2 + F(k)} = -\frac{a^2 + k^2 - 2Mk}{a^2 + k^2} \tag{1147}$$

Combining the first of Eqs (1131) and Eq (1147) we find that relation

$$a^2 + k^2 - 2Mk \geq 0 \tag{1148}$$

should hold. Therefore we must have $k \geq M+(M^2-a^2)^{1/2}$ or $k \leq M-(M^2-a^2)^{1/2}$. Since $r = k$ is the matching surface and the relation $a^2+r^2-2Mr = 0$ gives the horizons of the solution of Kerr the matching occurs outside or on

336

the outer horizon of the exterior solution of Kerr or inside or on the inner horizon of Kerr.

We shall consider three examples of solutions, which are regular, their $F(r)$ and $H(r)$ satisfy relations (1131) and only $\mu + P_r$ violates the WEC. We have violation in a small part of the interior region.

3.2.1 Example 3.2.1

Let us take

$$F(r) = \frac{k^3}{3k - 2r} + b(r - k)^2 = k^2\left(\frac{1}{3 - 2y} + b(y - 1)^2\right) \tag{1149}$$

$$H(r) = -2Mr + p(r - k)^2 = k^2\left(-(u^2 + 1)y + p(y - 1)^2\right) \tag{1150}$$

with

$$u = 1, \; b = -0.1 \text{ and } p = 3 \tag{1151}$$

In writing Eqs (1149) and (1150) we used the relations (1063) and also the relation

$$a^2 + k^2 - 2Mk = 0 \tag{1152}$$

which implies that the matching occurs at the horizons of the exterior solution of Kerr.

Plotting expression $\frac{1}{3-2y} - 0.1(y - 1)^2$ in the interior region $0 \le y \le 1$ we find that its minimum is at $y = 0$. Therefore we get in the interior region $0 \le r \le k$ $MinF(r) = \frac{0.7k^2}{3}$ and Eq (1122) is satisfied. Since relations (1123) are also satisfied the solution with the $F(r)$ and $H(r)$ of Eqs (1149) and (1150) is regular.

To find Eqs (1149) and (1150) we started from the simple expressions $\frac{k^3}{3k-2r}$ for $F(r)$ and $-2Mr$ for $H(r)$ which satisfy the matching conditions (997) and (998) we add to them the expressions $b(r - k)^2$ and $p(r - k)^2$ respectively which are chosen such that the matching conditions are not affected. We give to the constants u, p and p the above values such that relations (1131) hold and the violation of the WEC is minimal. The graphs of $V_1(y, x)$ and $V_2(r, x)$ for the above choice of the constants are given in Figures 304 and 305. Calculating with the help of a program of Mathematica [45], which in the following we shall call simply the program, the maximum of $V_1(y, x)$ and the minimum of $V_2(y, x)$ for $0 \le y \le 1$ and $0 \le x \le 1$ we get

$MaxV_1(y,x) = -2.31437 \times 10^{-16}$ at $x = 0.958558$ and $y = 1$
$MinV_2(y,x) = 0.303737$ at $x = 1.66237 \times 10^{-8}$ and $y = 0$

Therefore relations (1131) are satisfied, which mean that the eigenvalues B_1 and B_2 of R_μ^ν are eigenvalues of a timelike and a spacelike eigenvector respectively for $0 \le y \le 1$ and $0 \le x \le 1$.

The non vanishing components of the Ricci tensor its eigenvalues and the quantities μ, P_r, $\mu + P_r$, $\mu + P_\theta$, $\mu + P_\phi$, P_θ and P_ϕ can be obtained from Eqs (1115) - (1119), (1124)) - (1128) and (1132)) - (1138) for $0 \le y \le 1$ and $0 \le x \le 1$ but since they are long they will not be given explicitly. We shall present however in Figures 306 - 312 the graphs of $k^2\mu$, $k^2 P_r$, $k^2(\mu + P_r)$, $k^2(\mu + P_\theta)$, $k^2(\mu + P_\phi)$, $k^2 P_\theta$ and $k^2 P_\phi$ in the variables y and x for the above values of the constants. Also with the help of the program we can compute the minimum or maximum value of each of these quantities for $0 \le y \le 1$ and $0 \le x \le 1$. We get

$Min\ k^2\mu = -3.53395 \times 10^{-17}$ at $x = 5.37443 \times 10^{-11}$ and $y = 1$
$Max\ k^2 P_r = 0$ at $x = 0.96749 \times 10^{-8}$ and $y = 1$
$Min\ k^2(\mu + P_r) = -0.116677$ at $x = 3.49156 \times 10^{-9}$ and $y = 0.376302$
$Min\ k^2(\mu + P_\theta) = 0.101947$ at $x = 1$ and $y = 0.791764$
$Min\ k^2(\mu + P_\phi) = 0.101947$ at $x = 1$ and $y = 0.791762$
$Min\ k^2 P_\theta = 0.0893056$ at $x = 1$ and $y = 0.688886$
$Min\ k^2 P_\phi = 0.0893056$ at $x = 1$ and $y = 0.688883$

From the above relations we conclude that $k^2\mu, k^2(\mu + P_\theta)$ and $k^2(\mu + P_\phi)$ are non negative in the whole interior region $0 \le y \le 1$ and $0 \le x \le 1$, while $k^2(\mu + P_r)$ is negative in a portion of this region. Therefore the solution, which is regular, does not satisfy the WEC.

The line element d^2s of the solution is obtained from Eqs (999), (1149)) and (1150). We get for arbitrary values of the constants

$$d^2s = -(1 + \frac{(3k - 2r)(-2Mr + p(r - k)^2)}{k^3 + (3k - 2r)(b(r - k)^2 + a^2 cos^2\theta)})d^2t +$$

$$\frac{2asin^2\theta(3k - 2r)(-2Mr + p(r - k)^2)}{k^3 + (3k - 2r)(b(r - k)^2 + a^2 cos^2\theta)} dtd\phi +$$

$$\frac{k^3 + (3k - 2r)(b(r - k)^2 + a^2 cos^2\theta)}{k^3 + (3k - 2r)(-2Mr + (b + p)(r - k)^2 + a^2 cos^2\theta)} d^2r +$$

$$(\frac{k^3}{3k - 2r} + b(r - k)^2 + a^2 cos^2\theta)d^2\theta + sin^2\theta(\frac{k^3}{3k - 2r} + b(r - k)^2 +$$

338

$$a^2(1 - \frac{sin^2\theta(3k-2k)(-2Mr+p(r-k)^2)}{k^3+(3k-2r)(b(r-k)^2+a^2cos^2\theta)})d^2\phi \tag{1153}$$

The previous solution is obtained for $M = k$, $b = -0.1$, $p = 3$ and $a = k$.

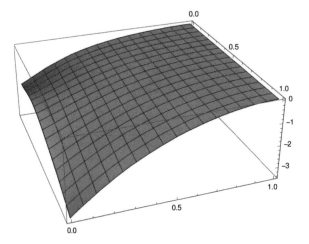

Figure 304: $V_1(y, x)$ of expression (1129) for the $F(r)$ and $H(r)$ of Eqs (1149) and (1150) with ($b = -0.1$, $p = 3$, $u = 1$)

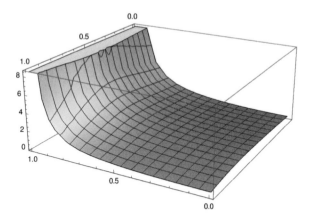

Figure 305: $V_2(y, x)$ of expression (1130) for the $F(r)$ and $H(r)$ of Eqs (1149) and (1150) with ($b = -0.1$, $p = 3$, $u = 1$)

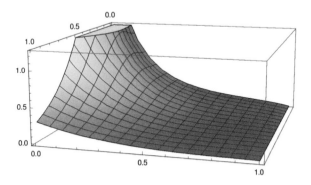

Figure 306: $k^2 \mu$ of expressions (1132) for the $F(r)$ and $H(r)$ of Eqs (1149) and (1150) with ($b = -0.1$, $p = 3$, $u = 1$)

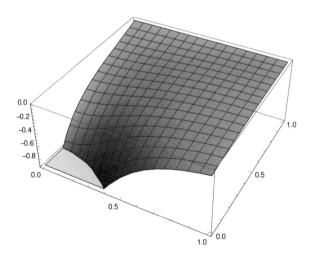

Figure 307: $k^2 P_r$ of expressions (1134) for the $F(r)$ and $H(r)$ of Eqs (1149) and (1150) with ($b = -0.1$, $p = 3$, $u = 1$)

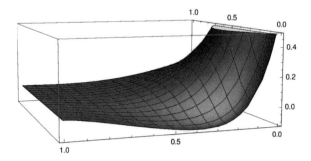

Figure 308: $k^2(\mu + P_r)$ of expressions (1136) for the $F(r)$ and $H(r)$ of Eqs (1149) and (1150) with ($b = -0.1$, $p = 3$, $u = 1$)

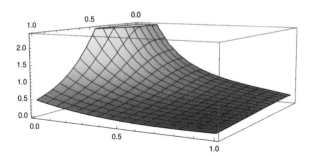

Figure 309: $k^2(\mu + P_\theta)$ of expressions (1137) for the $F(r)$ and $H(r)$ of Eqs (1149) and (1150) with ($b = -0.1$, $p = 3$, $u = 1$)

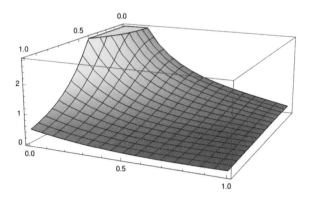

Figure 310: $k^2(\mu + P_\phi)$ of expression (1138) for the $F(r)$ and $H(r)$ of Eqs (1149) and (1150) with ($b = -0.1$, $p = 3$, $u = 1$)

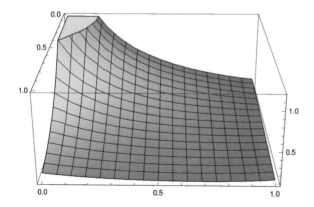

Figure 311: $k^2 P_\theta$ of expressions (1135) for the $F(r)$ and $H(r)$ of Eqs (1149) and (1150) with ($b = -0.1$, $p = 3$, $u = 1$)

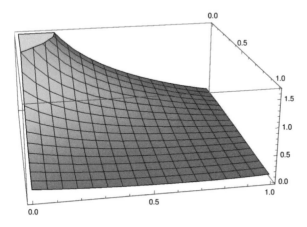

Figure 312: $k^2 P_\phi$ of expression (1133) for the $F(r)$ and $H(r)$ of Eqs (1149) and (1150) with ($b = -0.1$, $p = 3$, $u = 1$)

3.2.2 Example 3.2.2

Let us take

$$F(r) = (r - k)^2 (b + \frac{kv}{(w-1)^2(kw-r)}) + k(2r - k) =$$
$$k^2((y - 1)^2(b + \frac{v}{(w-1)^2(w-y)}) + 2y - 1) \qquad (1154)$$

$$H(r) = (r - k)^2(-b - \frac{v}{(w-1)^3} + 1) + \frac{p(r-k)^3}{k} - 2Mr =$$
$$k^2((y - 1)^2(-b - \frac{v}{(w-1)^3} + 1) - (u^2 + 1)y + p(y - 1)^3) \qquad (1155)$$

In writing Eqs (1154) and (1155) we used the relations (1063) and also the relation
$$a^2 + k^2 - 2Mk = 0 \qquad (1156)$$

which implies that the matching occurs at the horizons of the exterior solution of Kerr.

We easily find that the above $F(r)$ and $H(r)$ satisfy the matching conditions (997) and (998). If we take

$$b = -0.4, \quad w = 1.5, \quad v = 0.6, \quad p = -18 \quad \text{and} \quad u = 1 \qquad (1157)$$

relations (1131) are satisfied and the violation of the WEC for the above $F(r)$ and $H(r)$ is the smallest we could find.

Inserting in Eq (1154) the values of its constants and plotting the resulting expression $-1 + (-0.4 + \frac{2.4}{(1.5-y)})(-1 + y)^2 + 2y$ in the interior region $0 \leq y \leq 1$ we find that its minimum is at $y = 0$. Therefore we get in the interior region $0 \leq r \leq k$ $MinF(r) = 0.2k^2$ and Eq (1122) is satisfied. Since relations (1123) are also satisfied the solution with the $F(r)$ and $H(r)$ of Eqs (1154) and (1155) is regular.

The graphs of $V_1(y, x)$ and $V_2(r, x)$ for the above choice of the constants are given in Figures 313 and 314. Calculating with the help of the program the maximum of $V_1(y, x)$ and the minimum of $V_2(y, x)$ for $0 \leq y \leq 1$ and $0 \leq x \leq 1$ we get

$$Max \, V_1(r, x) = 2.22045 \times 10^{-10} \quad at \quad x = 2.09223 \times 10^{-9} \quad and \quad y = 1$$

$MinV_2(r, x) = 0.20646$ at $x = 3.31101 \times 10^{-7}$ and $y = 0$

We see that relations (1131) are satisfied, which mean that the eigenvalues B_1 and B_2 of R^ν_μ are eigenvalues of a timelike and a spacelike eigenvector respectively for $0 \le y \le 1$ and $0 \le x \le 1$.

We shall not give the explicit expressions for the non vanishing components of the Ricci tensor for its eigenvalues and for the quantities μ, P_r, $\mu + P_r$, $\mu + P_\theta$ and $\mu + P_\phi$ of this solution, which can be obtained from Eqs (1115) - (1119), (1124)) - (1128) and (1132)) - (1138), since they are long. We shall present however in Figures 315 - 321 the graphs of $k^2\mu$, k^2P_r, $k^2(\mu + P_r)$, $k^2(\mu + P_\theta)$, $k^2(\mu + P_\phi)$, k^2P_θ and k^2P_ϕ of the solution in the variables y and x for the above values of the constants. As we see from Figures 320 and 321 there is a small difference between the quantities P_θ and P_ϕ.

Also with the help of the program we can compute the minimum or maximum value of each of these quantities for $0 \le y \le 1$ and $0 \le x \le 1$. We get

$Min\, k^2\mu = -2.38702 \times 10^{-10}$ at $x = 0.963567$ and $y = 1$
$Max\, k^2P_r = 0$ at $x = 2.13169 \times 10^{-8}$ and $y = 1$
$Min\, k^2(\mu + P_r) = -0.0583008$ at $x = 0$ and $y = 0.602939$
$Min\, k^2(\mu + P_\theta) = 1.0113 \times 10^{-10}$ at $x = 0.999918$ and $y = 1$
$Min\, k^2(\mu + P_\phi) = 2.01461 \times 10^{-9}$ at $x = 0.96749$ and $y = 1$
$Min\, k^2P_\theta = -3.53395 \times 10^{-17}$ at $x = 7.68662 \times 10^{-8}$ and $y = 1$
$Min\, k^2P_\phi = 7.72351 \times 10^{-10}$ at $x = 0.979437$ and $y = 1$

From the above relations and the Figures 315 and 317 - 319 we conclude that $k^2\mu$, $k^2(\mu + P_\theta)$ and $k^2(\mu + P_\phi)$ are non negative in the whole interior region $0 \le y \le 1$ and $0 \le x \le 1$, while $k^2(\mu + P_r)$ is negative in a small portion of this region. Therefore the solution, which is regular, does not satisfy the WEC. Imaginary contribution of the order $10^{-10}i$ appearing in the calculation of $Min\, k^2(\mu + P_\theta)$ is ignored.

The line element d^2s of the solution is obtained from Eqs (999), (1154)) and (1155). We get for arbitrary values of the constants

$$d^2s = -(1 + \frac{(r-k)^2(-b - \frac{v}{(w-1)^3} + 1) + k^{-1}p(r-k)^3 - 2Mr}{(r-k)^2(b + \frac{kv}{(w-1)^2(kw-r)}) + k(2r-k) + a^2cos^2\theta})d^2t +$$

$$\frac{2asin^2\theta((r-k)^2(-b - \frac{v}{(w-1)^3} + 1) + k^{-1}p(r-k)^3 - 2Mr)}{(r-k)^2(b + \frac{kv}{(w-1)^2(kw-r)}) + k(2r-k) + a^2cos^2\theta}dtd\phi +$$

$$((r-k)^2(b + \frac{kv}{(w-1)^2(kw-r)}) + k(2r-k) + a^2cos^2\theta)((r-k)^2(b +$$

$$\frac{kv}{(w-1)^2(kw-r)}) + k(2r-k) + (r-k)^2(-b - \frac{v}{(w-1)^3} +$$
$$1) + k^{-1}p(r-k)^3 - 2Mr + a^2)^{-1}d^2r +$$
$$((r-k)^2(b + \frac{kv}{(w-1)^2(kw-r)}) + k(2r-k) + a^2cos^2\theta)d^2\theta +$$
$$sin^2\theta((r-k)^2(b + \frac{kv}{(w-1)^2(kw-r)}) + k(2r-k) + a^2(1 -$$
$$sin^2\theta \frac{(r-k)^2(-b - \frac{v}{(w-1)^3} + 1) + k^{-1}p(r-k)^3 - 2Mr}{(r-k)^2(b + \frac{kv}{(w-1)^2(kw-r)}) + k(2r-k) + a^2cos^2\theta}))d^2\phi \qquad (1158)$$

The above solution is obtained for $M = k$, $b = -0.4$, $w = 1.5$, $v = 0.6$, $p = -18$ and $a = k$.

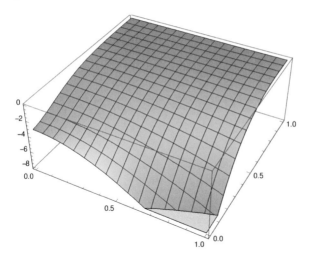

Figure 313: $V_1(y, x)$ of expression (1129)) for the $F(r)$ and $H(r)$ of Eqs (1154) and (1155) with ($b = -0.4$, $w = 1.5$, $v = 0.6$, $p = -18$, $u = 1$)

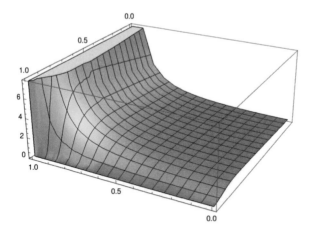

Figure 314: $V_2(y, x)$ of expression (1130)) for the $F(r)$ and $H(r)$ of Eqs (1154) and (1155) with ($b = -0.4$, $w = 1.5$, $v = 0.6$, $p = -18$, $u = 1$)

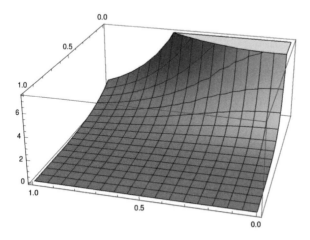

Figure 315: $k^2\mu$ of expression (1132)) for the $F(r)$ and $H(r)$ of Eqs (1154) and (1155) with ($b = -0.4$, $w = 1.5$, $v = 0.6$, $p = -18$, $u = 1$)

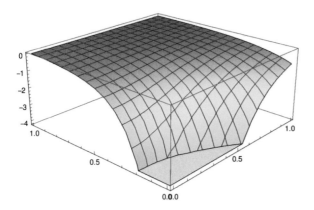

Figure 316: $k^2 P_r$ of expression (1134)) for the $F(r)$ and $H(r)$ of Eqs (1154) and (1155) with ($b = -0.4$, $w = 1.5$, $v = 0.6$, $p = -18$, $u = 1$)

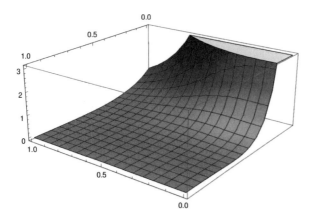

Figure 317: $k^2(\mu + P_r)$ of expression (1136)) for the $F(r)$ and $H(r)$ of Eqs (1154) and (1155) with ($b = -0.4$, $w = 1.5$, $v = 0.6$, $p = -18$, $u = 1$)

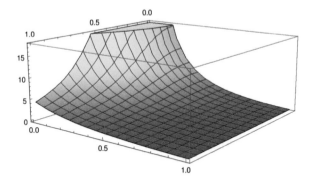

Figure 318: $k^2(\mu + P_\theta)$ of expression (1137)) for the $F(r)$ and $H(r)$ of Eqs (1154) and (1155) with ($b = -0.4$, $w = 1.5$, $v = 0.6$, $p = -18$, $u = 1$)

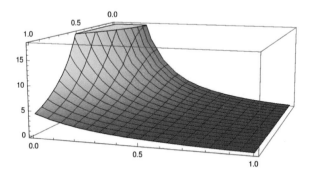

Figure 319: $k^2(\mu + P_\phi)$ of expression (1138) for the $F(r)$ and $H(r)$ of Eqs (1154) and (1155) with ($b = -0.4$, $w = 1.5$, $v = 0.6$, $p = -18$, $u = 1$)

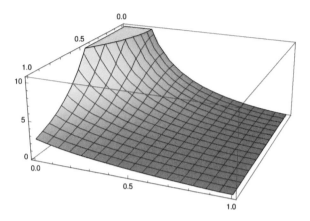

Figure 320: $k^2 P_\theta$ of expression (1135)) for the $F(r)$ and $H(r)$ of Eqs (1154) and (1155) with ($b = -0.4$, $w = 1.5$, $v = 0.6$, $p = -18$, $u = 1$)

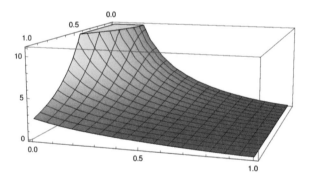

Figure 321: $k^2 P_\phi$ of expression (1133) for the $F(r)$ and $H(r)$ of Eqs (1154) and (1155) with ($b = -0.4$, $w = 1.5$, $v = 0.6$, $p = -18$, $u = 1$)

3.2.3 Example 3.2.3

Let us take

$$F(r) = b(r-k)^2 + \frac{p(r-k)^3}{k} + r^2 = k^2(b(y-1)^2 + p(y-1)^3 + y^2) \quad (1159)$$

$$H(r) = -2Mr - b(r-k)^2 + \frac{q(r-k)^3}{k} = k^2(-y(u^2+1) - b(y-1)^2 +$$
$$q(y-1)^3) \quad (1160)$$

In writing Eqs (1154) and (1155) we used the relations (1063) and also the relation

$$a^2 + k^2 - 2Mk = 0 \quad (1161)$$

which implies that the matching occurs at the horizons of the exterior solution of Kerr. For the above choice of $F(r)$ and $H(r)$ the matching conditions (997) and (998) are satisfied. If we take

$$b = 0.65, \quad p = 0.6, \quad q = -12, \quad \text{and } u = 1 \quad (1162)$$

relations (1131) are satisfied and the violation of the WEC for the above $F(r)$ and $H(r)$ is the smallest we could find.

Inserting in Eq (1159) the values of its constants and plotting the resulting expression $0.65(y-1)^2 + 0.6(y-1)^3 + y^2$ in the interior region $0 \le y \le 1$ we find that its minimum is at $y = 0$. Therefore we get in the interior region $0 \le r \le k$ $MinF(r) = 0.05k^2$ and Eq (1122) is satisfied. Since relations (1123) are also satisfied the solution with the $F(r)$ and $H(r)$ of Eqs (1159) and (1160) is regular.

The graphs of $V_1(y,x)$ and $V_2(r,x)$ for the above choice of the constants are given in Figures 322 and 323. Calculating with the help of the program the maximum of $V_1(y,x)$ and the minimum of $V_2(y,x)$ for $0 \le y \le 1$ and $0 \le x \le 1$ we get

$Max\, V_1(r,x) = 2.90201 \times 10^{-17}$ at $x = 0.955432$ and $y = 1$
$MinV_2(r,x) = 0.0513734$ at $x = 2.94949 \times 10^{-8}$ and $y = 0$ From the Figures and the above expressions we find that relations (1131) are satisfied, which mean that the eigenvalues B_1 and B_2 of R^ν_μ are eigenvalues of a timelike and a spacelike eigenvector respectively for $0 \le y \le 1$ and $0 \le x \le 1$.

The non vanishing components of the Ricci tensor its eigenvalues and the quantities μ, P_r, $\mu + P_r$, $\mu + P_\theta$, $\mu + P_\phi$, P_θ and P_ϕ can be calculated from

Eqs (1115) - (1119), (1124)) - (1128) and (1132)) - (1138) for $0 \leq y \leq 1$ and $0 \leq x \leq 1$ but we shall not give explicitly their expressions since they are long. We shall present however in Figures 324 - 330 the graphs of $k^2\mu$, k^2P_r, $k^2(\mu + P_r)$, $k^2(\mu + P_\theta)$, $k^2(\mu + P_\phi)$, k^2P_θ and k^2P_ϕ in the variables y and x for the above values of the constants. Also with the help of the program we can compute the minimum or maximum value of each of these quantities for $0 \leq y \leq 1$ and $0 \leq x \leq 1$. We get

$Min\ k^2\mu = 2.63822 \times 10^{-11}\ at\ \ x = 0.968611\ \ and\ \ y = 1$

$Max\ k^2P_r = -4.41744 \times 10^{-18}\ \ at\ \ x = 1.92687 \times 10^{-8}\ \ and\ \ y = 1$

$Min\ k^2(\mu + P_r) = -0.494875\ \ at\ \ x = 0\ \ and\ \ y = 0.392905$

$Min\ k^2(\mu + P_\theta) = 5.87312 \times 10^{-18}\ \ at\ \ x = 0.979437\ \ and\ \ y = 1$

$Min\ k^2(\mu + P_\phi) = 6.30622 \times 10^{-10}\ \ at\ \ x = 0.979437\ \ and\ \ y = 1$

$Min\ k^2P_\theta = -1.32523 \times 10^{-17}\ \ at\ \ x = 8.94712 \times 10^{-9}\ \ and\ \ y = 1$

$Min\ k^2P_\phi = 4.45917 \times 10^{-10}\ \ at\ \ x = 0.979438\ \ and\ \ y = 1$

From the above relations we conclude that $k^2\mu$, $k^2(\mu + P_\theta)$ and $k^2(\mu + P_\phi)$ are non negative in the whole interior region $0 \leq y \leq 1$ and $0 \leq x \leq 1$, while $k^2(\mu + P_r)$ is negative in a portion of this region. Therefore the solution, which is regular, does not satisfy the WEC. Imaginary contribution of the order of $10^{-10}i$ appearing in the calculation of $Min\ k^2(\mu + P_\theta)$ is ignored.

The line element d^2s of the solution is obtained from Eqs (999), (1159)) and (1160). We get for arbitrary values of the constants

$$ds^2 = -(1 + \frac{-2Mr - b(r-k)^2 + \frac{q(r-k)^3}{k}}{b(r-k)^2 + a^2\cos^2\theta + \frac{p(r-k)^3}{k} + r^2})dt^2 +$$

$$\frac{2asin^2\theta(-2Mr - b(r-k)^2 + \frac{q(r-k)^3}{k})}{b(r-k)^2 + a^2\cos^2\theta + \frac{p(r-k)^3}{k} + r^2}dtd\phi +$$

$$(a^2\cos^2\theta + b(r-k)^2 + \frac{p(r-k)^3}{k} + r^2)d\theta^2 +$$

$$\frac{a^2\cos^2\theta + b(r-k)^2 + \frac{p(r-k)^3}{k} + r^2}{a^2 + \frac{p(r-k)^3}{k} + \frac{q(r-k)^3}{k} - 2Mr + r^2}dr^2 + sin^2\theta(b(r-k)^2 + \frac{p(r-k)^3}{k}$$

$$+r^2 + a^2(1 - \frac{sin^2\theta(-b(r-k)^2 + \frac{q(r-k)^3}{k} - 2Mr)}{a^2\cos^2\theta + b(r-k)^2 + \frac{p(r-k)^3}{k} + r^2}))d\phi^2 \qquad (1163)$$

The previous solution is obtained for $M = k$, $b = 0.65$, $p = -0.6$, $q = -12$ and $a = k$.

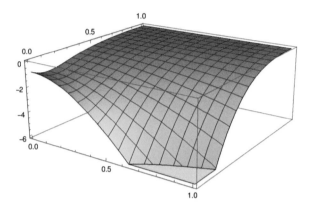

Figure 322: $V_1(y, x)$ of expression (1129)) for the $F(r)$ and $H(r)$ of Eqs (1159) and (1160) with ($b = 0.65$, $p = 0.6$, $q = -12$, $u = 1$)

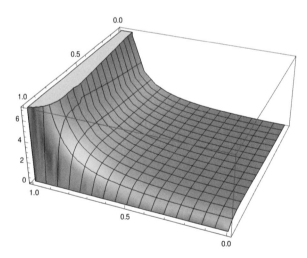

Figure 323: $V_2(y, x)$ of expression (1130)) for the $F(r)$ and $H(r)$ of Eqs (1159) and (1160) with ($b = 0.65$, $p = 0.6$, $q = -12$, $u = 1$)

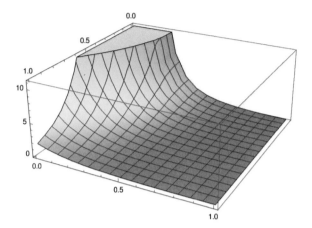

Figure 324: $k^2\mu$ of expression (1132)) for the $F(r)$ and $H(r)$ of Eqs (1159) and (1160) with ($b = 0.65$, $p = 0.6$, $q = -12$, $u = 1$)

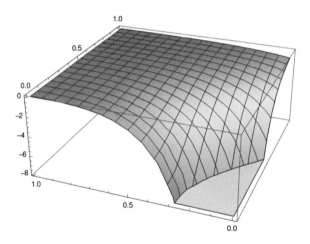

Figure 325: $k^2 P_r$ of expression (1134)) for the $F(r)$ and $H(r)$ of Eqs (1159) and (1160) with ($b = 0.65$, $p = 0.6$, $q = -12$, $u = 1$)

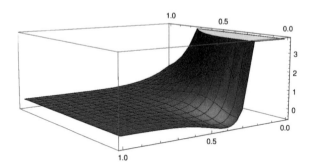

Figure 326: $k^2(\mu + P_r)$ of expression (1136)) for the $F(r)$ and $H(r)$ of Eqs (1159) and (1160) with ($b = 0.65$, $p = 0.6$, $q = -12$, $u = 1$)

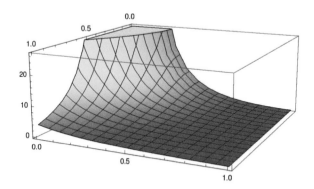

Figure 327: $k^2(\mu + P_\theta)$ of expression (1137)) for the $F(r)$ and $H(r)$ of Eqs (1159) and (1160) with ($b = 0.65$, $p = 0.6$, $q = -12$, $u = 1$)

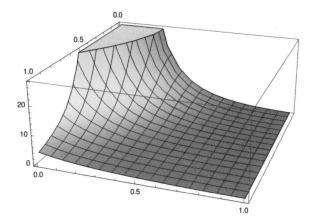

Figure 328: $k^2(\mu + P_\phi)$ of expression (1138) for the $F(r)$ and $H(r)$ of Eqs (1159) and (1160) with ($b = 0.65$, $p = 0.6$, $q = -12$, $u = 1$)

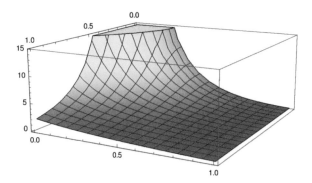

Figure 329: $k^2 P_\theta$ of expression (1135)) for the $F(r)$ and $H(r)$ of Eqs (1159) and (1160) with ($b = 0.65$, $p = 0.6$, $q = -12$, $u = 1$)

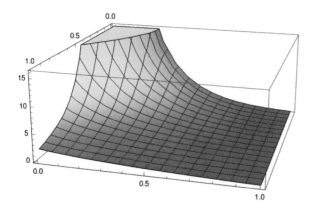

Figure 330: $k^2 P_\phi$ of expression (1133) for the $F(r)$ and $H(r)$ of Eqs (1159) and (1160) with ($b = 0.65$, $p = 0.6$, $q = -12$, $u = 1$)

References

[1] Lemos J. P. S. Regular Black Holes IV Black Holes Workshop , Universidade de Aveiro, Aveiro (19 December, 2011)

[2] Ansoldi S.Spherical Black Holes with Regular Center, Proceedings of the Conference on Black Holes and Naked Singularities (10-12 May 2007 Milan, Italy)(arXiv gr-gc /08020330)

[3] Dymnikova I. Gen. Rel. Grav. **24**, 235 (1992)

[4] Bardeen J. presented at GR5, Tiflis U.S.S.R. (1968); Borde A. Phys. Rev. **D 50**, 3692 (1994) (arXiv: gr-gc /9612057)

[5] Mbonye M. R. and Kazanas D. Phys. Rev. **D 72**, 024016 (2005)

[6] Hayward S. A. Phys. Rev. Lett. **96**, 031103 (2006) (arXiv: gr-gc/0506126)

[7] Gonzalez-Diaz P. F. Lett. Nuovo Cimento **32**, 161 (1981)

[8] Shen W. and Zhu S. Gen. Rel. Grav. **17**, 739 (1985)

[9] Poisson E. and Israel W. Class Quant. Grav. **5**, L201 (1988)

[10] Shen W. and Zhu S. Phys. Lett. **126 A**, 229 (1988)

[11] Frolov V. P. , Markov M. A. and Mukhanov V. F. Phys. Rev. **D 41**, 383 (1990)

[12] Barrabes C. and Isrel W. Phys. Rev. **D 43**, 1129 (1991)

[13] Mars M. Martin-Prats M. M. and Senovilla J. M. M. Class. Quant. Grav. **13**, L51 (1996)

[14] Magli G. Rep. Math. Phys. **44**, 407 (1999)

[15] Conboy S. and Lake K. Phys. Rev. **D 71**, 124017 (2005) (arXiv: gr-gc/0504036)

[16] www.inp.democritos.gr/ sbonano/RGTC/

[17] Sakharov A. D. Sov. Phys. JETP **22**, 241 (1966)

[18] Gliner E. B. Sov. Phys. JETP **22**, 378 (1966)

[19] Linde A. D.: *Particle Physics and Inflatiory Cosmology (Harwood Academic Press, Geneva, 1990)*

[20] Mazur P. O. and Mottola E. Gravitational Condensate Stars: An Alternative to Black Holes (arXiv: gr-gc /0109035)

[21] Visser M. and Wiltshire D. L. Class. Quant. Grav. **21**, 1135 (2004)

[22] Herrera L. and Santos N. O. Phys. Rep. **286**, 53 (1997)

[23] Krasinski A. Ann. Phys. **112**, 22 (1978)

[24] Des Mc Manus Class Quant. Grav. **8**, 863 (1991)

[25] Bicak J. and Ledvinka Phys. Rev. Lett. **71**, 1669 (1993)

[26] Pichon C. and Lynden-Bell D. Mon. Not. Roy. Astron. Soc. **280**, 1007 (1996)

[27] Viaggiu S. Int. J. Mod. Phys. D bf15, 1441 (1996)

[28] Drake S. P. and Turolla R. Class. Quant. Grav. **14**, 1883 (1997)

[29] Kyriakopoulos E. Int. J. Mod. Phys. D bf22, 1350051-1 (2013)

[30] Gonzalez-Romero L. M. Phys. Rev. **D 67**, 064011 (2013)

[31] Kyriakopoulos E. arXiv : gr-gc /1602.04067v1

[32] Hernandez-Pastora J. L. and Herrera L. Phys. Rev. **D 95**, 024003 (2017)

[33] Herrera L. and Hernandez-Pastora J. L. Phys. Rev. **D 96**, 024048 (2017)

[34] Ledvinka T. and Bicak J. Phys. Rev. **D 99**, 064046 (2019) arXiv : gr-gc /1903.01726v1.

[35] Boyer R. N. and Lindquist R. W. J. Math. Phys. **8**, 265 (1967)

[36] Darmois G. Memorial des Sciences Mathematiques Fasc. 25 (Gauthier-Villars, Paris)

[37] Lichnerowicz A. *Theories Relativistes de la Gravitation et de l'Electromagnetisme (Masson, Paris, 1955*)

[38] Gurses M. and Gursey F. J. Math. Phys. **16**, 2385 (1975)

[39] Torres R. and Fayos F. Gen. Rel. Grav. **49**, 739 (2017)

[40] Roos W. . Gen. Rel. Grav. **7**, 431 (1976)

[41] Kyriakopoulos E. arXiv : gr-gc /1602.0830v1

[42] Abramowitz M. and Stegun A (Ed.): *Handbook of Mathematical Functions with Formulas Graphs and Mathematical Tables (Dover, New York, 1970)*

[43] Dymnikova I. Gravit. Cosmol. **17**, 38 (2011)

[44] Kyriakopoulos E. Gen. Rel. Grav. **44**, 157 (2012)

[45] To find global minima or maxima we use Wolfram's programm [NMinimize....] and [NMaximize ...] for Numerical Nonlinear Global Optimization (Wolfram 2019). In the calculation of $Mink^2(\mu + P_\theta)$ of Example 3.2.2 in which we got the answer "Failed to converge to the requested accuracy or precision within 100 iterations" we used Wolfram's programm [NMinimize....Method - DifferentialEvolution].

The paper we present below was published in the Journal of Mathematical Physics. Cite as : J. Math. Phys. 63. 012501 (2022): http://doi.org/10.1063/5.0080367

Regular Interior Solutions to the Solution of Kerr which Satisfy the Weak and the Strong Energy Conditions

E. Kyriakopoulos

Department of Physics

National Technical University15780 Zografou, Athens, GREECE

E-mail: kyriakop@central.ntua.gr

Abstract

The line element of a class of solutions which match to the solution of Kerr on an oblate spheroid if the two functions $F(r)$ and $H(r)$ on which it depends satisfy certain matching conditions is presented. The non vanishing components of the Ricci tensor $R_{\mu\nu}$, the Ricci scalar R, the second order curvature invariant K, the eigenvalues of the Ricci tensor, the energy density μ, the tangential pressure $P_\perp$, and the quantity $\mu + P_\perp$ are calculated. A function $F(r)$ is given for which R and K and therefore the solutions are regular. The function $H(r)$ should be such that the solution it gives satisfies at least the Weak Energy Conditions (WEC). Several $H(r)$ are given explicitly for which the resulting solutions satisfy the WEC and also the Strong Energy Conditions (SEC) and the graphs of their μ, $P_\perp$ and $\mu + P_\perp$ for certain values of their parameters are presented. It is shown that all solutions of the class are anisotropic fluid solutions and that there are no perfect fluid solutions in the class.

1   Introduction

Soon after the discovery of the solution of Kerr [1] the problem of finding interior solutions to this solution became a major problem of the general theory of relativity. The efforts before 1978 are described in Ref [2]. According to this reference since all efforts were unsuccessful there appear an opinion, without however some proof, that the metric of Kerr may have no

361

other source than a black hole. Later attempts are described in references [3]-[8] and most resent attempts in references [9]-[12].

To find regular interior solutions to the solution of Kerr, which satisfy at least the WEC, we consider the line element of Eq (1) which depends on two functions $F(r)$ and $H(r)$ and which for $F(r) = r^2$ and $H(r) = -2Mr$ differs from the lime element of the solution of Kerr in Boyer-Lindquist coordinates [13] in the coefficient of dr^2, since this coefficient has an extra factor $cos^2(1-r/k)$. The exemption is necessary because it was found recently that for the Kerr like black hole spacetimes the regularity is linked to a violation of the WEC around the core of the rotating black hole [14].

Starting from the line element of Eq (1) we calculate the non vanishing components of the Ricci tensor $R_{\mu\nu}$, the Ricci scalar R, the second order curvature invariant K, the eigenvalues of the Ricci tensor, the eigenvalue which corresponds to the timelike eigenvector of the Ricci tensor, the energy density μ, the radial pressure P_r and the tangential pressure $P_\perp$. For all solutions of the model we have the equation of state $\mu + P_r = 0$. We calculate the normalized eigenvectors of the Ricci tensor and we prove that all solutions of the model are for arbitrary $F(r)$ and $H(r)$ anisotropic fluid solutions. Also we prove that perfect fluid solutions do not exist in the solutions of our model.

In a previous work [12] we presented many functions which at the matching surface $r = k$ satisfy the matching conditions of Eq (4). We take one of these functions as function $H(r)$ if it creates a solution which for some values of its parameters satisfies at least the WEC. Also we find with numerical computer calculations the range of values of its parameters for which this happens.

Having this in mind we find five solutions which satisfy the WEC and the SEC but not the Dominant Energy Conditions (DEC).Also we draw the graph of μ of $P_\perp$ and of $\mu + P_\perp$ of these solutions for certain values of their parameters.

2   The General Case

Consider the line element

$$d^2s = -(1 + \frac{H(r)}{F(r) + a^2cos^2\theta})dt^2 + \frac{2asin^2\theta H(r)}{F(r) + a^2cos^2\theta}dtd\phi +$$
$$\frac{cos^2(1 - r/k)(F(r) + a^2cos^2\theta)}{F(r) + H(r) + a^2}dr^2 + (F(r) + a^2cos^2\theta)d\theta^2 +$$

$$\sin^2\theta(F(r) + a^2 - \frac{a^2 \sin^2\theta H(r)}{F(r) + a^2\cos^2\theta})d\phi^2 \qquad (1)$$

where

$$F(r) = (1 - \sin(1 - r/k))^2 k^2 \qquad (2)$$

with k a constant. This line element can be the line element of an interior solution to the solution of Kerr if certain matching conditions are satisfied. The Darmois matching conditions on a surface $r = k$ are continuity of the first fundamental form and continuity of the extrinsic curvature (second fundamental form) on this surface [15]. With interior solution the solution with the above line element and exterior solution the solution of Kerr since the function $F(r)$ satisfy the relations

$$F(k) = k^2 \quad \text{and} \quad F'(k) = 2k \qquad (3)$$

continuity of the first and the second fundamental forms with Kerr's exterior solution in Boyer-Lindquist coordinates is obtained if the function $H(r)$ satisfies the relations

$$H(k) = -2Mk \quad \text{and} \quad H'(k) = -2M \qquad (4)$$

Also we find that if relations (4) are satisfied the interior metric (1) and the exterior Kerr metric as well as their first derivatives in coordinates are continuous at the matching surface $r = k$, which means that we have matching according to the matching conditions of Lichnerowicz [16]. The coordinates used are admissible. In the whole paper prime means derivative with respect to r. In Boyer-Lindquist coordinates the matching surface $r = k$ is an oblate spheroid [17].

We shall proceed in the calculations using the relation

$$\cos^2\left(1 - \frac{r}{k}\right) = \frac{F'(r)^2}{4F(r)} \qquad (5)$$

to eliminate the $\cos^2(1 - \frac{r}{k})$ from the line element of relation (1). Then the non-vanishing components of the Ricci tensor $R_{\mu\nu}$ the Ricci scalar R and the second order curvature invariant $K = R_{\mu\nu\rho\sigma}R^{\mu\nu\rho\sigma}$ (Kretschmann scalar) as functions of $F(r), H(r)$ and x defined by the relation

$$x = \cos\theta \qquad (6)$$

are

$$R_{tt} = \frac{1}{F'(r)^3 \left(a^2x^2 + F(r)\right)^3}(2F(r)(a^2 + F(r))F'(r)H''(r)(a^2x^2 + F(r))$$
$$+ H(r)(-2F(r)F''(r)H'(r)(a^2x^2 + F(r)) + 2F(r)F'(r)H''(r)(a^2x^2 +$$
$$F(r)) + F'(r)^2 H'(r)(a^2x^2 - F(r)) + F'(r)^3(F(r) - a^2(x^2 - 2))) + H'(r)$$
$$(F'(r)^2(a^4x^2 + 3a^2(x^2 - 1)F(r) - F(r)^2) - 2F(r)(a^2 + F(r))F''(r)(a^2x^2$$
$$+F(r))) + H(r)^2 F'(r)^3) \tag{7}$$

$$R_{t\phi} = \frac{1}{F'(r)^3 \left(a^2x^2 + F(r)\right)^3}(2F(r)(a^2 + F(r))F'(r)H''(r)(a^2x^2 + F(r))$$
$$+ H(r)(-2F(r)F''(r)H'(r)(a^2x^2 + F(r)) + 2F(r)F'(r)H''(r)(a^2x^2 +$$
$$F(r)) + F'(r)^2 H'(r)(a^2x^2 - F(r)) + F'(r)^3(F(r) - a^2(x^2 - 2))) + H'(r)$$
$$(F'(r)^2(a^4x^2 + 3a^2(x^2 - 1)F(r) - F(r)^2) - 2F(r)(a^2 + F(r))F''(r)(a^2x^2$$
$$+F(r))) + H(r)^2 F'(r)^3) \tag{8}$$

$$R_{rr} = \frac{1}{4F(r)F'(r)(a^2 + F(r) + H(r))(a^2x^2 + F(r))}(-2F(r)F'(r)H''(r)$$
$$(a^2x^2 + F(r)) + H'(r)(2F(r)F''(r)(a^2x^2 + F(r)) + F'(r)^2(F(r) - a^2x^2))$$
$$-H(r)F'(r)^3) \tag{9}$$

$$R_{\theta\theta} = \frac{H(r)F'(r) - 2F(r)H'(r)}{F'(r)\left(a^2x^2 + F(r)\right)} \tag{10}$$

$$R_{\phi\phi} = \frac{1}{F'(r)^3 \left(a^2x^2 + F(r)\right)^3}(x^2 - 1)(a^2\left(x^2 - 1\right)H(r)^2 F'(r)^3 + H(r)$$
$$(-2a^2(x^2 - 1)F(r)F''(r)H'(r)(a^2x^2 + F(r)) + 2a^2(x^2 - 1)F(r)F'(r)$$
$$H''(r)(a^2x^2 + F(r)) + a^2(x^2 - 1)F'(r)^2 H'(r)(a^2x^2 - F(r)) + (a^2 +$$
$$F(r))F'(r)^3(a^2(x^2 - 2) - F(r))) + (a^2 + F(r))(2a^2(x^2 - 1)F(r)F'(r)$$
$$H''(r)(a^2x^2 + F(r)) + H'(r)(F'(r)^2(a^4x^2(x^2 - 1) - a^2(x^2 - 3)F(r) +$$
$$2F(r)^2) - 2a^2(x^2 - 1)F(r)F''(r)(a^2x^2 + F(r))))) \tag{11}$$

$$R = \frac{-4F(r)F'(r)H''(r) - 2H'(r)\left(F'(r)^2 - 2F(r)F''(r)\right)}{F'(r)^3 \left(a^2x^2 + F(r)\right)} \tag{12}$$

$$K = \frac{1}{F'(r)^6 \left(a^2x^2 + F(r)\right)^6} 4(2H(r)^2 F'(r)^6 (7a^4x^4 - 34a^2x^2 F(r) +$$

$$7F(r)^2) + 2H(r)F'(r)^3(a^2x^2 + F(r))(H'(r)(2F(r)F''(r)(a^2x^2 - 3F(r))$$

$$(a^2x^2 + F(r)) + F'(r)^2(-a^4x^4 + 34a^2x^2 F(r) - 13F(r)^2)) - 2F(r)F'(r)$$

$$H''(r)(a^2x^2 - 3F(r))(a^2x^2 + F(r))) + (a^2x^2 + F(r))^2(4F(r)^2 F'(r)^2$$

$$H''(r)^2(a^2x^2 + F(r))^2 - 4F(r)F'(r)H'(r)H''(r)(a^2x^2 + F(r))(2F(r)$$

$$F''(r)(a^2x^2 + F(r)) + F'(r)^2(3F(r) - a^2x^2)) + H'(r)^2(4F(r)^2 F''(r)^2$$

$$(a^2x^2 + F(r))^2 + 4F(r)F'(r)^2 F''(r)(a^2x^2 + F(r))(3F(r) - a^2x^2) +$$

$$F'(r)^4(a^4x^4 - 18a^2x^2 F(r) + 13F(r)^2)))) \tag{13}$$

The calculations of the above quantities and all calculations of the paper were done with a computer program of Bonanos [18]

From Eq (2) we find that $F(r)$ and $F'(r)$ do not vanish in the interior region $0 \le r \le k$ and therefore the invariants R and K of Eqs (12) and (13) are not singular in this region if $H(r)$, $H'(r)$ and $H''(r)$ are not singular in this region. Therefore the solution is regular in the interior region if $H(r)$, $H'(r)$ and $H''(r)$ are not singular in this region.

The eigenvalues B_1 and B_2 of the Ricci tensor R^ν_μ are the following:

$$B_1 = B_r = \frac{1}{F'(r)^3 \left(a^2x^2 + F(r)\right)^2} (2F(r)F''(r)H'(r)\left(a^2x^2 + F(r)\right)$$

$$-2F(r)F'(r)H''(r)\left(a^2x^2 + F(r)\right) + F'(r)^2 H'(r)\left(F(r) - a^2x^2\right) - H(r)$$

$$F'(r)^3) \tag{14}$$

$$B_2 = B_\theta = \frac{H(r)F'(r) - 2F(r)H'(r)}{F'(r)\left(a^2x^2 + F(r)\right)^2} \tag{15}$$

To find the eigenvalues B_t and B_ϕ of the timelike eigenvector $(u_t)^\mu$ and the spacelike eigenvector $(u_\phi)^\mu$ of the Ricci tensor R^ν_μ respectively we consider the eigenvalue equation $R^\nu_\mu (u_i)^\mu = B_i (u_i)^\nu$. Writing for the eigenvectors $(u_i)^\mu$, $i = t$ and ϕ which correspond to the eigenvalues B_t and B_ϕ

$$(u_i)^\mu = \begin{pmatrix} b_i \\ 0 \\ 0 \\ c_i \end{pmatrix}$$

we get the relations

$$(R^t_t - B_i)b_i + R^t_\phi c_i = 0 \quad and \quad R^\phi_t b_i + (R^\phi_\phi - B_i)c_i = 0 \tag{16}$$

Therefore we have

$$\frac{c_i}{b_i} = -\frac{R_t^t - B_i}{R_t^\phi} = -\frac{R_\phi^t}{R_\phi^\phi - B_i} \tag{17}$$

Then we get $(u_i)_\mu (u_i)^\mu = b_i^2 V_i(r,x)$, where

$$V_i(r,x) = g_{tt} - 2\frac{R_\phi^t}{R_\phi^\phi - B_i}g_{t\phi} + (\frac{R_\phi^t}{R_\phi^\phi - B_i})^2 g_{\phi\phi} \tag{18}$$

If $V_i(r,x)$ is negative (positive) in the interior region $0 \leq r \leq k$ the eigenvalue B_i is eigenvalue of a timelike (spacelike) eigenvector $(u_i)^\mu$. For the metric of Eq (1) with the $cos^2(1 - r/k)$ replaced as in Eq (5) and arbitrary $F(r)$ and $H(r)$ we get

$$V_1(r,x) = -\frac{(a^2 + F(r) + H(r))(a^2 x^2 + F(r))}{(a^2 + F(r))^2} \tag{19}$$

$$V_2(r,x) = \frac{F(r) + a^2 x^2}{a^2(1 - x^2)} \tag{20}$$

For the $F(r)$ of Eq (2) we have $V_2(r,x) > 0$ and we shall choose a such that

$$a^2 + F(r) + H(r) > 0 \tag{21}$$

in which case we have $V_1(r,x) < 0$. Therefore we get

$$B_t = B_1 = B_r \tag{22}$$

and

$$B_\phi = B_2 = B_\theta \tag{23}$$

From relation (21) for $r = k$ and Eqs (3a) and (4a) we get

$$a^2 + k^2 - 2Mk > 0 \tag{24}$$

which means that $k > M + (M^2 - a^2)^{1/2}$ or $k < M - (M^2 - a^2)^{1/2}$. Therefore the matching occurs outside the outer horizon or inside the inner horizon of the exterior solution of Kerr.

The energy density μ, the radial pressure P_r, the tangential pressure $P_\perp = P_\theta = P_\phi$ and the quantities $\mu + P_r$ and $\mu + P_\perp$ are given by the expressions:

$$\mu = \frac{\frac{R}{2} - B_t}{8\pi} = \frac{kH'(r)\left(\tan\left(1 - \frac{r}{k}\right) - \sec\left(1 - \frac{r}{k}\right)\right) + H(r)}{8\pi\left(a^2x^2 + k^2\sin^2\left(1 - \frac{r}{k}\right) - 2k^2\sin\left(1 - \frac{r}{k}\right) + k^2\right)^2} \quad (25)$$

$$P_r = \frac{B_r - \frac{R}{2}}{8\pi} = -\frac{kH'(r)\left(\tan\left(1 - \frac{r}{k}\right) - \sec\left(1 - \frac{r}{k}\right)\right) + H(r)}{8\pi\left(a^2x^2 + k^2\sin^2\left(1 - \frac{r}{k}\right) - 2k^2\sin\left(1 - \frac{r}{k}\right) + k^2\right)^2} \quad (26)$$

$$P_\perp = \frac{B_\phi - \frac{R}{2}}{8\pi} = \frac{1}{16\pi k\,(a^2x^2 + k^2(\sin(1 - \frac{r}{k}) - 2)\sin(1 - \frac{r}{k}) + k^2)^2}$$

$$(2kH(r) - \frac{1}{4}\sec^3(1 - \frac{r}{k})(2kH''(r)\cos(1 - \frac{r}{k})(-2a^2x^2 + k^2(4\sin(1 - \frac{r}{k})$$

$$+ \cos(2 - \frac{2r}{k})) - 3k^2) + H'(r)(2(2a^2x^2 + k^2)\sin(1 - \frac{r}{k}) + 2k^2(4 -$$

$$(3\sin(1 - \frac{r}{k}))\cos(2 - \frac{2r}{k})))) \quad (27)$$

$$\mu + P_r = 0 \quad (28)$$

$$\mu + P_\perp = \frac{1}{64\pi k\left(a^2x^2 + k^2\left(\sin\left(1 - \frac{r}{k}\right) - 2\right)\sin\left(1 - \frac{r}{k}\right) + k^2\right)^2}$$

$$(-\sec^3(1 - \frac{r}{k})(2kH''(r)\cos(1 - \frac{r}{k})(-2a^2x^2 + k^2(4\sin(1 - \frac{r}{k}) +$$

$$\cos(2 - \frac{2r}{k})) - 3k^2) + H'(r)((4a^2x^2 + 3k^2)\sin(1 - \frac{r}{k}) + k^2(-5\sin(3 -$$

$$\frac{3r}{k}) + 12\cos(2 - \frac{2r}{k}) + 4)) - 16kH(r)\cos^3(1 - \frac{r}{k}))) \quad (29)$$

From Eqs (4), (25) and (26) we find that at the matching surface $r = k$ for all $H(r)$ we get $\mu = P_r = 0$. This is a very important feature of our solutions.

Expression (28), which holds for all solutions of the paper, is the equation of state of these solutions. An equation of state of the form $\mu + P_r = 0$ was introduced originally by Sakharov as an equation of state of a superdense fluid [19]. Gliner [20] argues that the meaning of a negative pressure is that the internal volume forces in the matter are not forces of repulsion but forces of attraction and also that an object with this equation of state might be formed in gravitational collapse. This equation arises in Grand Unified Theories at very high densities and it is used in the cosmological inflationary senario [21]. Also it is the equation of state in the de Sitter interior of the gravastar (gravitational vacuum star) model [22] [23].

We can show that the energy-momentum tensor $T_{\mu\nu}$ of the solutions with the line element of Eqs (1) and the $cos^2(1 - r/k)$ replaced as in Eq (5) has for arbitrary $F(r)$ and $H(r)$ the form of the energy-momentum tensor of an anisotropic fluid solution. To do that we consider the normalized eigenvectors $(u_\mu)_\nu$ $\mu, \nu = t, r, \theta, \phi$ of the Ricci tensor R_μ^ν, which are given by the relations

$$(u_t)_\mu = \frac{\sqrt{a^2 + F(r) + H(r)}}{\sqrt{a^2 x^2 + F(r)}}(-\delta_{\mu t} + a(1 - x^2)\delta_{\mu\phi}) \tag{30}$$

$$(u_r)_\mu = \sqrt{\frac{(a^2 x^2 + F(r))F'(r)^2}{4F(r)(a^2 + H(r) + F(r))}}\delta_{r\mu} \tag{31}$$

$$(u_\theta)_\mu = \sqrt{a^2 x^2 + F(r)}\delta_{\theta\mu} \tag{32}$$

$$(u_\phi)_\mu = \sqrt{\frac{1 - x^2}{a^2 x^2 + F(r)}}(-a\delta_{t\mu} + (F(r) + a^2)\delta_{\phi\mu}) \tag{33}$$

From the expression for $g_{\mu\nu}$ which is obtained from relations (1) and (5) and the expressions for $R_{\mu\nu}$, R, μ, P_r, $P_\perp$, $(u_t)_\mu$ and $(u_r)_\mu$ given by Eqs (7)- (12), (25) - (27), (30) and (31) we find that the energy-momentum tensor $T_{\mu\nu}$ of all solutions obtained for arbitrary $F(r)$ and $H(r)$ is given by the relation

$$T_{\mu\nu} = \frac{1}{8\pi}(R_{\mu\nu} - \frac{R}{2}g_{\mu\nu}) = (\mu + P_\perp)(u_t)_\mu(u_t)_\nu + P_\perp g_{\mu\nu} + (P_r - P_\perp)(u_r)_\mu(u_r)_\nu \tag{34}$$

which is the energy-momentum tensor of an anisotropic fluid solution [24].

We shall examine if functions $H(r)$ exist for which the line element (1) is the line element of a perfect fluid solution. To do that we shall use the relation $B_r = B_\theta$ which holds for perfect fluid solutions. From this relation and Eqs (14) and (15) we get

$$2F(r)F''(r)H'(r)\left(a^2 x^2 + F(r)\right) - 2F(r)F'(r)H''(r)\left(a^2 x^2 + F(r)\right) +$$
$$F'(r)^2 H'(r)\left(3F(r) - a^2 x^2\right) - 2H(r)F'(r)^3 = 0 \tag{35}$$

from which we get from the vanishing of the coefficients of the powers of x

$$F(r)(2F(r)F''(r)H'(r)-2F(r)F'(r)H''(r)+3F'(r)^2H'(r))-2H(r)F'(r)^3=0 \tag{36}$$

$$-2F(r)F''(r)H'(r)+2F(r)F'(r)H''(r)+F'(r)^2H'(r)=0 \tag{37}$$

Substituting in Eq (37) the $F(r)$ of expression (2), solving the resulting differential equation, and imposing on the solution $H(r)$ the matching conditions (4) we get

$$H(r)=-2kM\left(1-\sin\left(1-\frac{r}{k}\right)\right)=-2kM(F(r))^{1/2} \tag{38}$$

Since the expressions (2) and (38) of $F(r)$ and $H(r)$ respectively satisfy Eq (36) also, these expressions are the solution of the system of Eqs (36) and (37) which satisfies the matching conditions. But the solution with the line element of Eq (1) and the $F(r)$ and $H(r)$ of Eqs (2) and (38) respectively is the solution of Kerr. Therefore perfect fluid solutions we try to find do not exist.

All solutions we shall consider explicitly have the $F(r)$ of relation (2). To complete the solutions we must find the functions $H(r)$. These functions besides the relations (4) which they should satisfy they should give interior solutions which satisfy at least the WEC. In fact in the following Examples we shall find interior solutions whose $H(r)$ depend on a parameter b and we shall determined the values of b for which the resulting solutions satisfy the WEC and the SEC. The WEC are defined by the relations $\mu \geq 0$ and $\mu + P_i \geq 0$, $i=r,\theta,\phi$, the SEC by the relations $\mu + P_i \geq 0$ and $\mu + P_r + P_\theta + P_\phi \geq 0$ and the DEC by the relations $\mu \geq 0$ and $-\mu \leq P_i \leq \mu$. In the present case in which $\mu + P_r = 0$, and $P_\theta = P_\phi = P_\perp$ the SEC are satisfied if

$$\mu + P_\perp \geq 0 \quad \text{and} \quad P_\perp \geq 0 \tag{39}$$

A large number of function $H(r)$ which satisfy the matching conditions (4) are given in Ref [12].

We shall present some Examples. The $H(r)$ of these examples satisfy relations (4)

3 Examples

3.1 Example 1

The solution with the $H(r)$ of Eq (40), which is given below

$$H(r) = -2Mk(r/k + b(1 - r/k)^2) \tag{40}$$

For the above $H(r)$ the expressions for μ, $P_\perp$ and $\mu + P_\perp$ of Eqs (25), (27) and (29) in the variables y, n and u defined by the relations

$$y = r/k, \quad n = 2M/k \quad \text{and} \quad u = a/k \tag{41}$$

are the following:

$$\mu = -\frac{1}{2\pi k^2 \left(-2u^2 x^2 + 4\sin(1 - y) + \cos(2 - 2y) - 3\right)^2} n(by^2 - 2by +$$
$$(2b(y - 1) + 1)\tan(1 - y) + (-2b(y - 1) - 1)\sec(1 - y) + b + y) \tag{42}$$

$$P_\perp = -\frac{1}{64\pi k^2 \left(u^2 x^2 + \sin^2(1 - y) - 2\sin(1 - y) + 1\right)^2} n(\sec^3(1 - y)(-4b$$
$$\cos(1 - y)(-2u^2 x^2 + 4\sin(1 - y) + \cos(2 - 2y) - 3) - (2b(y - 1) + 1)$$
$$(2\sin(1 - y)(2u^2 x^2 - 3\cos(2 - 2y) + 1) + 8\cos(2 - 2y))) + 8(b(y - 1)^2$$
$$+y)) \tag{43}$$

$$\mu + P_\perp = -\frac{1}{64\pi k^2 \left(u^2 x^2 + (\sin(1 - y) - 2)\sin(1 - y) + 1\right)^2} n\sec^3(1 - y)$$
$$(-4b\cos(1 - y)(-2u^2 x^2 + 4\sin(1 - y) + \cos(2 - 2y) - 3) - (2b(y - 1)$$
$$+1)(4u^2 x^2 \sin(1 - y) - 5\sin(3 - 3y) + 3\sin(1 - y) + 12\cos(2 - 2y) + 4)$$
$$+16(b(y - 1)^2 + y)\cos^3(1 - y)) \tag{44}$$

Using numerical computer calculations we find that in the interior region we have

$$\mu \geq 0, \quad P_\perp \geq 0, \quad \mu + P_\perp \geq 0 \quad \text{for} \ b \leq 0 \tag{45}$$

Also with numerical computer calculations we find that there is no value of b for which $\mu - P_\perp \geq 0$ in the whole interior region. Therefore the solution with the metric (1) and the $F(r)$ and $H(r)$ of Eqs (2) and (40) with $b \leq 0$ satisfies the WEC and the SEC but there is no value of b for which the solution satisfies the DEC.

In addition the solution should satisfy the relation (21), which for the $F(r)$ and $H(r)$ of Eqs (2) and (40) respectively and the use of Eqs (41) becomes

$$u^2 > n(y - b(1 - y))^2 - (1 - \sin(1 - y))^2 \tag{46}$$

In Figures (1)-(3) we present the graphs of $k^2\mu$, $k^2P_\perp$ and $k^2(\mu + P_\perp)$ of Eqs (42), (43) and (44) for $b = 0$, $n = 1$ and $u = 0.8$ for which relation (46) is satisfied. With the help of a program [25] we can compute the minimum of these quantities for $0 \le y \le 1$ and $0 \le x^2 \le 1$. We find the relations .

$Min k^2\mu = 3.38947 * 10^{-18}$ $\;at\;$ $y = 1$, and $x = 0.979865$

$Min k^2 P_\perp = 0$, $\;at\;$ $y = 1$, and $x = 9.15476 * 10^{-6}$

$Min k^2(\mu + P_\perp) = 0$, $\;at\;$ $y = 1$, and $x = 4.10499 * 10^{-8}$

in agreement with relations (45), which verify that the solution indeed satisfies the WEC and the SEC.

From the expression for μ of this example we find that μ for constant x is monotonically decreasing for $0 \le y \le 1$ to the value $\mu = 0$ at $y = 1$. Also since $\mu + P_r = 0$ the radial pressure P_r is monotonically increasing to the value $P_r = 0$ at $y = 1$. The same thing happens to the examples which follow.

The line element of the solution is obtained from expression (1) with $F(r)$ and $H(r)$ given by relations (2) and (40) respectively. The line element for $b = 0$, which implies $H(r) = -2Mr$, is the line element of the simplest solution of our class of solutions. Explicitly this line element is

$$d^2s = -(1 - \frac{2Mr}{(1 - sin(1 - r/k))^2k^2 + a^2cos^2\theta})dt^2$$
$$- \frac{4asin^2\theta Mr}{(1 - sin(1 - r/k))^2k^2 + a^2cos^2\theta}dtd\phi$$
$$+ \frac{cos^2(1 - r/k)((1 - sin(1 - r/k))^2k^2 + a^2cos^2\theta)}{(1 - sin(1 - r/k))^2k^2 - 2Mr + a^2}dr^2$$
$$+ ((1 - sin(1 - r/k))^2k^2 + a^2cos^2\theta)d\theta^2 + sin^2\theta((1 - sin(1 - r/k))^2k^2$$
$$+ a^2 + \frac{2a^2sin^2\theta Mr}{(1 - sin(1 - r/k))^2k^2 + a^2cos^2\theta})d\phi^2 \qquad (47)$$

The above line element is obtained from the line element of the solution of Kerr if we multiply its coefficient of d^2r by $cos^2(1 - r/k)$ and replace its r^2 by $(1 - sin(1 - r/k))^2k^2$.

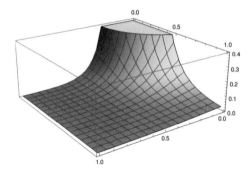

Figure 1: $k^2\mu$ of expression (42) for ($b = 0$, $n = 1$, $u = 0.8$)

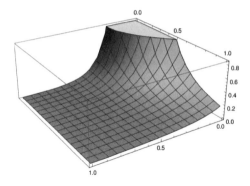

Figure 2: $k^2 P_\perp$ of expression (43) for ($b = 0$, $n = 1$, $u = 0.8$)

,

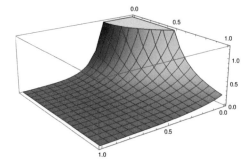

Figure 3: $k^2(\mu + P_\perp)$ of expression (44) for ($b = 0$, $n = 1$, $u = 0.8$)

3.2 Example 2

The solution with the $H(r)$ of Eq (48), which is given below

$$H(r) = -2Mk((1 - b)e^{(r-k)/k} + br/k) \tag{48}$$

For the above $H(r)$ the expressions for μ, $P_\perp$ and $\mu + P_\perp$ of Eqs (25), (27) and (29) in the variables y, n and u of Eqs (41) become

$$
\mu = -\frac{1}{2\pi k^2 \left(-2u^2x^2 + 4\sin(1 - y) + \cos(2 - 2y) - 3\right)^2} n(b(-e^{y-1})
$$
$$
+by + (b(-e^{y-1}) + b + e^{y-1})\tan(1 - y) + (b(e^{y-1} - 1) - e^{y-1})
$$
$$
\sec(1 - y) + e^{y-1}) \tag{49}
$$

$$
P_\perp = -\frac{1}{64\pi k^2 \left(u^2x^2 + \sin^2(1 - y) - 2\sin(1 - y) + 1\right)^2} n(\sec^3(1 - y)
$$
$$
(2(b - 1)e^{y-1}\cos(1 - y)(-2u^2x^2 + 4\sin(1 - y) + \cos(2 - 2y) - 3) +
$$
$$
(b(e^{y-1} - 1) - e^{y-1})(2\sin(1 - y)(2u^2x^2 - 3\cos(2 - 2y) + 1) +
$$
$$
8\cos(2 - 2y)) + 8((1 - b)e^{y-1} + by)) \tag{50}
$$

$$
\mu + P_\perp = -\frac{1}{64\pi k^2 \left(u^2x^2 + (\sin(1 - y) - 2)\sin(1 - y) + 1\right)^2} n\sec^3(1 - y)
$$

$$(2(b-1)e^{y-1}\cos(1-y)(-2u^2x^2+4\sin(1-y)+\cos(2-2y)-3)-$$
$$(b(1-e^{y-1})+e^{y-1})(4u^2x^2\sin(1-y)-5\sin(3-3y)+3\sin(1-y)+$$
$$12\cos(2-2y)+4)+16((1-b)e^{y-1}+by)\cos^3(1-y)) \tag{51}$$

Using numerical computer calculations we find that in the interior region $0 \leq y \leq 1$ and $0 \leq x^2 \leq 1$ the following relations are satisfied:

$$\mu \geq 0, \quad P_\perp \geq 0, \quad \mu + P_\perp \geq 0 \quad \text{for} \quad b \geq 1 \tag{52}$$

Therefore the solution for $b \geq 1$ satisfies the WEC and the SEC. Also using numerical computer calculations we find that there is no value of b for which $\mu - P_\perp \geq 0$ in the interior region. Therefore the solution does not satisfies the DEC.

According to our previous arguments the relation (21) should hold. For $F(r)$ and $H(r)$ given by Eqs (2) and (48) respectively and the use of Eqs (41) this relation becomes

$$u^2 > n\left((1-b)e^{y-1}+by\right)-(1-\sin(1-y))^2 \tag{53}$$

The graphs of $k^2\mu$, $k^2P_\perp$ and $k^2(\mu+P_\perp)$ are presented in Figures (4), (5) and (6) for $b = 2$, $n = 1$ and $u = 0.8$, which satisfy relation (53). With the help of a program [25] we can compute the minimum of these quantities for $0 \leq y \leq 1$ and $0 \leq x^2 \leq 1$. We find the relations

$Mink^2\mu = 0$ at $y = 1$ and $x = 3.38904 * 10^{-9}$

$Mink^2P_\perp = 0.0121307,$ at $y = 1,$ and $x = 1$

$Mink^2(\mu + P_\perp) = 0.0121307,$ at $y = 1,$ and $x = 1$

in agreement with relations (52), which verify that the solution indeed satisfies the WEC and the SEC.

The line element of the solution is that of Eq (1) where $F(r)$ and $H(r)$ are given by Eqs (2) and (48) respectively.

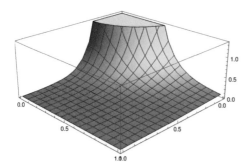

Figure 4: $k^2\mu$ of expression (49) for ($b = 2$, $n = 1$, $u = 0.8$)

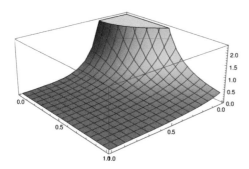

Figure 5: $k^2 P_\perp$ of expression (50) for ($b = 2$, $n = 1$, $u = 0.8$)

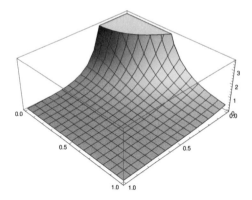

Figure 6: $k^2(\mu + P_\perp)$ of expression (51) for ($b = 2$, $n = 1$, $u = 0.8$)

3.3   Example 3

The solution with the $H(r)$ of Eq (54), which is given below

$$H(r) = -\frac{2M}{b}k^{1-b}\left((b-1)k^b + r^b\right) \tag{54}$$

For the above $H(r)$ the expressions for μ, $P_\perp$ and $\mu + P_\perp$ of Eqs (25), (27) and (29) in the variables y, n and u of Eqs (41) become

$$\mu = -\frac{n(yt(y^b + b - 1) + by^b \tan(1 - y) - by^b \sec(1 - y))}{2\pi bk^2 y(-2u^2x^2 + 4\sin(1 - y) + \cos(2 - 2y) - 3)^2} \tag{55}$$

$$P_\perp = \frac{1}{32\pi k^2 \left(u^2x^2 + (\sin(1 - y) - 2)\sin(1 - y) + 1\right)^2}n(y^{b-2}\sec^2(1 - y)$$
$$(-2bu^2x^2 + 4(b - 1)\sin(1 - y) + \cos(2 - 2y)(b - 3y\tan(1 - y) +$$
$$4y\sec(1 - y) - 1) - 3b + 2u^2x^2y\tan(1 - y) + 2u^2x^2 + y\tan(1 - y) + 3)$$
$$-\frac{4(y^b + b - 1)}{b}) \tag{56}$$

$$\mu + P_\perp = -\frac{1}{64\pi k^2 \left(u^2x^2 + (\sin(1 - y) - 2)\sin(1 - y) + 1\right)^2}n\sec^3(1 - y)$$

$$(-2(b-1)y^{b-2}\cos(1-y)(-2u^2x^2+4\sin(1-y)+\cos(2-2y)-3)-$$
$$y^{b-1}(4u^2x^2\sin(1-y)-5\sin(3-3y)+3\sin(1-y)+12\cos(2-2y)+4)$$
$$+\frac{16(y^b+b-1)\cos^3(1-y)}{b}) \tag{57}$$

Using numerical computer calculations we find that in the interior region $0 \le y \le 1$ and $0 \le x^2 \le 1$ the following relations are satisfied:

$$\mu \ge 0, \quad P_\perp \ge 0, \quad \mu + P_\perp \ge 0 \quad \text{for} \quad 0 < b \le 1 \tag{58}$$

Therefore the solution for $0 < b \le 1$ satisfies the WEC and the SEC. Also using numerical computer calculations we find that there is no value of b for which $\mu - P_\perp \ge 0$ in the interior region. Therefore the solution does not satisfies the DEC.

Also the relation (21) should hold. For $F(r)$ and $H(r)$ given by Eqs (2) and (54) respectively and the use of Eqs (41) this relation becomes

$$u^2 > \frac{n}{b}\left(y^b+b-1\right)-(1-\sin(1-y))^2 \tag{59}$$

The graphs of $k^2\mu$, $k^2P_\perp$ and $k^2(\mu+P_\perp)$ are presented in Figures (7), (8) and (9) for $b = 0.5$, $n = 1$ and $u = 0.8$, which satisfy relation (59). With the help of a program [25] we can compute the minimum of these quantities for $0 \le y \le 1$ and $0 \le x^2 \le 1$. We find the relations

$Min k^2\mu = 0$ at $y = 1$ and $x = 4.66932 * 10^{-8}$

$Min k^2 P_\perp = 0.00606536$, at $y = 1$, and $x = 1$

$Min k^2(\mu + P_\perp) = 0.00606536$, at $y = 1$, and $x = 1$

in agreement with relations (58), which verify that the solution indeed satisfies the WEC and the SEC.

The line element of the solution is that of Eq (1) where $F(r)$ and $H(r)$ are given by Eqs (2) and (54) respectively.

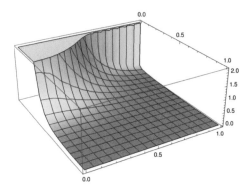

Figure 7: $k^2\mu$ of expression (55) for ($b = 0.5, \quad n = 1, \quad u = 0.8$)

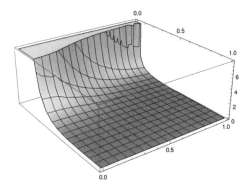

Figure 8: $k^2 P_\perp$ of expression (56) for ($b = 0.5, \quad n = 1, \quad u = 0.8$)

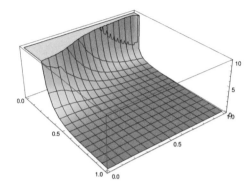

Figure 9: $k^2(\mu + P_\perp)$ of expression (57) for ($b = 0.5$, $n = 1$, $u = 0.8$)

3.4 Example 4

The solution with the $H(r)$ of Eq (60), which is given below

$$H(r) = -2M\left(bke^{\frac{r-k}{bk}} - bk + k\right) \tag{60}$$

For the above $H(r)$ the expressions for μ, $P_\perp$ and $\mu + P_\perp$ of Eqs (25), (27) and (29) in the variables y, n and u of Eqs (41) become

$$\mu = \frac{n\left(b\left(-e^{\frac{y-1}{b}}\right) - e^{\frac{y-1}{b}}\tan(1-y) + e^{\frac{y-1}{b}}\sec(1-y) + b - 1\right)}{8\pi k^2\left(u^2x^2 + \sin^2(1-y) - 2\sin(1-y) + 1\right)^2} \tag{61}$$

$$P_\perp = \frac{1}{8\pi bk^2(-2u^2x^2 + 4\sin(1-y) + \cos(2-2y) - 3)^2}n(\sec^2(1-y)$$
$$(b(2u^2x^2 + 1)\tan(1-y) + \cos(2-2y)(1 - 3b\tan(1-y)) - 2u^2x^2 - 3)$$
$$+4b(b(-e^{\frac{y-1}{b}}) + b - 1) + 4b\cos(2-2y)\sec^3(1-y) + 4\tan(1-y)$$
$$\sec(1-y)) \tag{62}$$

$$\mu + P_\perp = \frac{1}{16\pi bk^2(-2u^2x^2 + 4\sin(1-y) + \cos(2-2y) - 3)^2}n(e^{\frac{y-1}{b}}$$
$$\sec^2(1-y)(b(4u^2x^2 + 3)\tan(1-y) - 4u^2x^2 + 2\cos(2-2y) - 6) + 16b$$
$$(b(-e^{\frac{y-1}{b}} + b - 1) + 8e^{\frac{y-1}{b}}\tan(1-y)\sec(1-y) + be^{\frac{y-1}{b}}\sec^3(1-y)(-5$$
$$\sin(3-3y) + 12\cos(2-2y) + 4)) \tag{63}$$

With numerical computer calculations we find that in the interior region $0 \leq y \leq 1$ and $0 \leq x^2 \leq 1$ the following relations are satisfied:

$$\mu \geq 0, \quad P_\perp \geq 0, \quad \mu + P_\perp \geq 0 \quad \text{for} \quad b < 0 \tag{64}$$

Therefore the solution for $b < 0$ satisfies the WEC and the SEC. Also with numerical computer calculations we find that there is no value of b for which $\mu - P_\perp \geq 0$ in the interior region. Therefore the solution does not satisfies the DEC.

The relation (21), which should hold, becomes for $F(r)$ and $H(r)$ given by Eqs (2) and (60) respectively and the use of Eqs (41)

$$u^2 > n \left(be^{\frac{y-1}{b}} - b + 1 \right) - ((y-1)\sin +1)^2 \tag{65}$$

The graphs of $k^2\mu$, $k^2 P_\perp$ and $k^2(\mu + P_\perp)$ are presented in Figures (10), (11) and (12) for $b = -1$, $n = 1$ and $u = 0.8$, which satisfy the above relation. With the help of a program [25] we can compute the minimum of these quantities for $0 \leq y \leq 1$ and $0 \leq x^2 \leq 1$. We find the relations
$Min k^2\mu = 0$ at $y = 1$ and $x = 2.36449 * 10^{-8}$
$Min k^2 P_\perp = 0.0121307$, at $y = 1$, and $x = 1$
$Min k^2(\mu + P_\perp) = 0.0121307$, at $y = 1$, and $x = 1$
in agreement with relations (64), which verify that the solution indeed satisfies the WEC and the SEC.

The line element of the solution is that of Eq (1) where $F(r)$ and $H(r)$ are given by Eqs (2) and (60) respectively.

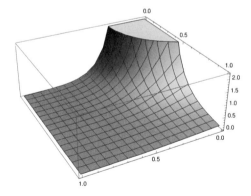

Figure 10: $k^2\mu$ of expression (61) for ($b = -1$, $n = 1$, $u = 0.8$)

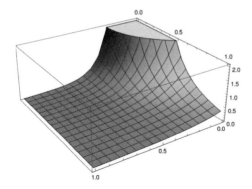

Figure 11: $k^2 P_\perp$ of expression (62) for ($b = -1, \; n = 1, \; u = 0.8$)

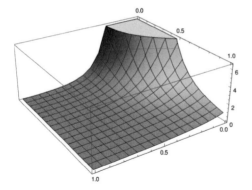

Figure 12: $k^2(\mu + P_\perp)$ of expression (63) for ($b = -1, \; n = 1, \; u = 0.8$)

3.5 Example 5

The solution with the $H(r)$ of Eq (66), which is given below

$$H(r) = -\frac{2kM(br - k)}{(b - 2)k + r} \tag{66}$$

For the above $H(r)$ the expressions for μ, $P_\perp$ and $\mu + P_\perp$ of Eqs (25),

(27) and (29) in the variables y, n and u of Eqs (41) become

$$\mu = -\frac{n}{2\pi k^2(b+y-2)^2(-2u^2x^2+4\sin(1-y)+\cos(2-2y)-3)^2}(b^2y+$$
$$by^2-2by+(b-1)^2\tan(1-y)+(b-1)^2(-\sec(1-y))-b-y+2) \quad (67)$$

$$P_\perp = \frac{n}{64\pi k^2(b+y-2)^3\left(u^2x^2+(\sin(1-y)-2)\sin(1-y)+1\right)^2}((b-1)^2$$
$$\sec^3(1-y)((b+y-2)(2\sin(1-y)(2u^2x^2-3\cos(2-2y)+1)+$$
$$8\cos(2-2y))-4\cos(1-y)(-2u^2x^2+4\sin(1-y)+\cos(2-2y)-3))+$$
$$8(b+y-2)^2(1-by)) \quad (68)$$

$$\mu+P_\perp = \frac{n}{64\pi k^2(b+y-2)^3\left(u^2x^2+(\sin(1-y)-2)\sin(1-y)+1\right)^2}$$
$$\sec^3(1-y)-4(b-1)^2\cos(1-y)(-2u^2x^2+4\sin(1-y)+\cos(2-2y)$$
$$-3)+(b-1)^2(b+y-2)(4u^2x^2\sin(1-y)-5\sin(3-3y)+3\sin(1-y)$$
$$+12\cos(2-2y)+4)-16(b+y-2)^2(by-1)\cos^3(1-y)) \quad (69)$$

With numerical computer calculations we find that in the interior region $0 \le y \le 1$ and $0 \le x^2 \le 1$ the following relations are satisfied:

$$\mu \ge 0, \quad P_\perp \ge 0, \quad \mu+P_\perp \ge 0 \quad \text{for} \quad b > 2 \quad (70)$$

which imply that the solution for $b > 2$ satisfies the WEC and the SEC. Also with numerical computer calculations we find that there is no value of b for which $\mu - P_\perp \ge 0$ in the interior region. Therefore the solution does not satisfies the DEC.

The relation (21), which should hold, becomes for $F(r)$ and $H(r)$ given by Eqs (2) and (66) respectively and the use of Eqs (41)

$$u^2 > -\frac{n-bny}{b+y-2} - (1-\sin(1-y))^2 \quad (71)$$

The graphs of $k^2\mu$, $k^2P_\perp$ and $k^2(\mu+P_\perp)$ are presented in Figures (13), (14) and (15) for $b=3$, $n=1$ and $u=1.2$, which satisfy the above relation. With the help of a program [25] we can compute the minimum of these quantities for $0 \le y \le 1$ and $0 \le x^2 \le 1$. We find the relations

$Mink^2\mu = 0$ *at* $y = 1$ *and* $x = 8.62525 * 10^{-8}$
$Mink^2P_\perp = 0.00815343$, *at* $y = 1$, *and* $x = 1$
$Mink^2(\mu + P_\perp) = 0.00815343$, *at* $y = 1$, *and* $x = 1$

in agreement with relations (70), which verify that the solution indeed satisfies the WEC and the SEC.

The line element of the solution is that of Eq (1) where $F(r)$ and $H(r)$ are given by Eqs (2) and (66) respectively.

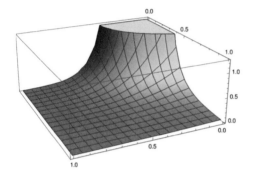

Figure 13: $k^2\mu$ of expression (67) for ($b = 3$, $n = 1$, $u = 1.2$)

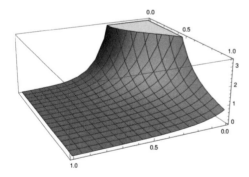

Figure 14: $k^2P_\perp$ of expression (68) for ($b = 3$, $n = 1$, $u = 1.2$)

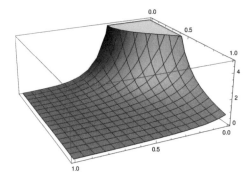

Figure 15: $k^2(\mu + P_\perp)$ of expression (69) for ($b = 3$, $n = 1$, $u = 1.2$)

References

[1] Kerr R. P. Phys. Rev. Lett. **11**, 237 (1963)

[2] Krasinski A. Ann. Phys. **112**, 22 (1978)

[3] Des Mc Manus Class Quant. Grav. **8**, 863 (1991)

[4] Bicak J. and Ledvinka T. Phys. Rev. Lett. **71**, 1669 (1993)

[5] Pichon C. and Lynden-Bell D. Mon. Not. Roy. Astron. Soc. **280**, 1007 (1996)

[6] Viaggiu S. Int. J. Mod. Phys. D **15**, 1441 (2006)

[7] Drake S. P. and Turolla R. Class. Quant. Grav. **14**, 1883 (1997)

[8] Kyriakopoulos E. Int. J. Mod. Phys. D **22**, 1350051-1 (2013)

[9] Hernandez-Pastora J. L. and Herrera L. Phys. Rev. **D 95**, 024003 (2017)

[10] Herrera L. and Hernandez-Pastora J. L. Phys. Rev. **D 96**, 024048 (2017)

[11] Ledvinka T. and Bicak J. Phys. Rev. **D 99**, 064046 (2019) arXiv : gr-gc /1903.01726v1.

[12] Kyriakopoulos E. *Interior Solutions to the Solution of Schwarzschild and to the Solution of Kerr (Lambert Academic Publishing, Beau Basin, 2021)*

[13] Boyer R. N. and Lindquist R. W. J. Math. Phys. **8**, 265 (1967)

[14] Torres R. and Fayos F. Gen. Rel. Grav. **49**, 739 (2017)

[15] Darmois G. *Memorial des Sciences Mathematiques (Gauthier-Villars, Paris, 1927) Fasc. 25*

[16] Lichnerowicz A. *Theories Relativistes de la Gravitation et de l'Electromagnetisme (Masson, Paris, 1955)*

[17] Gurses M. and Gursey F. J. Math. Phys. **16**, 2385 (1975)

[18] Bonanos S: Riemannian Geometry and Tensor Calculus. In: Wolfram Research, Inc. Mathematica, Version 11.0, Champaign Il. (2016) www.inp.democritos.gr/ sbonano/RGTC/

[19] Sakharov A. D. Sov. Phys. JETP **22**, 241 (1966)

[20] Gliner E. B. Sov. Phys. JETP **22**, 378 (1966)

[21] Ilic S. Kunz M. Liddle A. R. and Frieman J. A. Phys. Rev. **D 81**, 103502 (2010)

[22] Mazur P. O. and Mottola E. Gravitational Condensate Stars: An Alternative to Black Holes (arXiv: gr-gc /0109035)

[23] Visser M. and Wiltshire D. L. Class. Quant. Grav. **21**, 1135 (2004)

[24] Herrera L. and Santos N. O. Phys. Rep. **286**, 53 (1997)

[25] To find global minima we use Wolfram's programm [NMinimize....] and [NMaximize ...] for Numerical Nonlinear Global Optimization (Wolfram 2019).

Contents

Interior Solutions to the Solution of Schwarzschild and to the
Solution of Kerr 1

Regular Interior Solutions to the Solution of Kerr which satisfy
the Weak and the Strong Energy Conditions 361

Printed by
Schaltungsdienst Lange o.H.G., Berlin